SECRETS TO HEALTHY AGING

FROM THE EDITORS OF BOTTOM LINE

BottomLineBooks

BottomLineInc.com

Contents

REPORT #3
DON'T LET YOUR HOME KILL YOU

REPORT #4
CAREGIVER CONFIDENTIAL: HOW TO TAKE CARE OF YOURSELF WHILE TAKING CARE OF OTHERS

REPORT #5
DEADLY MEDICAL MISTAKES AND HOW TO AVOID THEM

REPORT #11
HOW TO GET VIP TREATMENT WHEREVER YOU GO

REPORT #12

Retirement Riches: Have All the Money You Need... for the Life You Want

Get What's Yours from Social Security

Laurence J. Kotlikoff, PhD, professor of economics at Boston University and a former senior economist with the President's Council of Economic Advisers. He has spent years studying the Social Security system and developing software to help people navigate it. He is president of Economic Security Planning Inc., which develops financial-planning software, and coauthor of *Get What's Yours: Revised and Updated—The Secrets of Maxing Out Your Social Security.* MaximizeMySocialSecurity.com

You're not supposed to have to worry about Social Security. It's supposed to provide the simple, reliable and predictable portion of your retirement income. Instead, the program is a quagmire of thousands of rules that make it difficult to understand and difficult to make crucial choices.

It isn't just regular people who don't understand the ins and outs of Social Security—if you ask a question at a Social Security office, there's a good chance that the response you receive will be wrong or incomplete. That faulty guidance could cost you a fortune in lost benefits (more on that below). To make matters worse, Social Security rules are occasionally changed in important ways that you might never hear about.

We asked economics professor Laurence J. Kotlikoff, PhD, a longtime Social Security expert who recently moved his "Ask Larry" column from the PBS News Hour website to the Forbes website, to provide answers to some of the important and tricky Social Security questions that people have now. Here he focuses on questions related to eligibility, options for claiming benefits, paying taxes on your benefits and earning money during your retirement years.

I read that the rules about claiming "spousal benefits" have changed. My wife turns 66 this year. Is she still eligible to claim those benefits, and would it be wise to do so?

You are correct that the rules have changed, but people who turned 62 on or before January 1, 2016, still can claim spousal benefits once they reach their "full" retirement age and they also can earn "delayed-retirement credits" on their own benefits. (Full retirement age is 66 for anyone born between January 2, 1943, and January 1, 1955.) In other words, if you yourself already are receiving Social Security retirement or disability payments, your spouse can start collecting benefits based on your income history while the benefits based on her own income history will continue to grow by 8% for each year that she delays starting those benefits until she turns 70.

But because of the rule change, people who turned 62 after January 1, 2016, and who file for spousal benefits at full retirement age will be "deemed" to also have filed for their own retirement benefits, which means that they will not continue to earn those valuable delayed-retirement credits. To be clear, these people will not receive two benefits. Instead, their monthly check will be equal to the larger of the two types, with the smaller one essentially lost.

Keep in mind that even though the spousal benefit often is described as being half of the wage earner's benefit, your wife's spousal benefits will not necessarily be exactly half of your benefits. If, for example, you earned delayed-retirement credits by waiting beyond your full retirement age to file, your wife's monthly check will not be 50% of the amount reflecting those credits—it will be 50% of the amount you would have received each month had you filed earlier at your full retirement age.

I waited beyond my full retirement age to start my Social Security benefits so that my monthly checks would be larger—but when I received my first check, it was less than I expected. Is Social Security shortchanging me?

Probably not. People who apply to start their retirement benefits after their full retirement age but before age 70 often discover that their initial checks are slightly lower than they expected. That's because the Social Security Administration takes time to calculate delayed-retirement credits for partial calendar years. For example, say you reached your full retirement age in April 2015 but did not start receiving benefits until July 2016 (15 months later). Your initial checks should include the delayed-retirement credits that you earned between April and December of 2015 (eight months' worth) but not the credits you earned from January through June 2016. Those credits won't be payable until you reach January 2017. Even then, it may take the Social Security Administration as long as two years to figure out exactly how much you are owed for the partial year, but when it does, it will not only increase your monthly checks to include your additional delayed-retirement credits, it also will pay you the money that you should have been receiving since January 2017.

My local Social Security office gave me bad information that caused me to start my benefits sooner than I should have, costing me money. Is there any way to get Social Security to compensate me for this?

Possibly, if you can prove that the Social Security Administration gave you the wrong information. But far too often, the Social Security Administration will not make good on the benefits you lost because of its erroneous guidance or, in some cases, even its outright mistakes.

Example: In one case I know, a widow in her 60s asked the Social Security Administration to start her "survivor benefits"—the benefits she was entitled to based on her deceased husband's earnings. The Social Security employee instead processed her applications for both her survivor benefits and her own retirement benefits—the benefits she was entitled to based on her own earnings history. This widow never asked to start her own retirement benefits, and there was absolutely no advantage to doing so—it did not increase her monthly check by even a penny. On the contrary, starting her own benefits cost this widow the opportunity to earn delayed-retirement credits. The mistake will cost her $357 per month starting on her 70th birthday and continuing for the rest of her life. If she lives to 90, the Social Security employee's blunder will have cost her more than $85,000.

It is possible to appeal when a Social Security error or faulty advice costs you money, and it could be worth contacting an attorney to represent you if the appeal fails.

I'm about to start receiving my Social Security retirement benefits. My wife is not a US citizen. Can she receive spousal benefits?

The fact that a spouse is not a US citizen does not affect his/her eligibility for spousal or survivor benefits as long as the spouse is living in the US. Your wife will be eligible to receive spousal benefits based on your earnings as long as she meets the eligibility requirements that apply to all spouses—she must be at least 62 years old, for example, and you must have been married for at least one year. (If the two of you were divorced, the marriage would have to have lasted at least 10 years for your ex to qualify.)

If your spouse is not a US citizen, does not have a green card and lives outside the US for six consecutive calendar months or longer, he/she may lose benefits. However, in general, such a spouse could continue to receive benefits if he/she is a citizen and/or a resident of any of more than 20 countries including Canada, Chile, Japan, South Korea and most of Western Europe. Such a spouse also likely could receive benefits if the two of you previously lived together in the US for at least five years. (See SSA.gov/international/index.html for details.)

My Social Security benefits will be taxed only if I have a lot of other income during retirement, correct?

Unfortunately, that's increasingly not the case. When the taxation of Social Security benefits began in 1984, we were told that this would affect only the wealthiest of retirees—and, indeed, in 1984, fewer than 10% of beneficiaries paid federal income tax on any part of their benefits. But there was a trap hidden in these tax rules—the income thresholds that triggered the taxation of benefits did not automatically rise to keep pace with inflation.

Individuals who have a "combined income" (explained below) of just $25,000 to $34,000 must pay income tax on as much as 50% of their Social Security benefits ($32,000 to $44,000 for married couples filing jointly)…and individuals who have a combined income of $34,000 or more must pay income tax on as much as 85% of their benefits ($44,000 or more for married couples filing jointly).

Those thresholds seemed pretty high in 1984, but as of 2015, more than half of beneficiaries exceeded these thresholds and were required to pay taxes on some of their benefits—and that percentage will continue to climb due to inflation. It is not unreasonable to say that the government is setting us all up to pay income tax on 50% to 85% of our Social Security benefits in the future.

Warning: Don't assume that you will be safe just because you expect your adjusted gross income (AGI) to be below the thresholds cited above. The "combined income" figure that is used to determine Social Security benefit taxation is your adjusted gross income plus any nontaxable interest you received plus half of your Social Security benefits.

My husband recently passed away, and I started receiving survivor's benefits. My 15-year-old daughter started receiving survivor's benefits, too. How will her benefits affect my taxes?

They will not affect your taxes at all. Children younger than 18 (younger than 19 if still in high school) often are eligible to receive Social Security benefits if a parent dies or retires. But these children's benefits are considered taxable income for the child, not for the parent. That's true even if the child's benefit checks are made out to the parent.

Your daughter probably will not have to pay taxes on her benefits, either. Social Security benefits are taxable only if the recipient exceeds certain income thresholds, which very few minors do. To make sure, combine one-half of the child's annual Social Security benefits (do not include your own benefits in this calculation) with all of the child's other income, including any tax-exempt interest. As long as the total is no greater than $25,000 in a given year, no part of the child's Social Security benefits is taxable.

I recently returned to the workforce at age 68, and I am making more money now than I did during the early years of my career. I'm already receiving my Social Security retirement benefits—but will my future benefit checks increase because of the additional income I am now earning?

Your retirement benefits are based on your highest 35 years of inflation-adjusted earnings. These 35 years can be recalculated even after you have started receiving your benefits, so, yes, if you earn more on an inflation-adjusted basis this year than you did in your thirty-fifth-best earnings year, your benefit checks should increase slightly. Unfortunately, the Social Security Administration can be slow in recalculating benefits in these cases—but when it does get around to it, you will be paid retroactively any money that you are owed. If you want to speed along this process, you can visit a Social Security office in person and request a manual recalculation of your benefits. Bring your W-2 forms or other proof of your recent income.

There is a downside to earning significant income while receiving Social Security retirement benefits—the income might mean that as much as 85% of your benefits are subject to federal income tax. Don't let this stop you from working, however, because the income you earn will more than make up for any extra taxes.

I intend to retire in the middle of this year, at age 64—even though I know that I'm not at full retirement age—and I'd like to start my Social Security benefits as soon as I retire. But if I earn a significant amount of income during the first half of this year (before I retire), will I exceed Social Security's annual earnings limits and lose a lot of my benefits for the rest of the year?

Not necessarily. It's true that Social Security has an "earnings test" that, as of 2017, can reduce recipients' benefits by $1 for every $2 earned in excess of $16,920. (This earnings test applies to recipients who have not yet reached their "full retirement age" year, as you have not. Different earnings test rules apply during the calendar year in which you reach your full retirement age. There is no earnings test after the year in which you reach your full retirement age.)

But there also is an alternative monthly earnings test that you can opt to use in the first year that you receive Social Security benefits. Under this monthly test, your benefits will not be reduced during any month in which you earn less than $1,410, which is one-twelfth of the $16,920 annual limit. (You also must not "perform substantial services in self-employment" during these months. See the publication *How Work Affects Your Benefits* at SSA.gov for additional details.)

Thanks to this alternative monthly earnings test, you could, for example, earn $8,000 per month from January through June, then retire, start your benefits in July and not have any of your benefits withheld even though the $48,000 you earned during the first half of the year easily exceeds the $16,920 annual earnings test.

There is one common misconception that's worth clearing up about the "earnings test." Many people believe that if they do have benefits withheld because of earnings, they have lost that money forever. That is not true.

Future benefits are adjusted upward starting at your full-retirement age to compensate you for any benefits that you did not receive previously because of the earnings test. Of course, if you switch to a different benefit at or after full retirement, such as a widow(er) benefit, this adjustment will be of no real value.

MORE FROM LAURENCE J. KOTLIKOFF, PHD

How Social Security Feasts On Your Paycheck

The Social Security tax rate has not gone up in many years—but that doesn't mean your Social Security taxes haven't grown. The government has been using a sneaky, backdoor way to dramatically increase Social Security taxes and take a bigger bite out of many workers' income.

Although the Social Security tax rate has stayed more or less steady since 1990 (the only exception was a temporary reduction in 2011 and 2012)—at 6.2% of wages from employees (and the same from employers)—the amount of earnings that is subject to this tax rate each year has jumped from $65,400 in 1997...to $97,500 in 2007...to $127,200 in 2017. Those increases are well above the overall rate of inflation—in fact, the jump in earnings subject to taxation for 2017 alone is 7.3%, far higher than the recent inflation rate of less than 2%.

Result: If you earn $127,200 or more this year in Social Security–covered employment, you and your employer will each have to pay $539 more than last year in Social Security tax.

Social Security and Inflation

MarketWatch.com and *The Wall Street Journal.*

Social Security checks rose just 0.3% in 2017. The estimated average monthly benefit will be $1,360, up from $1,355. There was no Social Security cost-of-living adjustment in 2016.

How to Never Run Out of Money

Jeff Yeager is AARP's official "Savings Expert" and host of a weekly AARP web show on YouTube. He is the author of four popular books about frugal living, including his most recent, *How to Retire the Cheapskate Way*. UltimateCheapskate.com

Comedian Henny Youngman used to tell a story about meeting with his advisers to discuss his finances and retirement prospects. What Youngman said he told his advisers is, "I've got all the money I'll ever need...if I die by four o'clock."

But the prospect of running out of money in retirement is no laughing matter. For my book *How to Retire the Cheapskate Way*, I asked more than 100 happily retired frugal folks how they planned for and manage their finances in retirement to avoid running short. *Here are their winning strategies...*

•**Test-drive your retirement budget.** Many people wait until they are on the cusp of retirement—or even fully retired—before they crunch the numbers and put in place a realistic household budget based on the actual income they will have to work with in retirement. As a result, their lifestyles often change abruptly as the effect of less income takes hold. Then their newly minted budgets are quickly shelved as they return to their previous spending patterns—a move that can quickly drain their resources.

In contrast, the successfully retired people I spoke with often "test-drove" their retirement budgets in the years leading up to retirement, experiencing what it would be like to live on their projected retirement incomes. This allowed them to more gradually adjust their spending. Sometimes, as a result of the test-drive, they even decided that they needed to postpone retirement, and when they did finally retire, their lifestyles changed very little, making it much easier for them to stick to their budgets.

•**Fix your expenses to fit your fixed income.** Speaking of retirement budgets, the safest model to avoid running out of money during retirement is pretty straightforward. If you can limit your fixed expenses—the true necessities of life, including food, housing and health care—so that your guaranteed or fixed income (such as Social Security and any pensions or annuity income) will at least cover those expenses, you should be OK even in the worst-case scenario. Assuming that you have other, variable income (such as income from an investment account or from working part-time), then that can be allocated for your variable expenses—the "wants" as opposed to the "needs" in your life—or put back into savings. You might ask, *Aren't regular withdrawals from an IRA and other investments also fixed income?* If the assets are invested in a no-risk or very low-risk portfolio and the withdrawal rate is ultraconservative based on your potential life span, then perhaps it's safe to consider that income "fixed." But otherwise, plan for the absolute worst-case scenario and assume that those funds might not always be available. For people who have lots of money (even millions) in higher-risk investments and think that those investments afford them the ability to splurge on housing, food and other fixed expenses—be careful! You are safe only as long as you move enough money into low-risk investments to cover these splurges. (Obviously if there's any chance that your combined fixed income and variable income may not cover even your fixed expenses, you have a problem and should consider postponing retirement and/or downsizing your spending to fit within your income.)

•**Don't count on Social Security alone—but don't count it out, either.** It's important to know that Social Security was never intended to be the sole source of income for a comfortable retirement. In fact, the system was designed to replace only 30% to 40% of most recipients' preretirement income. With the average monthly Social Security retirement benefit currently at $1,360, you'll be living only a little above the official US poverty threshold if that's your sole source of income. This is why it's important to have a pension, 401(k), IRA or other supplemental income before retiring. That said, at the other end of the spectrum, a lot of people planning for retirement—particularly younger people—discount Social Security entirely, buying into the common myth that our Social Security system is nearing extinction. While the issues are complicated and Social Security does face a number of financial challenges, they are not as serious or insurmountable as many people seem to believe. Benefits may be reduced and/or the qualifying ages to receive benefits may be extended by lawmakers, but I'm among the many who strongly believe that if you're old enough to be reading this article today, you still can count on a not insignificant level of Social Security support by the time you retire. Visit the Social Security Administration's user-friendly website (SSA.gov) for the latest news on the program and to calculate exactly what your benefits will be under different retirement scenarios. While you should never plan to retire on Social Security alone, you should plan to have it and work to reduce expenses so that you can stretch it to at least cover routine monthly bills.

●**Retire your debt before you retire yourself.** This is a tough concept for many would-be retirees to accept, and some financial advisers beg to differ, at least with regard to paying off home mortgage debt. But my happily retired "cheapskates" take a hard-line approach on the issue of debt, insisting that you should retire all of your debt—including your home mortgage—before you stop working. Once you're debt-free, you can use the money you would otherwise spend on interest for other things in retirement and you've also safeguarded your other assets against creditors (since you have no creditors). In fact, most frugal retirees I interviewed were successful in fully paying off their debts before they retired even if it meant postponing retirement or selling off other assets in order to do so.

●**Medicare is wonderful, but never underestimate health-care costs.** Under current policies, most Americans turning 65 today qualify for Medicare health-care coverage, and that really is an extremely valuable benefit you've earned and need to understand (visit Medicare.gov). So breathe a sigh of relief once you've qualified for Medicare—but don't for a minute think that your health-care-cost worries are over. In fact, Fidelity Benefits Consulting estimates that a couple retiring these days will spend an average of $260,000 of their own money on premiums, deductibles and other out-of-pocket

health-care costs in retirement. Talk about a retirement nest egg buster! Buying an appropriate Medicare supplement insurance policy ("Medigap"), which covers some of the costs not covered by Medicare, is worth it to hedge your bets. There are up to 10 different types of Medigap plans (depending on your state). When choosing, you should factor in your projected health, lifestyle, risk tolerance, ability to pay and other factors. For help with all that, search for "Choosing a Medigap Policy" at Medicare.gov. And if you can afford it, consider long-term-care insurance, which can cover nursing home costs.

●**Stay active…and keep earning.** Staying active in retirement not only increases quality of life, but it can help keep you healthy and reduce your medical costs. And it also can supplement your retirement income if, like an increasing number of Americans, you choose to work part-time during retirement. A Gallup poll found that about 60% of Americans say they intend to work part-time during at least a portion of their retirement years, and most of them are choosing to do so primarily to stay active, not just to supplement their income. A common scenario for many of my frugal retirees who are under full retirement age is to work at least enough to generate the $16,920 they are allowed to earn annually under current law without reducing the Social Security benefits they are drawing at the same time (once they reach full retirement age, there's no reduction in benefits regardless of their earnings from a job or self-employment).

That's smart. Beyond that annual earning threshold, you still will continue to receive Social Security benefits at a reduced rate. So if you truly enjoy your part-time work, go ahead and earn more—that's smart, too!

●**Practice income procrastination.** As a cheapskate, I've always been a proponent of "spending procrastination"—putting off buying something today when you can just as well buy it tomorrow instead. In my opinion, that's good advice for anyone of any age, but in retirement, "income procrastination" also is an important concept worth considering. The idea is to delay as long as possible drawing on the funding sources you have available to you in retirement (such as Social Security, an IRA or a 401(k) account, reverse mortgage, etc.), both to ensure that you don't outlive your resources and to allow those resources to continue to increase in value as long as possible. For example, if you postpone drawing Social Security retirement benefits until age 70, under current policies your monthly benefit check will be 32% more than it would be if you started collecting at 66. Of course, most retirement accounts do have required minimum distributions (RMDs) starting at age 70½—but while you have to withdraw a certain amount of money from these accounts starting at that age, you don't have to spend that money right away! According to the Society of Actuaries, more than half of pre-retirees underestimate how long they are going to live. Hopefully you'll be one of the lucky ones who outlives your own prediction—and spends wisely in the meantime.

Power Up Your 401k

Ric Lager, president of Lager & Company, which advises 401(k) plan participants, Golden Valley, Minnesota. He is author of *Forget the Pie: Recipe for a Healthier 401(k).* LagerCo.com

I f you are among the 90 million Americans who invest in a 401(k) retirement plan, you might be surprised by the big opportunities you are missing and the costly mistakes you are making in how you handle that account.

Here are some of the most surprising things you should know about your 401(k)—or a similar 403(b)—whether you have it at a current employer...still hold one from a former employer...are considering shifting it to an IRA...or will be taking distributions soon.

A CURRENT EMPLOYER'S 401(K)

Employees often pay much less attention to the assets they have in their employer-sponsored 401(k) accounts than to the assets they have in IRAs or taxable accounts. In many cases, they think they can rely on the employer to keep them from making big mistakes. That leaves them open to various surprises.

SURPRISE: **Your funds could be switched.** Your employer or 401(k) administrator can drop a fund that you are in and shift your assets to a different fund it chooses. This may happen when a lower-cost fund becomes available...as a way to make the investment menu more attractive by replacing a fund that has done poorly over the past year with one that has done well over that period...or because the management of a fund or the administrator of your 401(k) plan has changed. You typically are notified by mail and/or e-mail at least 30 to 90 days before this switch, known as "mapping," takes effect, but the notifications are easy to overlook.

What to do: Check the new fund's five- and 10-year record rather than just the one-year record, and consider whether there is another fund available that is more attractive.

SURPRISE: **You're in the wrong target-date fund.** A target-date fund—a very popular type of fund in 401(k)s—is designed to shift its mix of investments to reduce risk as the fund's target year gets nearer. Even though it is common for an employee to choose the version of the fund whose target year coincides with his/her planned retirement year, that is not always wise.

For instance, you might end up working several years longer than you expected. Or you might have other sources of substantial income—ranging from a pension and Social Security to money-market accounts and certificates of deposit (CDs)—that you can draw on before you tap the target-date fund. If so, you may want to choose a target-date fund with a later target year (which means that it is weighted more toward stocks).

A FORMER EMPLOYER'S 401(K)

It might make sense to keep your money in a 401(k) even after you have stopped working for the employer that sponsors it rather than roll it over to an IRA.

SURPRISE: **Once you have left the employer, you could withdraw assets from the 401(k) without penalty if you are at least 55 years old—** you could not do this until 59½ with an IRA.

A twist: If this possibility seems enticing and you still are working for the employer that sponsors the 401(k), you might want to think ahead and do a "reverse rollover"—moving assets from a traditional IRA into your current employer's 401(k). That could increase the amount available to withdraw from the 401(k) after you leave your current employer. About two-thirds of 401(k) plans allow these reverse rollovers.

ROLLING OVER A 401(K)

About 60% of all 401(k) participants transfer or "roll over" their accounts into an IRA when they leave a company or retire, but they should first consider some surprising advantages and disadvantages. (For more, see our article at BottomLineInc.com/job401k.)

SURPRISE: **In some cases, you can invest in mutual funds that are closed to new investors if you roll over your 401(k) to an IRA.**

Example: At T. Rowe Price, you can gain access to any fund that is closed to new investors, including highly ranked funds such as Capital Appreciation, Mid-Cap Value and New Horizons. Caveat: The fund can't be completely closed—it still must be accepting additional assets from investors who have already invested in it.

SURPRISE: **If you are rolling over a 401(k) to an IRA, in some cases—but not all—you must liquidate your mutual funds and then transfer the cash to the IRA, where you can reinvest it.** This is always true if you are rolling over the 401(k) from one investment firm to a different one, even if the same mutual funds are available in the IRA at the second firm. And it usually is true even if you are staying within the same investment firm for any funds that are not managed by that investment firm.

Examples: If you have a Fidelity fund in a 401(k) that is administered by Vanguard and you want to roll it over to an IRA at Vanguard, you must cash it out first, repurchase the shares at Vanguard and typically pay Vanguard a transaction fee. You also would have to sell your shares if your 401(k) account includes one of the "institutional" class Vanguard funds, which charge extremely low fees, because that class is not available in IRAs. You then could purchase the same fund in a class with higher expenses (but no transaction fee).

What to do: Before rolling over a 401(k) to an IRA, check with the company that will hold your IRA to determine all of the fees and ongoing expenses that will be involved, and take this into account when deciding which funds to choose.

TAKING REQUIRED DISTRIBUTIONS

Many investors assume that the IRS requires them to take required minimum distributions (RMDs) from their 401(k)s starting at age 70½ because they must do that for their IRAs.

SURPRISE: **The rules regarding RMDs are different for 401(k)s and IRAs.** For instance, if you still are working at age 70½, the IRS does not require you to take RMDs from your current employer's 401(k) until you retire or leave the company. For both 401(k)s and IRAs, the amount you take is based on a life-expectancy formula that is calculated each year and on the value of your accounts. But for 401(k)s, you must calculate the RMD formula separately for each 401(k) requiring an RMD and take the appropriate amount from each.

In contrast, for IRAs, you apply the formula to the total amount in all your IRAs—whether you are employed or not—and then you get to choose which IRA or combination of IRAs the distribution comes from. Keep this in mind when deciding whether and when to roll over a 401(k) into an IRA.

The Best Funds from Vanguard, Fidelity and T. Rowe Price

Daniel Wiener is editor of the Independent Adviser for Vanguard Investors newsletter and is chairman and CEO of Adviser Investments LLC, Newton, Massachusetts. The firm was named one of Barron's top 100 independent advisers in the US for 2016. AdviserOnline.InvestorPlace.com

Jim Lowell is editor in chief of the Fidelity Investor newsletter and chief investment officer at Adviser Investments, a money-management firm overseeing more than $3 billion in assets, Newton, Massachusetts. FidelityInvestor.Investor-Place.com

Katie Rushkewicz Reichart, CFA, is an analyst who covers T. Rowe Price funds and associate director covering equity strategies for Morningstar Inc., Chicago, which tracks 530,000 investment offerings. Morningstar.com

As an investor, you can create a mutual fund portfolio that includes offerings from a vast array of fund firms. But many investors like to keep things simpler and potentially cheaper by using funds from only one giant fund company—often Vanguard, Fidelity or T. Rowe Price. To help our readers who want to stick with one of these firms, we asked three investment experts to tell us what they consider to be the best-of-the-best in-house funds available to new investors at each of the above companies. The experts did not consider index funds, which are very similar at all three fund firms. Here are the actively managed funds they chose—across a variety of investing categories—that you can use to build or augment your portfolio.

VANGUARD

Vanguard is the biggest fund company in the US, with $4 trillion in assets. Although it is best known for its index funds, the company also offers 68 actively managed funds, most with far lower fees than those charged by other fund firms in similar categories.

•**Equity Income (VEIPX)** invests in about 150 to 200 stocks, primarily of large US companies with strong cash flow that pay above-average dividends. Over the past 10 years, the fund's performance ranks in the top 5% of its category, and its annual expense ratio is 0.26%.

Performance: 8%.*

Recent yield: 2.7%.

•**Selected Value (VASVX).** This fund, which owns mostly mid-cap stocks, uses three high-quality subadvisers, each looking for deep-bargain stocks and holding them for long periods but with three somewhat different approaches. One subadviser looks for strong balance sheets but above-average yields...another for hidden earnings potential...and the third for companies that will pull out of short-term problems.

Performance: 7.8%.

Recent Yield: 1.4%.

•**Health Care (VGHCX).** This sector has great long-term potential thanks to the aging populations in many nations. The fund focuses on large pharmaceutical and medical-equipment companies and waits to buy until the stock prices make them bargains.

Performance: 11.3%.

•**Global Equity (VHGEX)** invests nearly half its assets in US stocks and spreads its foreign investments among giant, large, medium-sized and small companies, including 8% of its investments in emerging markets recently.

Performance: 4%.

Recent yield: 1.4%.

•**International Growth (VWIGX)** invests mostly in large-cap growth stocks in developed nations but keeps about 20% of its assets in emerging-market companies. Its performance ranks in the top 3% of its category over the past year and the top 15% over the past 10 years.

Performance: 3.3%.

•**Intermediate-Term Investment-Grade (VFICX)** keeps 60% to 80% of assets in high-credit-quality corporate bonds but has been able to boost yields and capital appreciation by investing the rest in mortgage-backed securities, foreign bonds and US Treasuries and government agency debt.

Performance: 5.1%.

Recent yield: 2.7%.

*Performance figures are annualized returns for the 10 years through March 10, 2017, unless otherwise noted.

FIDELITY INVESTMENTS

Fidelity, which has $1.7 trillion in mutual fund assets and 220 actively managed funds, is reluctant to close a fund to new investors even when its assets have grown unwieldy. But even some of the biggest funds deliver impressive returns and consistency.

- **Contrafund (FCNKX).** This large-cap growth fund has swelled to $107 billion in assets. But shrewd stock-picking by Will Danoff, who has been the fund manager since 1990, has enabled the fund to outperform the Standard & Poor's 500 stock index by an annualized 1.3 percentage points over the past decade.

Performance: 9%.

- **Large Cap Stock (FLCSX)** seeks mostly large-cap undervalued stocks and lately has focused on financial-services, health-care and energy stocks. There typically is a smattering of medium-sized and small companies as well. Its 10-year returns rank in the top 6% of its category.

Performance: 8.6%.

Recent yield: 1.3%.

- **Low-Priced Stock (FLPSX).** Since the fund was launched in 1989, manager Joel Tillinghast has taken a patient, low-risk approach with little annual turnover. The fund limits its new purchases to stocks that sell for $35 or less per share. Nearly 40% of $39 billion in assets is in mid-cap stocks, with nearly one-third in large-cap and the rest in small- and micro-cap stocks. And 36% of assets are in foreign stocks.

Performance: 7.8%.

- **International Growth (FIGFX).** This fund hunts mostly for stocks of large companies with strong growth potential from developed nations, including US stocks, which accounted for 22% of assets recently.

Five-year performance: 6.5%.

- **Total Bond (FTBFX).** The fund invests 80% of its holdings in a diversified mix of high-quality bonds and puts its remaining assets in riskier fare such as high-yield and emerging-market bonds. This strategy has helped the fund outperform the benchmark Barclays US Aggregate Bond Index by nearly one-half percentage point a year over the past decade.

Performance: 4.8%.

Recent yield: 2.6%.

T. ROWE PRICE

T. Rowe Price is smaller than the other two fund firms, managing $811 billion in assets and overseeing 128 actively managed funds, but still is one of the most popular firms for in-house funds. About 90% of T. Rowe Price actively managed funds have outperformed funds in the same categories over the past 10 years.

- **Blue Chip Growth (TRBCX).** Larry Puglia, manager since the fund's inception in 1993, looks for US blue chips with earnings that can grow strongly even if the global economy continues to grow slowly. It has outperformed the S&P 500 annually by nearly two percentage points, on average, over the past 10 years.

Performance: 9.6%.

- **Dividend Growth (PRDGX)** focuses on large-cap US growth and value stocks, especially those that can keep raising dividends over time and seem reasonably priced.

Performance: 7.9%.

- **QM US Small-Cap Growth Equity (PRDSX)** uses computer models to help find companies with decent valuations and solid earnings growth. This quantitative approach has led to performance in the top 2% of its category over the past decade with less than average volatility.

Performance: 10.7%.

- **International Discovery (PRIDX).** The fund invests mostly in rapidly growing small- and mid-sized companies in countries ranging from Japan and the UK to China and India.

Performance: 5.6%.

- **Spectrum Income (RPSIX).** This fund spreads its investments over 15 income-producing T. Rowe Price funds, including core, high-yield, foreign and inflation-protected bonds, floating-rate loans and intermediate-term Treasuries.

Performance: 5.2%.

Recent yield: 3%.

Great Stocks That Are Great Deals

Hilary Kramer, chief investment officer of A&G Capital Research, New York City, and editor in chief of the subscription newsletter Breakout Stocks. She is author of *The Little Book of Big Profits from Small Stocks.* GameChangers.Investor Place.com

A global travel agency...a brewer...and a maker of robotic cancer surgery systems. These companies have very little in common except for one thing—their stocks have been trading at $10 (or significantly lower) per share. With the stock market at or near record highs recently and many individual stocks in nosebleed territory, some of these low-priced stocks stand out as overlooked bargains, according to expert stock picker Hilary Kramer.

We asked Kramer how she finds winning low-priced stocks and which ones are her favorites now...

UNDISCOVERED GROWTH

I focus on two categories of low-priced stocks. The first is "undiscovered growth" companies, typically very small—under half-a-billion dollars in stock market value—with the potential to increase their revenues quickly. Most investors have never heard of these companies because they're in unglamorous or niche industries...are tapping into emerging trends that aren't fully appreciated...or are overshadowed by larger competitors. *Here are my favorite undiscovered growth stocks now...*

•**Accuray (ARAY).** This medical technology company makes advanced radiation therapy systems that help doctors treat tumors with less damage to healthy cells. Such systems are very expensive, and hospitals and surgical centers have been slow to adopt them. The company, which is tiny compared with robotic surgery industry leader Intuitive Surgical, still is not profitable, and that's one reason its stock is 85% below its all-time high. But it has a backlog of more than $400 million in orders, and once more of those systems are in place, I believe recurring revenue from tech support, parts and repair will explode.

Recent share price: $4.60.*

•**Century Casinos (CNTY).** This company, with its two casino/hotel resorts in the Rocky Mountains, is regarded by many as a marginal player in the industry. But it has a strong balance sheet, as well as the flexibility to move into fast-growing markets that are too small to interest major competitors. Such markets include Eastern Europe and the cash-rich oil-sands region of Alberta, Canada. Century also operates casinos on 13 luxury cruise ships.

Recent share price: $8.02.

•**Evolution Petroleum (EPM).** Many energy stocks are unlikely to go much higher anytime soon now that oil prices seem to have hit a ceiling. But I think this Houston-based oil-and-gas company is an exception. It acquires the rights cheaply to wells that have been depleted using traditional extraction methods and then uses proprietary technology to extract more. The stock nearly doubled in the past year, but it could move much higher as the company extends its technology to more wells in the US and abroad.

Recent share price: $7.62.

•**FNCB Bancorp (FNCB).** Small, profitable banks are likely to be stock market leaders over the next few years.

Reason: They haven't gotten as much attention from investors as giant, well-known banks, but they benefit from the same positive trends including the potential rollback in business regulations and corporate taxes proposed by the Trump administration and higher interest rates. This Pennsylvania community bank has attractive growth prospects as it expands in the state, and I think it could be taken over by a larger regional bank at a premium to its current share price.

Recent share price: $7.50.

•**Hudson Technologies (HDSN).** Hudson is a refrigerant-services company that serves businesses such as supermarket chains that rely on commercial refrigerators, freezers and large central-air-conditioning systems. Its stock jumped 170% last

*Figures as of May 26, 2017.

year on the basis of a multiyear contract with the US Department of Defense that could be worth as much as $400 million. I think the share price can go much higher because revenues have been growing quickly and because the company may attract business from other federal government customers.

Recent share price: $8.13.

•**Patriot National (PN).** This outsourcing firm provides insurance carriers with back-end services such as employee-benefits management, claims administration and fraud investigation. The company went public two years ago at an awful time, when growth in the insurance industry was sluggish. But the insurance business is turning around now, and large carriers are spending more on outsourcing.

Recent share price: $2.73.

•**Travelzoo (TZOO).** Online travel agencies are a great growth business, providing a fast, cost-effective way to sell billions of dollars worth of unfilled airline seats and hotel rooms at discounts. Travelzoo, which books air-and-hotel travel packages for more than 28 million members in North America, Europe and the Asia-Pacific region, is a reasonably priced way to tap into this industry's long-term potential.

Recent share price: $10.85.

FALLEN ANGELS

The second category where I look for low-priced stocks is the one I call "fallen angels." These are well-known medium-sized and large companies with total stock market values ranging from $5 billion to $100 billion. Their stock prices have plummeted because of setbacks ranging from dramatic changes in their industries to calamitous slowdowns in their markets. But these former highfliers still are profitable, and they have potential earnings catalysts that have been overlooked.

My favorite fallen angels now…

•**AmBev (ABEV).** This Brazilian beverage company is the fifth-largest brewer in the world, with premium-brand beers such as Brahma and Skol. A severe recession coupled with soaring inflation in Brazil, AmBev's largest market, has hurt earnings and driven the stock price down about 40% be-

low its five-year high. But Brazil will recover, and the company is profiting from the near-monopolies it has in most other Latin American markets. Anheuser-Busch InBev SA/NV, the world's largest brewer, owns 62% of AmBev, which trades separately.

Recent share price: $5.80.

•**Banco Santander (SAN).** Spanish banks have been a disaster since the end of the global recession in 2009 because of Spain's low interest rates, high unemployment and a lingering real estate downturn. Recently, Banco Santander's stock was 44% below its five-year high, and the company is closing 13% of its branches in the country. But investors are missing the fact that the bank is a global player that derives nearly half its profits from stronger economies such as the US, the UK and Mexico. Its stock recently offered a very attractive 4.1% yield.

Recent share price: $6.58.

•**Xerox (XRX).** More and more offices have reduced the use of paper documents. Xerox, the global leader in photocopiers and printing equipment, responded by expanding into a variety of other industries—and lost focus and floundered. This past January, Xerox, prodded by activist investor Carl Icahn, who owns 10% of the company, spun off its ancillary businesses. Icahn believes that a leaner, focused Xerox can compete more effectively even in an industry in slow decline. I do, too, and I like the generous yield, recently 3.6%.

Recent share price: $6.96.

Discounts for Grown-Ups: Start Saving at Age 55

David Smidt, founder and president of SeniorDiscounts. com, a website based in Albuquerque, New Mexico, that tracks discounts available to people age 50 and older.

It's no secret that some businesses, museums, parks and zoos offer discounts to seniors. But many shoppers are surprised to discover that they don't necessarily need to be "senior citizens" to qualify—some of these discounts are available to people who are as young as 55.

The wide range of businesses offering senior discounts may come as a surprise, too. In addition to getting discounts at restaurants and retailers, you might get a discount on a round of golf, a plumber's services or even a highway toll. But in most cases, you need to know to ask for senior discounts—few businesses offer them unless they're specifically requested by the customer.

Opportunities to save...*

RETAIL STORES

Among the senior discounts available at retail stores...

•**Ace Hardware.** Many locations offer a 10% senior discount every day. Age requirement: 55.

•**CJ Banks and Christopher & Banks.** Women's apparel retailer Christopher & Banks and women's plus-size apparel retailer CJ Banks offer a 10% senior discount on Wednesdays.

Age requirement: 60.

•**Dressbarn.** This budget-minded women's wear chain offers senior discounts one day each week at most locations. Details vary by location, but the typical offer is a 10% discount on either Tuesdays or Wednesdays. Ask at your local Dressbarn for details.

Age requirement: Varies by location, but sometimes as young as 55.

•**Goodwill.** Goodwill is a nonprofit organization that sells mostly secondhand apparel, furniture, housewares, books and other merchandise for very reasonable prices. Most locations offer a 10%-to-20% senior discount on certain days of the week. Ask for details at your local Goodwill.

Age requirement: Varies by location, but often 55.

*Always confirm senior discount terms before making a purchase. These discounts might not be available on all merchandise or services. In some cases, they cannot be combined with other discounts or coupons. Other restrictions might apply as well, and discount terms might change without warning and vary by store.

•**Hallmark.** Most locations offer a 10% senior discount on regularly priced merchandise. At some locations, this discount is available only one day each week.

Age requirement: Varies by location, but often 55.

•**Kohl's.** The department store chain offers seniors a 15% discount on non-sale merchandise every Wednesday.

Age requirement: 62.

RESTAURANTS

Senior discounts are fairly common at mom-and-pop diners and family-style restaurants. Many fast-food chains including Burger King, Chick-fil-A, Chili's, McDonald's, Dairy Queen, Mrs. Fields Cookies, Subway, TCBY and Wendy's offer seniors discounts or specials, too—often either 10% off or a bargain-priced beverage. These fast-food senior discounts tend to vary by location within each chain, so don't assume that the discount you get at one Burger King or Subway will be the same at the one down the road.

Other senior discounts available at restaurant chains...

•**International House of Pancakes (IHOP).** Many locations offer 10% senior discounts and/or special senior menus featuring discounted prices and smaller portions. Some locations also offer half-price dinners for seniors one night each week.

Age requirement: Varies, but sometimes as young as 55.

•**Dunkin' Donuts.** Many locations offer seniors reduced prices on coffee and other beverages. Some offer 10% off the entire purchase.

Age requirement: Varies by location, but sometimes as young as 55.

•**Applebee's Restaurants.** Sign up for the Senior Golden Apple Card, which provides 10% to 15% off food purchases at this midpriced American family-fare chain. This senior discount is not available at every location and is not usually well advertised, so be sure to ask about availability and restrictions that apply.

Age requirement: 60.

•**El Pollo Loco.** This chain specializing in grilled chicken and Mexican entrées offers a 10% senior discount.

Age requirement: Varies by location, usually 60.

ENTERTAINMENT

Seniors sometimes qualify for discounts on popular pastimes, including the following…

•**Golfing.** Many public and private golf courses offer senior discounts. These discounts occasionally are restricted to weekday hours when most nonretirees are working. Savings can be as much as 20% to 50%. Call courses in your area for details.

•**Skiing.** Ski slopes often offer senior discounts on lift tickets and season passes. Discounts typically are available starting at age 60 or 65, but the savings might increase with age. By age 70 or 80, you might be able to ski virtually for free.

Example: At Killington in Vermont, skiers age 65 and older can save $400 on an unlimited season pass, a 31% discount. They can save $12 to $13 on a one-day lift ticket, which is a discount of 13% to 15%. Skiers age 80 and older can ski all season for just $59. Killington.com

UNEXPECTED SAVINGS

Here are three senior discounts on services that you might not expect to be discounted…

•**New Jersey E-ZPass.** Drivers age 65 and older who sign up for a New Jersey E-ZPass account can fill out a special form to receive discounts on certain New Jersey highway and Delaware River crossing tolls. You don't have to be a New Jersey resident to sign up for a New Jersey E-ZPass. The discount often is 10% and is restricted to off-peak hours. For details, visit EZPassNJ.com, select "E-ZPass Information," then "Plan Descriptions." Scroll down to the "Senior Citizens Discount Plan" section.

•**Pet-adoption organizations and veterinarians.** Many municipal and private pet-adoption facilities offer discounted or free spaying or neutering for pets adopted by seniors. Some veterinarians offer senior discounts as well—that is, discounts for older pet owners, not for older pets. Call local vets' offices to ask if such discounts are available.

•**Plumbers, heating/air-conditioning contractors and landscapers.** An increasing number of local home-care professionals have begun offering senior discounts. Check your local Yellow Pages in search of ads mentioning senior discounts. Or enter the type of service provider you require, your city or region, and the phrase "senior discount" into an online search engine to see if anything comes up.

Homesharing Can Help

Janet Witkin, executive director, Alternative Living for the Aging, West Hollywood, California, which has matched more than 7,800 seniors with roommates.

Home sharing may allow seniors to stay in their homes. Some seniors offer a spare room rent-free to a younger person in exchange for cooking and light housecleaning. Others charge rent and expect no services but feel more comfortable knowing that a younger person is nearby in case of an emergency. Younger people benefit because these arrangements tend to cost less than living in a rented apartment.

For more information visit Nationalsharedhousing.org or in the New York area, NYFSC.org/home-sharing.

Be an Airbnb "Superhost"

Brian X. Chen, Airbnb "Superhost," writing in *The New York Times.* A Superhost has hosted many guests and consistently received five-star reviews—only about 7% of Airbnb hosts are Superhosts.

How to run a successful Airbnb rental: Be honest about the pluses and minuses of your home so that guests do not expect more than you offer, become disappointed and give you bad reviews. Solve problems quickly when they arise, whether that means calling a plumber about a broken fixture or having a spare remote control in case one is lost. Hire top-notch professional cleaners so that your home meets the highest possible cleanliness standards at all times. Document everything valuable in your home by taking photos of countertops, appliances, furniture and electronic equipment—if anything is damaged, Airbnb will need before-and-after photos to prove that guests caused the damage.

What You Don't Know About IRAs Could Hurt You

Bob Carlson, editor of the monthly newsletter *Retirement Watch*. He is a managing member of Carlson Wealth Advisors, LLC, Centreville, Virginia, and chairman of the board of trustees of the Fairfax County (Virginia) Employees' Retirement System. RetirementWatch.com

Do you know all you need to know about your IRA? You probably don't. That's because getting the most out of these tremendously popular retirement accounts—and avoiding traps that can cost you money—doesn't just depend on which investments you choose and how much you contribute. It also requires that you follow some little-known rules that affect whether you can withdraw assets without penalty...how protected your money will be from creditors...and how much in taxes you eventually will pay.

AVOIDING WITHDRAWAL PENALTIES

You may know that most advisers recommend not tapping money in a traditional IRA before age 59½, in part because you might incur a 10% penalty on the withdrawn amount. But it is possible to avoid the penalty in certain circumstances. *Examples...*

•**You agree to withdraw all the funds in your IRA in "substantially equal periodic payments,"** known as SEPP payments. You must spread out the withdrawals over at least five years or until you turn 59½, whichever time period is longer. For more information, search for "SEPP" at IRS.gov.

•**You use withdrawn IRA assets** to pay unreimbursed medical expenses for yourself and/or

your family that are in excess of 10% of your adjusted gross income (AGI). In that case, there is no penalty.

•**You become permanently disabled,** meaning that you are unable to perform any substantially gainful employment. In that case, you can use the withdrawals for any purpose without penalty, but your withdrawals will be taxed as income.

SEPARATING IRAS

You generally can split up a traditional IRA into separate IRAs without tax consequences. This goes against conventional wisdom, which says that if you have several IRAs of the same type (such as IRAs rolled over from 401(k)s ...or inherited IRAs), you should combine them into a single IRA to make it easier to manage investments and to calculate required minimum distributions (RMDs) starting when you turn 70½. But in some cases, having more IRAs is preferable. *Examples...*

•**If you have several beneficiaries,** you may want to split a large IRA into separate ones for each beneficiary. This would make it easier to choose and pass on particular investments for each beneficiary based on such factors as the beneficiary's age, income and financial needs. For instance, you might want to leave one child a rental property and another one dividend-paying stocks.

•**To use some of your IRA assets for an investment that requires a specialized IRA custodian,** it may make sense to create a separate IRA for that investment.

Example: Legal tender gold coins, mortgages or a small business may require a specialized custodian.

CONTRIBUTING FOR A NONWORKING SPOUSE

You can contribute to an IRA for your spouse—even if he/she has no income. You are allowed to put up to $5,500 into your own IRA as long as you had at least that much earned income for the year ($6,500 if you are age 50 or over)...and you also can contribute to an account in your spouse's name regardless of whether the spouse's income was enough to normally qualify. What matters is that your combined earned income must be at least as much as your combined contributions to the two accounts and that neither contribution can be more than the individual limits stated above. (Roth IRA contributions are allowed only if your income is below a certain level.)

401(K) CONTRIBUTIONS VS. IRA CONTRIBUTIONS

You are allowed to contribute to both your 401(k) plan at work and an IRA in the same year. If your employer matches part of your 401(k) contributions, it typically makes sense to first contribute enough to get your full employer match. Contributions to a traditional 401(k) are not taxed until you withdraw money from the 401(k).

Caution: When you are covered by an employer plan such as a 401(k), the tax deduction you can take on your contributions to a traditional IRA depend on your modified adjusted gross income (MAGI).

Example: For married couples filing jointly, if they both have retirement plans at work, they can take a full deduction on IRA contributions up to the allowable amounts if their MAGI in 2016 is $98,000 or less...a partial deduction if their MAGI is more than $98,000 but less than $118,000...and no deduction if their MAGI is $118,000 or more. For 2017, the ability to take a deduction is phased out between $99,000 and $119,000. If only one spouse has a retirement plan at work, the ability to claim a deduction is phased out between $184,000 and $194,000 for 2016 and between $186,000 and $196,000 for 2017.

PROTECTING ASSETS

There may be limits on how much you can protect your IRA assets from creditors if you declare bankruptcy or get sued. This is different from the rules for some other retirement accounts, such as most 401(k)s, which may receive near-ironclad protection from creditors under federal law if you face bankruptcy or a personal-injury or other lawsuit. (You are not protected from federal tax liens or spousal/child support payments, among other exceptions.) *Examples...*

•**Inherited IRAs receive no federal bankruptcy protection unless you inherited the account from your spouse.** For traditional and Roth IRAs, the current amount shielded from bankruptcy creditors is capped at a total of $1,283,025 for all of your IRAs combined. Rollover IRAs from employer 401(k) plans, Simplified Employee Pension (SEP) plans and SIMPLE IRAs do get federal protection from creditors in a bankruptcy, but like all IRAs, state laws define the protection you get from other creditors such as an individual who wins a civil lawsuit against you.

Say you injure someone in a car accident...the injured person's claims exceed your insurance coverage...and he/she sues you. Most states provide some protection for your IRA assets, but how much varies drastically.

Examples: In California, you can exempt only as much as a judge deems "reasonably necessary" to support your dependents. In Ohio, traditional and Roth IRAs are protected, but SEP plans and SIMPLE IRAs are not. For rules in your state, consult an estate-planning attorney.

Self-defense: If you have a very large amount of assets in your IRAs, you may want to consider a personal umbrella liability policy and/or malpractice insurance if, say, you are a surgeon or in some other occupation at high risk from creditors. Or if you plan to leave your IRA to a child who has financial problems and could wind up seeking bankruptcy protection, you may want to name a trust as beneficiary of the IRA instead and let the trust distribute the money to the child.

FUNDING AN HSA

You can fund a Health Savings Account (HSA) with your IRA without facing a penalty or paying taxes. Transfer money directly from your IRA to your HSA using a Qualified HSA Funding Distribution (QHFD). You may take only one QHFD in your lifetime, and the transferred money can be used only for qualified medical expenses. For more information, including limits on the amount transferred, see Form 8889, Health Savings Accounts (HSAs), at IRS.gov. This transaction is not taxable or subject to the 10% penalty.

MAKING REQUIRED MINIMUM DISTRIBUTIONS (RMDS)

• **You don't have to liquidate an investment in your IRA in order to take an RMD.** You can do this by making an "in-kind" distribution rather than a cash withdrawal. Have your IRA custodian transfer IRA investments with a value at least equal to the RMD amount into a taxable account.

Example: You can transfer shares of a mutual fund or stock or, if you own real estate, you can transfer all or part of the property.

Advantages: You get to keep investments that you want to hold long-term or that you might have trouble selling in a timely and profitable fashion, such as real estate.

• **You may be able to avoid RMDs by using a "reverse rollover" to a 401(k) at your current employer.** You might know that you can roll an employer retirement account such as a 401(k) into a traditional IRA. But some employers allow you to do the opposite—roll assets from an IRA into a 401(k). This strategy is attractive for individuals who have reached age 70½ but still are working and don't need additional income. The IRS does not require you to begin taking RMDs from your 401(k) accounts until April 1 of the year following the end of your employment.

Get More for Your Dollar

Roundup of experts on retirement planning, reported at GoBankingRates.com.

Stretch retirement savings as far as possible by moving to a city where money goes further. The 10 most economical cities: In Oklahoma City, the annual cost of living is about $41,355—including housing, utilities, taxes, health care and everyday living expenses. The annual cost is $41,510 in Tucson, Arizona...$41,748 in Albuquerque, New Mexico...$42,636 in Salt Lake City...$42,694 in Rochester, New York...$43,091 in Kansas City, Mis-souri...$43,149 in Madison, Wisconsin...$43,162 in Tulsa...$43,529 in Sioux Falls, South Dakota... and $43,816 in Dallas.

For a full list of cities and estimated costs: Go BankingRates.com (click the magnifying glass, and search for "Retirement Cities").

Retirement Tax-Friendly Cities

Where to Retire. WheretoRetire.com

These tax-friendly cities have low or no income tax and reasonable sales, personal-property and estate taxes, and they tend to have small-to-moderate-sized populations...

Granbury, Texas, 70 miles southwest of Dallas, population 9,052...Greeley, Colorado, 60 miles north of Denver, population 98,596...Lake Havasu City, Arizona, 200 miles northwest of Phoenix, population 53,103...Pensacola, Florida, far west on the Florida panhandle, population 53,068... Rome, Georgia, 70 miles northwest of Atlanta, population 35,997...San Juan Islands, Washington, 100 miles northwest of Seattle, population 16,015...Summerville, South Carolina, 25 miles northwest of Charleston, population 46,974... West Feliciana Parish, Louisiana, 30 miles northwest of Baton Rouge, population 15,406.

Note: Be sure to consider climate, health care, proximity to family and availability of cultural and outdoor activities that are important to you—in addition to taxes and other costs—when choosing a retirement location.

7 Things You Didn't Know Are Taxable

Greg Rosica, CPA, CFA, partner with Ernst & Young LLP in the private client services practice in Tampa. He is a contributing author for the EY Tax Guide 2016. EY.com/eytaxguide

Buried treasure...generous gifts from your employer...and that iPad you got as a gift for opening a bank account—they all have something in common. The IRS defines them as income and expects you to pay federal tax on their cash value.

Americans underreport an estimated $68 billion in personal income annually, sometimes intentionally but often because they don't realize it counts as taxable income. Many establishments such as casinos aren't even required to notify the IRS that you have received income unless the income tops a certain threshold. But in some cases, failing to report taxable income can trigger an audit and/or result in civil penalties ranging from "failure to file" penalties (up to $135 if you are more than 60 days late) to "failure to pay" penalties (0.5% of the amount of unpaid tax per month).

Surprising things that are taxable...

BANK OR CREDIT CARD GIFTS

Many financial institutions offer incentives for opening new accounts, ranging from cash and electronic gadgets to frequent-flier miles. These generally are considered taxable income unless you must spend a certain amount on a credit card or debit card within a limited time period. Important: Frequent-flier miles and cash back that you receive when you use a credit or debit card are not taxable because they are rebates.

CANCELED CREDIT CARD DEBT

When someone negotiates a settlement with a credit card issuer to pay less than the full amount owed, the IRS treats the forgiven debt as income. So if you owe, say, a balance of $25,000 and the issuer settles for $18,500, the $6,500 difference counts as taxable income.

Exceptions: Credit card debt discharged in a Chapter 11 bankruptcy does not count as income.

And in cases of insolvency, you may not have to pay tax on all or possibly any of your forgiven credit card debt. Just before any of the debt is forgiven, if your total debt exceeds your total assets (excluding assets that creditors can't seize, such as 401(k) accounts), you are insolvent by that excess amount. You subtract the insolvency amount from the forgiven debt to get the amount of taxable income. So if your total debt exceeds your assets by $5,000 and your credit card issuer forgives $6,500, you report $1,500 of the forgiven debt as income.

ILL-GOTTEN GAINS

Whether you rob a bank or win an illegal football betting pool at the office, the IRS expects you to pay tax on any ill-gotten gains, although few lawbreakers choose to do so. Although the IRS technically must keep the contents of your tax returns confidential, there are enough legal loopholes that law-enforcement agencies are likely to find out if you are including ill-gotten gains as part of your income. For instance, if the IRS audits you, it is allowed to reveal certain information to law-enforcement authorities that it gathers from outside sources, such as witnesses to your illegal activities.

There's a better way to gain from illegal profits—report other people who are tax evaders. The IRS Whistleblower Office paid out more than $103 million in awards in 2015 to tipsters—they typically get 15% to 30% of the amount the government eventually collects. And yes, any money you get as a whistleblower is regarded as taxable income on your own return.

More information: IRS.gov/uac/Whistleblower-Informant-award.

EMPLOYER PERKS

Generally, you aren't required to pay tax on gifts you receive from family and friends no matter how much they're worth. But most sizable gifts from your boss or company are regarded as taxable compensation subject to federal and state income tax withholding as well as FICA taxes. This includes everything from golf clubs to the use of a company-owned apartment for a vacation.

Two exceptions: "De minimis" fringe benefits—gifts of minimal value, which some employers define as $75 or less but which the IRS has not defined—generally are not taxable. That includes, for example, a holiday gift basket, group meals and picnics, and local transportation after hours if it is required because of security concerns. Cash and gift cards generally are not included under the de minimis rule—they typically are taxable—but cash and gifts awarded to employees to recognize their achievements for "length of service" are not taxable if you have been with the company for at least five years and the value of the award is $1,600 or less.

GAMBLING PROCEEDS

The IRS expects you to report all "gambling" winnings, no matter how small, whether they come from church bingo games, raffles, sweepstakes, lotteries, casinos or online sports fantasy betting sites. If you win more than a certain amount, ranging from $1,200 (bingo and slot machines) to $5,000 (poker tournaments and lotteries), the gambling establishment typically withholds a 25% flat tax and must notify the IRS...and then you adjust that for your tax bracket when you file tax forms. The good news: If you itemize, gambling losses are deductible up to the amount of winnings you report as income. You must be able to prove your losses through documentation such as receipts, tickets, payment slips and/or a gambling diary with specific dates, the type of gambling, and the names and addresses of the establishments and the names of other people accompanying you at the establishments.

RENTING OUT YOUR HOME

Services such as Airbnb.com that enable you to rent out available rooms in your house or apartment to travelers have allowed hundreds of thousands of home owners to earn extra income. The IRS considers any short-term rental income taxable if you rent out space for 15 or more days a year. Be aware that additional taxes imposed by your local and state government also may apply.

Example: Chicago, Philadelphia, San Diego and San Francisco are among cities that impose a "transient occupancy" or hotel tax on every short-term rental stay.

You can reduce the taxes you owe on rental income by taking related deductions. In addition to a portion of your own rent or mortgage payments, utilities and insurance expenses, you can deduct items such as the cost of sheets and linens that you designate for the exclusive use of your guests...toiletries for guests...and cleaning fees.

Helpful: Get more strategies at websites of the major online lodging services, LearnAirbnb.com and Community.HomeAway.com.

A TREASURE TROVE

"Treasure Trove" is a fanciful term used by the IRS to categorize any lost or abandoned cash and/or valuables that you find. Precedent for taxing treasure troves dates back to a famous 1964 case in which an Ohio couple bought a used piano for $15 and found $4,467 in cash inside while cleaning it. Recent cases involve fans who have caught historic home run baseballs in stadiums. The balls are taxable based on "fair market value."

Common Tax-Filing Mistakes

Kay Bell, contributing tax editor, Bankrate.com.

Common tax-filing mistakes. Input—double-check to make sure that you're entering your figures correctly. Missing out—look out for credits and special deductions and a larger standard deduction if you are age 65 or older. Misspelled or different names—be sure yours matches whatever the Social Security Administration has on record. Direct-deposit errors—be sure the routing and account numbers are correct. Additional income—be sure to record it from forms such as 1099-MISC, 1099-INT and 1099-DIV. Social Security number omissions—be careful to write it wherever it is called for. Charitable contributions—follow all donation tax rules carefully. Signature omission—the return must be signed before mailing or signed electronically if it is filed online.

Moving Company Traps and Hidden Costs

Roundup of experts on moving, reported at GoBanking Rates.com.

Estimates made over the phone are likely to be inaccurate and may be scams—have movers visit your home, and get estimates from at least three companies. Additional fees can raise costs—for instance, packing and unpacking, temporary warehousing and specific-date delivery. Movers that insist on a deposit probably are scammers—up-front payments may disappear. Cardboard boxes—save by getting them for free from liquor stores and other retailers or look for giveaways on Craigslist. Moving permits may be required to park the moving van. Check the website of the city you're moving to. Full-value coverage can be costly, but it requires movers to pay replacement value for lost or damaged goods. Hidden costs of renting a truck to move on your own—these include gas, charges per mile driven, damage coverage and supplies such as furniture pads.

Don't Let a Financial Adviser Rip You Off

Mark Cortazzo, CFP, CIMA, founder and senior partner of Macro Consulting Group LLC in Parsippany, New Jersey, which oversees $380 million in client assets. Cortazzo has been named one of the 250 best financial advisers in America by Worth and one of America's top financial advisers by both *Barron's* and *Fortune*. MacroConsultingGroup.com

Do you ever suspect that financial advisers put a greater priority on earning commissions and making profits for themselves than looking out for you and your nest egg—whether they are suggesting a stock, a fund, an annuity or something else?

An Obama-era federal rule sought to require advisers who work with tax-advantaged retirement savings to put client interests first. President Donald Trump has told the Department of Labor to review and possibly revise or scrap that "fiduciary rule," suggesting that the rule may hurt investors by limiting their access to certain investment products and advice.

If you have a financial adviser or are considering hiring one, it's important for you to understand how the adviser gets paid and what conflicts of interest he/she may have. We asked highly rated financial adviser Mark Cortazzo to explain how you can be sure that you're getting financial advice that is given in your interest—regardless of the fate of the fiduciary rule.

Here are seven questions Cortazzo suggests you ask to help you understand how your current or prospective financial adviser gets paid and how that might influence the advice you receive...

THE KEY QUESTIONS TO ASK

Is your advice to me subject to a fiduciary standard?

With the government's fiduciary rule in limbo, this is a good question to start the discussion. You may get a simple "yes," as in the case of a registered investment adviser (RIA), who already is subject to a fiduciary standard and typically charges clients a fee that's a percentage of the clients' assets rather than commissions on specific products.

Or you may get a more complicated answer if you're talking to a broker, wealth manager or insurance agent. The term "fiduciary" just means that there's a commitment to put the client's interests first. Even if your adviser is not subject to a legal requirement, the firm may have rules in place meant to approximate such a standard. Make sure that the firm's rules are explained clearly and in writing.

Some advisers might answer you by saying, "Part of the time." For example, an adviser could act as a fiduciary when recommending mutual funds but not when selling you an insurance product such as an annuity. Be more skeptical of anything offered under such an exception, and don't hesitate to go elsewhere to buy or get advice on that product.

Helpful: A designation of CFP, or certified financial planner, from the CFP Board of Standards, an industry group, requires that the adviser meet a fiduciary standard, but there is no guarantee of full compliance. Also, you can ask your investment adviser to notify you, in writing, of any instance in which he will not be acting as a fiduciary.

Have you changed your standards or practices at all since the fiduciary rule was announced?

Some investment firms have said that they would go ahead with changes to how their advisers function no matter what happens with the federal rule. For instance, Merrill Lynch has said it will stop offering new commission-based IRAs through advisers. Instead, it will allow customers to choose whether to work with human advisers by paying fees based on the amount of assets in the account...or to use commission-based self-directed brokerage accounts...or to use fee-based automated robo-adviser accounts.

Some advisers will tell you that there is no need for a change. If that's because the individual or firm has been subject to a fiduciary requirement all along, fine. If the adviser starts talking about the flexibility to offer you more products or get you a better deal—or if he seems most interested in talking about the importance of his own compensation—be wary. Consider going elsewhere.

Will you earn more by putting my money into this fund rather than something similar from another company?

The answer with the least potential for a conflict of interest is that the adviser collects an advisory fee based on your account value rather than commissions or transaction-based fees of any kind, because that isn't going to create an incentive to sell a particular product. An adviser whose compensation will vary depending on what funds or investments you buy faces a conflict. You should make certain that you understand all the costs and how they compare with competing products and services. Of course, if you highly value a particular adviser's advice, you might choose to accept higher costs than you would be charged elsewhere.

You can arm yourself for this discussion with this simple step: Read your adviser's business card. If the name on a fund or other financial product that you are offered is the same as any name on the card—the name of the firm in large type or an affiliate in the fine-print disclosures—then you should ask a lot more questions.

Helpful: Even if your adviser has answered this question to your satisfaction, consider the next question.

Are you more loyal to your clients or to your employer?

The answer may not always be completely honest, but it is worth raising the issue of whether your adviser is pushing the "house brand" of investments—and whether that's appropriate. Even if the adviser has no direct financial incentive, he still might recommend the company's own products because selling more of them might earn an attaboy from the boss.

Helpful: Ask whether selling more company products is a factor in deciding promotions, and if the answer is yes, consider whether the honesty the person is showing outweighs the conflict of interest.

Do you go on "due-diligence" trips?

Due-diligence trips offer advisers a chance to meet investment managers and learn about their funds and other products. And that can be a good thing. For instance, last year I went on a two-day due-diligence trip during which I spent six to eight hours a day listening to speakers, including three Nobel Prize laureates, and I didn't play any golf or tennis or go swimming. But if these trips involve less time learning about the investments and more time dining, drinking and golfing, that's not a good thing. If an adviser seems nervous and evasive in describing the agendas and details of his past three trips, be wary.

Is the product I'm investing in the lowest-cost share class?

Mutual funds and exchange-traded funds (ETFs) often have different classes with identical management but different expense ratios. Everyone wants low costs, which boost investment returns, but there sometimes are trade-offs worth considering. For example, an investor with a small amount of money might choose a share class that's slightly more expensive but has no transaction fees when it's bought or sold. If this investor is rebalancing his portfolio (and therefore selling/buying shares) multiple times a year, this could be cost-effective.

Helpful: At some large brokerages, you may find that a more expensive share class lowers your advisory fee, but make sure that the cost trade-offs have been explained clearly and completely.

The 5 Worst Social Security Scams

Steven J. Weisman, JD, senior lecturer in the department of law, tax and financial planning at Bentley University in Waltham, Massachusetts. He is founder of the scam-information website Scamicide.com.

Your Social Security account is a tempting target for scammers whether you are already collecting benefits or will be in the future. Few people understand all the ins and outs of this complex government program, and the bad guys have developed ways to exploit this confusion. *Watch out for these five scams...*

SCAMS THAT APPLY TO EVERYONE

•**Online account hijacking.** The Social Security Administration is encouraging beneficiaries and future beneficiaries to set up "My Social Security" accounts on its website, SSA.gov. If you set up an account, you can check on the size of future Social Security benefits or make changes to your account, such as altering your mailing address or bank information, without visiting an office or waiting on hold for a phone rep. Unfortunately, this system is proving convenient for scammers, too. They have been setting up accounts in the names of benefit recipients (and people who are eligible to receive benefits but have not yet done so)...and then routing benefits to the scammers' bank accounts or debit cards.

Scammers can do this only if they know a victim's Social Security number, date of birth and other personal information, but thanks to recent data breaches, that information often is easily accessible. If a scammer hijacks your benefits, Social Security will reimburse you, but it could take months to sort this out, during which time you could have financial trouble if you depend on your benefits.

What to do: Set up an account at SSA.gov/myaccount before a scammer sets up a bogus account in your name—the sooner, the better. You can set up an account even if you have not yet reached retirement age and/or do not yet wish to start receiving your benefits (accounts may be set up only for people who are at least 18 years old). When you set up your account, click "Yes" under the "Add

Extra Security" heading on the online form. That way, a new security code will be texted to your cell phone each time you try to log onto your account. Access to the account will be allowed only if you enter this code, making it extremely unlikely that a hacker would be able to hijack your account.

•**Fake data-breach scam.** There have been so many data breaches in recent years that it would hardly come as a surprise if the Social Security Administration's database were hacked. Scammers use this fear of data breaches to their advantage.

It works like this: The scammer contacts a victim, claims to work for the Social Security Administration and says that its computers have been breached. The scammer says that in order to find out which accounts have been hacked and altered, he/she must check whether he has the correct bank and account number for the beneficiary. He gives account information that he knows does not pertain to the victim. When victims say the account mentioned is not theirs, they are asked to provide the correct bank information and perhaps other information as well. In reality, victims who provide the requested information might have their bank accounts robbed and their benefits and/or identity stolen as well.

What to do: Always ignore calls and e-mail messages about Social Security data breaches—the Social Security Administration never initiates contact with recipients via phone or e-mail. If you receive a letter claiming you must take action because of a data breach, this, too, could be a scam—call the Social Security Administration at 800-772-1213 (not at a number provided in the letter) to ask whether the letter is legitimate. Be extremely wary if someone who contacts you about a Social Security data breach asks you to provide sensitive information, such as bank account details—the real Social Security Administration would never ask for this.

SCAMS THAT APPLY ONLY TO CURRENT BENEFICIARIES

•**Cost-of-living adjustment scam.** Social Security benefits increase in most years to keep pace with inflation. This year was an exception—falling energy prices kept inflation down last year, so there was no 2016 cost-of-living adjustment. To scammers, this exceptional situation represents an opportunity.

Victims receive an e-mail, text, letter or phone call explaining that the Social Security Administration has noticed that they did not apply for their cost- of-living increase this year. Apply soon, these victims are warned, or this benefit boost will be forfeited. An application form might be provided or possibly a link to a website. In reality, victims who supply the requested information will have their identities and/or Social Security benefits stolen.

What to do: Ignore any notices or calls suggesting that you must apply for a Social Security cost-of-living adjustment. These adjustments are made automatically in years when they occur. And never assume that a phone call is legitimate because your phone's caller ID says that it is coming from the Social Security Administration—scammers have ways to fool caller-ID systems.

●**Social Security card scam.** It seems perfectly reasonable that the old paper Social Security cards might be due for an upgrade—after all, the latest credit cards contain computer chips. In fact, Social Security card modernization is a scam.

Scammers contact benefits recipients, claim to work for the Social Security Administration and say that no further benefits can be issued until the beneficiary's old, out-of-date paper card is replaced with a modern, chip-enabled card. These scammers offer to expedite replacement-card requests if the beneficiary provides some identification details. If this information is provided, the victim's benefits and/or identity will be stolen.

What to do: Ignore anyone who says you need a new, high-tech Social Security card. There is no such thing.

●**Fake-scam scam.** Scammers have come up with a way to steal Social Security benefits by exploiting people's fear of being scammed. The scammer contacts victims, claims to work for the Social Security Administration, and says the Administration's scam-spotting software noticed a suspicious change to the victim's account—did the victim recently reroute his benefits to a bank account in a

different state? When the victim says no, the helpful Social Security "employee" warns that a scammer must have hijacked the victim's account. The scammer says that he will help the victim fix the problem, but the person must act fast. As part of the process, this fake government employee will request information such as Social Security number and bank account details that will allow him to steal the victim's benefits and/or identity.

What to do: Never provide any information to anyone who contacts you with a warning that you might be the victim of a Social Security benefits scam. Instead, contact the real Social Security Administration at 800-772-1213, describe the warning you received and ask if your account is truly at risk.

Tax Scam Alert

Adam Levin, JD, founder of the cyber-security company CyberScout and author of Swiped. IDT911.com

The IRS will start using private debt collectors to pursue unpaid taxes, which could lead to scams.

What to do: Never provide Social Security numbers or credit card details. The debt collectors are not authorized to take payments. Be especially suspicious if you did not receive an official letter about a debt beforehand. If you get a call, contact the IRS directly at 800-829-1040.

Fake Websites

Robert Siciliano, security analyst and CEO of IDTheftSecurity.com, Boston. He has more than 30 years of experience in cyber and real-world security and is author of *99 Things You Wish You Knew Before Your Identity Was Stolen.* RobertSiciliano.com

Until recently, if you made a typo and left out the "c" when typing "Netflix.com" into a web browser, the website you landed on might have told you to update your software to watch videos.

Sites like these with addresses that are only slightly different from those of trustworthy sites often are a scam sometimes referred to as "typosquatting." Victims reach these bogus sites when they accidentally type incorrect addresses...or when they click a link in an e-mail or at a website that contains the dangerous address, not noticing the minor alteration.

These bogus sites then might ask you to enter financial information, such as a credit card number, setting the stage for cyberthieves to misuse that information. Or they might ask you to update some software on your computer or download some other file, which actually contains spyware or malware. Or they might trick you into overpaying for products or services that are much less expensive on the site that you meant to go to.

Victims often lower their guard and comply, believing that they are on trustworthy sites.

Example: If you use a search engine to locate your state's Department of Motor Vehicles (DMV) site, similarly named fake sites likely will appear high in the listings as well. These sites might then ask you to pay for information or services that are provided for free by the real DMV. The fake sites typically end with .com or .org. Websites with the domain name .gov are much more likely to be a real DMV site.

What to do: Double-check that you have typed web addresses properly before hitting Enter. If you often make typos, create bookmarks in your web browser for sites that you visit often. Download and install a free web browser add-on such as McAfee SiteAdvisor (SiteAdvisor.com/download)* for Windows or Web of Trust (MyWOT.com) for Windows or Mac that will help protect you against fake sites, malware and scams.

*Disclosure: McAfee is among Siciliano's clients.

Ways to Earn Extra Money

Kiplinger.com

Be a tutor in a second language, math, science or writing—$15 to $60 per hour. Model for artists—an average session lasts three hours at $12 to $13 per hour. Join a street team to promote products—$20 to $25 per hour. Walk dogs—$15 to $30 per hour. Become a driver for Uber or Lyft—earnings can be $19 to $35 per hour. Do substitute teaching—salary averages $90 to $120 per day (qualifications for substitute teaching vary by state).

Watch Out for Misleading Reverse Mortgage Pitches

The New York Times.

Fines for misleading reverse-mortgage pitches have been levied on three companies by the Consumer Financial Protection Bureau (CFPB). The firms' ads, dating to 2012, claimed that consumers could not lose their homes with a reverse mortgage, a type of home loan that allows older Americans to access the equity they have built up in their homes. But foreclosures do happen—for failure to provide proof of residency, failure to pay taxes or failure to keep the home in good repair. The companies were fined a total of $800,000, half of which was assessed against the largest reverse-mortgage lender in the US, American Advisors Group...and the rest against Reverse Mortgage Solutions and Aegean Financial. The firms did not admit or deny wrongdoing. To complain about a reverse-mortgage lender: Contact the CFPB online at ConsumerFinance.gov or by phone at 855-411-2372.

How to Help Parents in Financial Need

Robert Mauterstock, CFP, CLU, ChFC, a financial adviser with Parent Care Planning, LLC, based in Brewster, Massachusetts. He specializes in helping families address the financial needs of aging parents. He is author of *Can We Talk? A Financial Guide for Baby Boomers Assisting Their Elderly Parents (Soar with Eagles).* ParentCarePlanning.com

Your retirement and your spouse's retirement might not be the only ones you have to pay for. More than 20% of Americans age 40 to 59 are providing financial support to an aging parent, according to a recent Pew Research Center report. Many of these adult children will continue providing support well into their 60s, delaying or curtailing their own retirement plans.

If your parents need your financial help, don't assume that handing over cash is the only solution. There often are wiser options (these strategies also can be used to help other older relatives, except as noted)…

●**Help the parent investigate programs that provide financial assistance to the elderly.** It is important to investigate assistance programs before giving your parent significant cash gifts, which could make him/her ineligible for means-tested programs. The best-known of these is Medicaid, which covers long-term-care and medical costs for those who have very limited assets and income (Medicaid.gov).

Another is the Aid and Attendance and Housebound Improved Pension benefit offered by the Department of Veterans Affairs, which provides about $2,000 per month to veterans (or about $1,000 per month to their surviving spouses) who served during wartime and now cannot afford caregiver assistance. Visit the VA's website for eligibility requirements and other details (Benefits.va.gov/pension).

The paperwork for benefits such as these can be challenging, so your parent might value your assistance. Or help your parent find a local non-profit Council on Aging or Agency on Aging that can provide guidance on these and other assistance programs.

●**Offer your parent a private reverse mortgage.** This is a loan from you to your parent that's secured by an interest in the parent's home. It can provide the parent with cash in a lump sum, monthly income or a line of credit. The home is sold upon the parent's death to pay back the loan. This strategy allows you to provide your parent with needed cash without him having to give up the home…pay the potentially steep costs of a commercial reverse mortgage…or feel like a burden for taking your money. The parent must have significant equity in the home for this to be a viable option. The strategy even could turn out to be a reasonable investment for you—if the home gains significant value—compared with the low interest rates currently offered by other safe investments.

Don't do this informally—the reverse mortgage should be written up by an estate-planning attorney and recorded with the Registry of Deeds in your parent's county to ensure that the funds from the sale of the home go back to you after the parent's death, rather than to other creditors or heirs.

●**Pay your parent's bills.** Rather than hand cash to your parent, consider making payments directly to his service providers and creditors. This keeps you in control of how the money is spent, eliminating the risk that it might be squandered if your parent can no longer manage his finances effectively or spot con artists, which can happen with age. It also prevents your money from winding up in your parent's estate upon his death, where it might have to pass through the court-supervised probate process or be divided among multiple heirs.

Money paid directly to your parent's medical providers does not count against your $14,000 annual gift tax exemption or your lifetime estate tax exemption. It even could be tax-deductible for you if you can claim your parent as a dependent and your total medical spending for the entire family, parent included, exceeds 10% of your adjusted gross income (7.5% if you or your spouse is age 65 or older).

If you pay this parent's nursing home or assisted-living-facility bills, the cost of care is a deductible medical expense, but the cost of room and board is not. Ask the facility to break down the bill.

Helpful: For your parent to be your dependent, you generally must provide more than half of his support and the parent must not earn more than $4,000 in 2017 (excluding Social Security benefits but including investment income). If the parent lives in your home, you can include in your calculations the fair market value of food and housing that you provide. IRS rules limit you to claiming only certain relatives as dependents, but the list of who is allowed is lengthy and includes siblings, aunts and uncles, grandparents, great-grandparents, stepparents and others in addition to parents. See IRS Publication 501, Exemptions, Standard Deduction, and Filing Information, for additional details.

•**Lend money to your parent.** A parent who is too proud to accept your money as a gift might be willing to accept it as a loan. As with a private reverse mortgage, this improves your odds of recovering any remaining funds after the parent dies—as a creditor, you'll be paid back before any remaining assets are divided among the heirs. However, the loan must be properly documented for you to be treated as a creditor by the estate. Write down the loan terms, and have both parties sign this document.

Warning: Consider charging your parent interest if the loan is larger than $14,000. If you don't charge interest, the IRS will treat the loan as a gift, which could have tax consequences. Search online for "Applicable Federal Rates" to find the IRS's minimum qualifying interest rates for loans. These minimum rates currently are quite low, and you even can forgive the parent's interest payments if you like, essentially making a gift of the interest payments as they arise.

Have an "in-law apartment" added to your home. In-law apartments allow older parents to have some privacy and independence, as well as assistance from family just steps away.

Having a parent live on your property also increases the odds that you will be able to claim him as a dependent—assuming that you pay for the housing and food, you can include the fair market value of room and board in your calculations. Alternately, if your parent has assets remaining, those could be transferred to you in the form of rent, increasing the odds that he later will qualify for means-tested programs such as Medicaid (see box on page six). When your parent passes away, the in-law apartment will already be part of your property, so it won't face probate, state estate tax issues or disputes over ownership from other heirs.

AVOID TRIGGERING MEDICAID LIMITS

When helping a parent financially, be careful not to let his/her assets grow to the point that they could disqualify him from Medicaid health coverage in the future. Generally, a person with total "countable" assets (including cash and investments but typically not a home) of no more than $2,000 can qualify for Medicaid coverage, although the limit is somewhat higher in some states. In addition, the person's spouse cannot have countable assets that exceed $115,920. (For more information, go to ElderLawAnswers.com.)

What to do...

If you put money into a trust for a parent and the parent, as the beneficiary, has access to the principal in the trust, that principal would count as part of total countable assets. Instead, you could set up an "income only" trust that would provide access to only the income, not the principal.

Reverse mortgages and loans (see the main article) also could push someone beyond the allowable asset limit. To avoid exceeding the limit, you could provide income for a parent through a "Medicaid annuity." The principal transferred into the annuity would not count toward total countable assets, although the income would. These annuities have strict requirements and are available from only a few specialized insurers.

Go to LongTermCareLink.net for links to companies offering Medicaid annuities, among other resources (click "Links," then "Insurance Products," and search for Medicaid annuity options and information among the annuity providers listed).

Unlike trusts, Medicaid annuities provide a guaranteed amount of monthly income. They are likely to provide the parent with more income each month than a trust could, assuming that a similar amount of cash is placed in each. On the downside, the parent's heirs will not receive any remaining principal upon the parent's death.

Yes, You Can Cut Big Medical Bills Down to Size

Susan Dressler, president of Health Claim Assistance, Inc., a medical billing advocacy company located in West Chicago, Illinois (HealthClaimAssistance.net). She previously spent 17 years working in insurance industry claims departments and is one of the founders of the Alliance of Claims Assistance Professionals, a nonprofit professional association.

Major medical problems can turn into major financial problems for those who lack Medicare or health insurance. They can be just as costly for those who do have health coverage if Medicare or insurance won't cover the bills.

There may be a way out. Insurance or Medicare can be convinced to pay up, or health-care providers can be convinced to pare down charges.

BEFORE AND DURING TREATMENT

Before receiving any potentially expensive non-emergency medical treatment...

●**Ask your insurance company to confirm that the health-care provider is in its provider network.** If you have Medicare, ask the provider to confirm that it has a participation agreement with Medicare and accepts Medicare's approved amount as payment in full. If it doesn't, find a health-care provider that does.

●**Read your insurance plan's benefits booklet (or online benefits summary).** Pay special attention to the section labeled "Exclusions" or "Not Covered." If you have any doubt that the procedure will be covered, contact your insurance company.

●**Don't agree to the treatment without knowing how much it will cost** if you do not have insurance or Medicare or if the treatment is not covered by your plan. Confirm with your doctor that the treatment is necessary.

●**Keep a log of every drug, test and procedure.** Do this yourself, or ask a family member to remain on hand throughout your treatment and keep the log for you. When your bill arrives, this log will help you confirm that your bill is accurate.

DON'T PAY WHAT YOU DON'T OWE

Health-care providers, insurance companies and Medicare sometimes bill patients improperly. *What to do...*

●**Compare the bills you receive from providers with the "Explanation of Benefits" (EOB)** statements you receive from your insurance company or "Medicare Summary Notices" (MSNs) you receive from Medicare. The amounts that these EOBs or MSNs say you were charged should match the amounts on the health-care providers' bills. If they don't, call the provider's patient financial services department. It might be a simple billing error. Or it could be a case of "balance billing," where you're billed for the uncovered portion of the provider's charges. (Sometimes charges are combined and it isn't always clear what's been paid for.)

●**Request itemized bills from health-care providers.** Standard medical bills don't always fully break down charges. With an itemized bill, you can spot double billing and charges for services not rendered.

Note: You must get these from the provider—Medicare and insurance companies will not provide itemized bills.

●**Scan the paperwork sent to you by Medicare** or your insurance company to determine why a procedure or product was not covered or was only partially covered. Often the explanation will be that a procedure wasn't "medically necessary," that the bill was larger than is "reasonable and customary" or that you were outside the age range for which the procedure is covered.

Your doctor might be able to convince your insurance company or Medicare that the refusal is incorrect. Ask the doctor to write a letter explaining why the procedure was medically necessary in your case or to provide a reason why the bill was larger than usual. You can continue to appeal this decision if it isn't initially reversed.

●**Ask the health-care provider to confirm that the procedure was coded properly.** Insurance and Medicare claims sometimes are rejected simply because someone in the provider's office entered the wrong billing code.

•**Determine whether an out-of-network charge is justified.** If you visited a health-care provider that is not part of your insurer's network (or one that does not have a participation agreement with Medicare), you might have to pay a significant share of the bill. If you visited this health-care provider because of a medical emergency, however, the bills should be treated as if they came from an in-network or participating provider. Sending copies of emergency room reports or police accident reports to the insurance company or Medicare could convince them that this was a legitimate emergency.

Helpful: Out-of-network bills also should be covered if no in-network provider was qualified to provide the type of care required.

NEGOTIATE A LOWER BILL

The amount a health-care provider charges is not chiseled in stone. *To get a better price…*

•**Discuss money before the procedure.** Your negotiating power is strongest before receiving treatment, though it still might be possible to haggle afterward.

•**Ask the provider's patient financial services department for a "charity case application"** if you are financially unable to pay a large health-care bill. If your application is approved, your bill might be dramatically reduced or waived entirely.

Helpful: If you have a stack of bills from hospitals, doctors, labs and other health-care providers, request this hardship discount from the largest company first—typically, the hospital. Once you have written evidence that the hospital has granted you a discount, the smaller medical providers might match this discount.

•**Ask for a discount from the health-care provider's patient financial services department in exchange for prompt out-of-pocket payment.** Some health-care providers are willing to cut their prices by anywhere from 10% to 50%, though others never budge.

Tip: Stress that you want to pay, but the bill is so large that you are financially unable to do so. This is likely to be more effective than creating an adversarial relationship by arguing that the bills are exorbitant and unfair.

•**Hire a professional claims advocate to assist with your negotiations if the provider won't lower your bill.** The Alliance of Claims Assistance Professionals (888-394-5163, Claims.org) or Medical Billing Advocates of America (855-203-7058, Bill Advocates.com) can help you find assistance in your region.

Make sure that the advocate you hire has at least 10 years of experience in claims assistance or medical billing, is familiar with the health-care providers that you are dealing with and can provide at least three former clients as references.

Expect to be charged between $30 and $150 an hour, depending on region and experience level, or around 15% to 35% of the amount that the claims assistance professional saves you.

How to Get Health Care Regardless of Your Ability to Pay

FindaHealthCenter.HRSA.gov

Here are some places to look for free or reduced-cost health care, if you are beyond your insurance limits or have very low income.

•**Community health centers provide health care regardless of your ability to pay and even if you have no health insurance.** To find the closest community health center, go to FindaHealthCenter.HRSA.gov.

If you don't have internet access, call your city or county government to find a community health center. Phone the center for information or for an appointment.

•**Hill-Burton Facilities.** About 200 health care facilities nationwide are obligated to provide free or reduced-cost care to people with very low incomes who are unable to pay. They are known as Hill-Burton obligated facilities after the law that created them. Each facility chooses which services it will provide at no or lowered cost and who will receive them. Eligibility is based on family size and income. You may apply at a Hill-Burton obligated facility for free or reduced-cost care either before or after you receive care. Be sure to follow the application's guidelines carefully. To find one, call the Hill-Burton Hotline 800-638-0742; 800- 492-0359 in Maryland.

•**State medical assistance programs** help people with incomes under certain limits pay for prescription medications, visits to the doctor, hospitalizations, and insurance premiums. Each program is different and not all states have medical assistance programs. Contact your local department of social services or a local hospital's social worker to see if your s tate has a program and if you might be eligible to apply.

•**The National Breast and Cervical Cancer Early Detection Program** for low-income women helps them afford mammograms and Pap tests. Find a free or low-cost mammogram and Pap test in your State.

Contact: Centers for Disease Control and Prevention, Division of Cancer Prevention and Control, 4770 Buford Hwy, NE, MS K-64, Atlanta, GA 30341-3717. Call 800-CDC-INFO; TTY 888-232-6348; fax 770-488-4760; E-mail *cdcinfo@cdc.gov*.

•**Veterans Medical Benefits provide care to enrolled veterans.** If you served in the military and were discharged in other than dishonorable conditions, you are probably eligible. For more information, see the US Department of Veteran Affairs web site *VA.gov*.

VA Benefits: 800-827-1000.

Health care benefits: 877-222-8387.

How to Cut Costs of Heart Disease, Cancer, Diabetes and Other Chronic Conditions

David Nganele, PhD, president of Solutions to Healthcare, a health-education company based in New York City. He is author of several books, including *The Best Healthcare for Less*. He is founder of Harmony Health Communications, where he developed award-winning disease-management programs in cooperation with doctors, drug companies and community groups.

A chronic disease can be financially devastating even for someone who has health insurance. Benefit limits often are reached before the condition is under control.

People without insurance may be forced to borrow money or sell assets when faced with such conditions as recurring cancers, heart disease, depression and diabetes.

Making lifestyle changes—quitting smoking, improving your diet and exercising—can reduce the need for medication for many conditions. In addition, sufferers can eliminate some costs entirely by understanding how hospitals, drug companies and doctors do business. *Most effective cost-saving strategies…*

AT-HOME CARE

•**Become an expert.** Learning all you can about your illness may help you discover lower-cost treatments and aspects of the condition that even your doctor may not know about. You'll also benefit psychologically from putting yourself in charge instead of relying solely on your doctor.

•**Contact associations specializing in your condition.** They can help you to locate low-cost treatment centers and suggest ways to prevent your condition from worsening.

Example: Adding supplemental chromium, magnesium and vanadium to your diet may help with diabetes.

Associations for several common illnesses…

•**American Cancer Society.** 800-227-2345, Cancer.org.

●**American Diabetes Association.** 800-342-2383, Diabetes.org.

●**American Heart Disease Association,** 800-242-8721, AmericanHeart.org.

●**American Kidney Fund,** 800-638-8299, KidneyFund.org.

●**Depression and Bipolar Support Alliance,** 800-826-3632, DBSAlliance.org.

If you're unsure of the appropriate organization, contact the American Medical Association for a referral (800-621-8335, AMA-assn.org).

●**Investigate alternative treatments, such as acupuncture and biofeedback.** Many now are covered by insurance. Even if they're not, they may cost less and be more effective than conventional treatments. For information, contact the federal government's National Center for Complementary and Alternative Medicine at 888-644-6226, NCCAM.nih.gov.

●**Buy drugs in large quantities to save on co-payments.** Most insurers charge a copayment for each prescription, regardless of the drug's cost. Copayments today can be as high as $50.

Ask your doctor to write 90-day prescriptions, instead of 30-day. You will reduce your copayment by two-thirds.

Example: If you take eight prescription medicines—not unusual for someone with a chronic condition—and have a $30 copayment, your cost will fall by $1,920, or two-thirds—from $2,880 (8 x $30 x 12) to $960 (8 x $30 x 4).

If your insurance company won't allow more than a 30-day supply of a drug from a local pharmacy, ask your health insurer if it uses a mail-order drug service. They typically supply 90-day quantities. Most insurers prefer that you order by mail because it holds down their costs.

●**Ask your doctors for free samples.** Pharmaceutical companies give away billions of dollars worth of samples for doctors to pass on to patients. Don't be embarrassed to ask. If your doctor doesn't have samples, ask him to prescribe generic drugs. For all but a very small percentage of patients, generics are just as effective as brand-name drugs. If you do have insurance, you may have a smaller copayment with generic drugs.

Example: A patient who suffers from depression and doesn't have drug coverage typically pays about $687 for 90 tablets of Prozac in 40-milligram (mg) strength. The generic equivalent represents a saving of 30% or more.

●**Take part in a clinical trial.** Each year, thousands of people with chronic ailments receive free treatment by taking part in trials designed to assess new drugs and procedures. The drug industry or National Institutes of Health (800-411-1222, ClinicalTrials.gov) coordinates most of these trials.

Important: Participants are given a consent form explaining the trial. Read it, and ask questions before signing.

Some trials are open—all the participants are given the medicine being tested and are informed about the results of the trial at each stage.

Other trials are double-blind—some participants are given the treatment while others receive a placebo. This prevents test results from being skewed by psychological factors. Patients—and often the doctors who administer the drug—aren't told who has received the drug and who has received the placebo.

Despite the risk that you won't receive any treatment, don't rule out a double-blind trial. If you take part in one, you have about a 50-50 chance of receiving cutting-edge medication.

Even if you get the placebo, doctors typically take you out of the trial if your condition worsens, so you can resume treatment on your own.

HOSPITAL-BASED CARE

●**When you are hospitalized, put your primary-care physician in charge.** Doctors who are unfamiliar with your health history might recommend costly, unnecessary procedures.

Primary physicians, as a rule, recommend fewer procedures than other doctors at a hospital. Your primary doctor already is familiar with your condition and may have tried a variety of treatments for you in the past.

You even might ask your primary physician to help check your hospital bill for inaccuracies. As a patient with a chronic illness, you need to be vigilant about not reaching insurance policy limits sooner than necessary.

●**Consider treatment at a teaching or government-run hospital or clinic.** These institutions usually charge patients according to their ability to pay. They can make sense for people with limited incomes, especially those who lack insurance or have passed their insurance limit.

Information: Health Resources and Services Administration, 800-400-2742. HRSA.gov.

●**Negotiate with the hospital and other providers.** Pay what you can now, and work out a payment plan for the rest. Or ask for a fee reduction. A hospital or doctor nearly always will compromise because reducing the bill may be cheaper than paying a collection agency or not collecting at all.

●**Get the opinion of more than one doctor before any procedure.** Second opinions increase your chance of finding less expensive—and perhaps more effective—treatment.

Example: Cancer treatments vary greatly in cost and outcome. Since few doctors are experts in all procedures, it's best to weigh the options with different specialists.

Many chronic disease sufferers don't get more than one opinion because they think that their insurance won't pay for a second one. In fact, most policies pay for two or three consultations as long as the doctors are in the insurer's network of approved physicians.

Unraveling the Medicare Insurance Maze

Charles B. Inlander, health-care consultant and founding president of the People's Medical Society, a consumer advocacy organization active in the 1980s and 1990s. He is the author of 20 books, including *Take This Book to the Hospital with You: A Consumer Guide to Surviving Your Hospital Stay.*

Having turned 65 this month, I am now officially on Medicare. Enrolling was a snap. I did it on the Medicare.gov website in less than five minutes. This can also be done by mail or at your local Social Security office. What wasn't a snap was deciding whether I should purchase a Medigap policy to supplement my traditional Medicare coverage or opt for a different type of program known as a Medicare Advantage Plan.* *To select the right plan for you...*

●**Know the pros and cons.** Medigap is a type of private health insurance that helps pay some of the health-care costs ("gaps") that traditional Medicare doesn't cover, such as copayments and deductibles. However, Medicare Advantage Plans do not just fill in the gaps. While also sold by Medicare-approved private insurance companies, they provide all of the usual Medicare-approved services within their own network of doctors and hospitals. To attract members, most Advantage plans offer some additional services, such as dental and vision benefits. Advantage plans substitute for traditional Medicare, so you do not carry a Medigap policy if you join.

When Medigap may be better: If you travel a lot or spend several months each year in another state, traditional Medicare supplemented with a Medigap policy is probably the better choice for you. This combination allows you to use any doctor or hospital in the country that accepts Medicare without any financial penalty. In contrast, with a Medicare Advantage Plan, if a doctor or hospital is not in the plan's network, you must pay an often hefty out-of-network charge.

Insider tip: Premiums for Medigap policies can differ significantly from company to company—even for the exact same coverage. Carefully compare the premiums to ensure you're getting the most for your money.

When an Advantage plan may be better: Medicare Advantage Plans are good for people who are most concerned about finding the lowest possible premium—even if they have to switch doctors to find one within the plan's network.

*If you're already enrolled in Medicare, you can switch your Medigap or Advantage plan once annually (usually mid-October to early December). This means you can buy a different Advantage or Medigap plan or jump from a Medigap to an Advantage plan (or vice versa).

Insider tip: Be sure to call the company whose plan you're considering (or check its website) to confirm exactly which doctors and hospitals are included in the network.

●**Consider getting help.** Many insurance brokers sell Medigap and Medicare Advantage Plans and can be extremely helpful in comparing programs and prices. Contact your state insurance department for a list of licensed brokers in your area. To do your own research, go to the Medicare.gov website and click on the "Find health & drug plans" (for Advantage plans) and "Find and compare medigap policies" tabs. Each will display the Medicare-approved plans and policies available in your zip code and allow you to compare benefits and prices. Or call Medicare at 800-MEDICARE (633-4227), and ask for the information to be sent to you. For more help with Medicare, see pages 33 and 45.

Appealing a Medicare Claim

Roundup of experts in Medicare appeals, reported in *Kiplinger's Retirement Report*. Kiplingers.com

Appealing a denial of a Medicare claim has a good chance of succeeding, although it can be slow and time-consuming. Government reviewers at the first level of the appeals process reversed denials in 40% of cases involving Medicare Part A...53% involving Part B...and 44% relating to durable medical equipment. Before appealing, talk with the doctor, hospital and Medicare to see if the denial was caused by something that can be easily corrected, such as wrong coding. If that does not work, read the appeal rules on the back of your quarterly Medicare summary notice. Appeals range from reconsideration by a Medicare contractor to going to US District Court. There are special rules for Medicare Advantage plans and Part D prescription-drug appeals. For help with an appeal, contact your local State Health Insurance Assistance Program (SHIP). For information, go to SHIPTalk.org.

Get More from Your Insurance

Charles B. Inlander, health-care consultant and founding president of the People's Medical Society, a consumer advocacy organization active in the 1980s and 1990s. He is the author of 20 books, including *Take This Book to the Hospital with You: A Consumer Guide to Surviving Your Hospital Stay.*

With the Affordable Care Act (ACA), the traditional "open season" that gives us a chance to sign up or switch health insurance plans has a few more moving parts. Open season now includes three basic categories of health insurance—Medicare and employer health plans, as in the past, and ACA health policies for people who buy insurance on their own, who haven't been able to afford it or who have been denied coverage. Regardless of the type of insurance you have or need, making the right choices can be complicated. *Key points to consider…*

●**Cost.** No matter what type of health policy you might be shopping for, one of the biggest mistakes people make is paying more attention to a policy's premium cost than its actual coverage. In addition to the premium cost, consider the co-payments, deductibles and other out-of-pocket costs you'll owe if you use doctors, hospitals or medications not fully covered by the plan. These issues apply to Medicare, employer plans (if multiple plans are offered where you work) and to those plans that will be offered via the Obamacare Health Insurance Marketplaces, also known as Health Exchanges.

What helps: Make a list of the doctors, hospitals, medications and services you use, and see whether they are covered by any plan you are considering. Then compare the co-pays for those services or any limits on the number of treatments allowed (such as 20 physical therapy sessions per year) for each plan. Add those costs to the premiums before choosing a policy.

●**Does the plan fit your needs?** While cost is important, it's crucial that you opt for a plan that meets your family's health-care needs. For example, if your 55-year-old spouse has Parkinson's disease, you can anticipate needing more health services in the future than you did prior to that diagnosis.

What helps: Ask your doctor what health services you (and your family members) may need in the next year or two. Use that as a guide to find a plan that best matches your needs.

●**Don't miss the deadline!** Believe me, this is one deadline you don't want to miss. If you do, you'll keep your current plan (except in circumstances such as marriage or divorce).

Here are the specific dates you need to know: If you're on Medicare, open season is October 15 through December 7. If you have an employer plan, open season usually occurs during November and December—check with your employer. If you're buying an individual or family health policy from a private insurance company or are purchasing through an ACA-created Health Exchange, you need to sign up by December 15 for coverage to begin January 1. The last day to enroll or change a health plan for 2017 was January 31, 2016.

Best places to get help: Medicare's website, Medicare.gov, compares various Medicare plans on a state-by-state basis. Or call 1-800-MEDICARE. If you're shopping for an individual or a family plan under the new Health Exchanges, Healthcare.gov is an excellent resource or call 1-800-318-2596. If you have an employer plan, check with the company's human resources office.

Choosing a Medicare Advantage Plan? These Common Mistakes Can Cost You BIG

Frederic Riccardi, MSW, director of programs and outreach with the Medicare Rights Center, a nonprofit consumer rights organization with offices in New York City and Washington, DC. MedicareRights.org

---

The choice of a Medicare Advantage plan can be a crucial one when it comes to the cost and quality of your health care.

Trap: People who are eligible often overlook important factors when considering the many plans that are offered by private health insurers.

The Medicare Plan Finder (Medicare.gov/find-a-plan) is useful for comparing the Advantage plans available in your area.

Important: Open-enrollment period runs from October 15 through December 7 (not to year-end).

As you make your decision, be wary of these eight common mistakes...

●**Signing up for a plan that doesn't include your doctor.** Just because a doctor's office (or hospital or skilled nursing facility) accepts Medicare doesn't guarantee that it will accept your Medicare Advantage plan. If it doesn't, you may have to pay substantial out-of-network costs (or switch doctors). Check with all your health-care providers before choosing an Advantage plan.

Warning: If you split your year between homes in different parts of the country, be particularly wary of plans that impose hefty out-of-pocket costs for seeing out-of-network providers.

●**Failing to check the drug list.** Before signing up for any plan, scan its formulary—the list of prescription drugs covered—to confirm that all of the medications you currently take are included without excessive co-pays or a requirement that you try less expensive drugs first. If an otherwise appealing plan does not include one of your medications, ask your doctor whether another drug that is covered by the plan would work as well for you.

Failing to confirm the quality of dental, vision and hearing coverage. Medicare Advantage plans often include dental, vision and hearing benefits—coverage that traditional Medicare lacks. Unfortunately, these benefits often are much less valuable than they seem, sometimes offering little more than basic eye and hearing exams or discounted dental cleanings.

What to do: Don't rely solely on the plan's brochure. Look for the plan's "Evidence of Coverage" on its website for details. Use the Medicare Plan Finder to determine which plans have the best coverage for a reasonable cost.

●**Ignoring the kinds of cost differences that aren't obvious.** Rather than comparing just premiums and deductibles—the two costs that most people focus on—also compare out-of-pocket maximums set by various plans, plus co-payments and co-insurance charged for doctor office visits...hospital stays...diagnostic tests...visits to specialists... emergency care...ambulance services...the cost of purchasing medications you take on an ongoing basis...and other medical services. These can be found in descriptions available at Medicare.gov.

•**Ignoring the annual notice of change.** If you already belong to an Advantage plan, you should receive an update each year explaining how your plan is changing in the coming year. Read this carefully—plans can change substantially from one year to the next.

Accidentally voiding retiree coverage from a former employer. If you have retiree health coverage, speak with your former employer's benefits manager before signing up for a Medicare Advantage plan. Some retiree coverage may be voided if participants sign up for a Medicare Advantage plan or Part D.

•**Overlooking Part B premiums when calculating a plan's cost.** Part B covers doctor's services, outpatient care and home health services, among other medical services. If you opt for an Advantage plan, it will provide these services, but you still will have to pay the Part B premium, in addition to any premium charged by an Advantage plan.

•**Ignoring the downside of Medicare Advantage disenrollment.** The Medicare system offers an escape route for those who quickly become disenchanted with their Medicare Advantage plans. They can disenroll from their plans between January 1 and February 14 and rejoin traditional Medicare. But depending on your state's laws, that might be too late for you also to sign up for a Medigap policy—an insurance policy offered by a private company that pays co-insurance and deductibles associated with traditional Medicare. Without a Medigap policy, you might have to pay significant medical costs out of pocket, perhaps for the rest of your life. It's wiser to make an informed choice during the annual election period than to depend on disenrollment.

You Can Negotiate to Pay Less for Health Care

Charles B. Inlander, health-care consultant and founding president of the People's Medical Society, a consumer advocacy organization active in the 1980s and 1990s. He is the author of 20 books, including *Take This Book to the Hospital with You: A Consumer Guide to Surviving Your Hospital Stay.*

Most people never think about negotiating fees with a doctor or other health-care provider. Negotiating is something we do with a car dealer or at a flea market. But the truth is, doctors and hospitals negotiate fees with insurance companies and the government all the time. So why not with you? If you have health insurance, you can save by negotiating such health-care fees as copayments. If you are uninsured or need a medical treatment that is not covered by your insurance, you can save even more. *How to negotiate fees for health care and medical products...*

•**Don't be afraid to ask.** Most doctors are willing to lower their fees for people with limited budgets who may not have health insurance (or only very basic coverage). But you must initiate the negotiation.

My advice: If the quoted fee is more than you can pay, ask if some other payment arrangement, such as paying in monthly installments, can be made or if the fee can be lowered.

What you might say: "What is the fee for this treatment/service? Unfortunately, I can't afford that. Can we negotiate?" If you have been treated by the health-care provider for many years, mention your loyal patronage.

•**Talk to the right person.** In a recent report published in *U.S. News & World Report,* a hospital's chief financial officer (CFO) noted that it is common for hospitals to reduce charges by 30% for needy or uninsured patients who contact the CFO directly. He noted that most hospitals give large health insurers discounts of 60% or more, so deals with individual patients are still profitable to the facility.

My advice: Always negotiate with a decision-maker. For fee reductions at a hospital, before you receive surgery or any other treatment, call the hospital and ask the operator to connect you to the office of the CFO or the assistant CFO—one of them must sign off on all of the hospital's financial negotiations. At a doctor's office, talk directly to the doctor about lower fees—not the nurse, office manager or receptionist.

What you might say to a doctor or hospital CFO: "What does Medicare pay you for the service or treatment I am going to get? Will you accept the same payment from me?"

•**Request a discount on medical products.** Several years ago, I took a friend to a hearing-aid shop, and we negotiated 40% off the lowest quoted price. Since most stores that sell hearing aids, wheelchairs and other types of durable medical equipment are privately owned, and typically mark up products by 50% to 100%, you usually can strike a good bargain with the owner.

My advice: Shop around before negotiating and don't forget to check prices on the Internet. Then start by offering 20% less than the best price you found elsewhere. Offer to pay in cash rather than by credit card or check—this saves the merchant a processing fee.

The worst that can happen if you try to negotiate a medical fee is that your request will be turned down. But chances are you'll save a tidy sum with little effort on your part.

Free Medical Screenings

Jim Miller, an advocate for senior citizens, writes "Savvy Senior," a weekly information column syndicated in more than 400 newspapers nationwide. Based in Norman, Oklahoma, he offers a free senior newswire service. SavvySenior.org

In addition to a nutritious diet, regular exercise and not smoking, health screenings are the best way to stay healthy as you age. But for the approximately 46 million Americans living without health insurance and millions more who are underinsured, health screenings may be a luxury they can't afford.

Fortunately, free or low-cost health screenings for a wide range of medical conditions are provided through various national, state and local organizations, government agencies and even businesses.

The best way to find these screenings in your area is by calling the health department of your city, county or state. Also check with hospitals, pharmacies, senior centers and your "area agency on aging."

National and local health associations that focus on particular diseases also may help you. For example, to search for free or low-cost cancer screenings, call the American Cancer Society (800-227-2345) or the National Cancer Institute (800-422-6237).

Other national and regional screening programs and services...

CARDIOVASCULAR DISEASE

•**Legs for Life.** This program offers free screenings for peripheral arterial disease (PAD), a "hardening of the arteries" condition that affects an estimated 8 million to 10 million Americans. Individuals with PAD have much greater risk for heart attack, stroke and even leg amputation. Some screening sites also can test for related diseases, such as abdominal aortic aneurysm and carotid artery disease. Most screenings take place in September and require an appointment. 703-691-1805, Sirweb.org.

•**WISEWOMAN Program.** For low-income, uninsured and underinsured women between the ages of 40 and 64, the Centers for Disease Control and Prevention (CDC) offers free blood pressure and cholesterol tests in 20 states. Some sites also offer testing for diabetes and osteoporosis. 800-232-4636, CDC.gov/wisewoman.

SKIN CANCER

•**American Academy of Dermatology** offers free skin cancer screenings by volunteer dermatologists across the US. 888-462-3376, AAD.org/ (type "screenings" in search box).

•**Skin Cancer Foundation** operates a nationwide "Road to Healthy Skin Tour" that starts in April and runs through September. 800-754-6490, SkinCancer.org.

BREAST AND CERVICAL CANCER

•**National Breast and Cervical Cancer Early Detection Program.** This CDC program is for low-income, uninsured and underinsured women. It offers free or low-cost mammograms and Pap tests year-round in all 50 states, the District of Columbia and five US territories. 800-232-4636, CDCgov/cancer. (Click on "How can I get a free or low-cost mammogram or Pap test?" in the right column of the website page.)

PROSTATE CANCER

•**Prostate Cancer Awareness Week.** Each year, during the third full week of September, the Prostate Cancer Educational Council coordinates with hundreds of sites across America to offer free or low-cost screenings to all men over age 45 and to high-risk men (African-Americans and men who have a family history of the disease) over age 40. The screening consists of a prostate-specific antigen (PSA) blood test and digital rectal exam. 866-477-6788, PCAW.org.

•**Zero, the Project to End Prostate Cancer** offer free screenings from mobile screening units that tour the country. 888-245-9455, ZeroCancer.org.

COLORECTAL CANCER

•**CDC** currently provides funding for 25 state programs that give free or low-cost colon and rectal cancer screenings to people ages 50 and older who have no insurance and low incomes. Specific state contact numbers include Maryland (800-477-9774)...Washington (888-438-2247)...Nebraska (800-532-2227)...and New York (866-442-2262). CDC.gov/cancer/colorectal.

•**Fight Colorectal Cancer** offers free information about colorectal cancer research, free or low-cost screenings, diagnoses and treatment options. FightColorectalCancer.org, 877-427-2111.

KIDNEY DISEASE

•**Kidney Early Evaluation Program** (KEEP). Sponsored by the National Kidney Foundation, this program offers free screenings for those at elevated risk, including adults with high blood pressure, diabetes or a family history of kidney disease. It also offers free screenings in at least 20 cities on World Kidney Day, the second Thursday in March. 800-622-9010, Kidney.org/news/keep/index.cfm.

•**American Kidney Fund** offers free kidney screenings to anyone age 18 and older in the At-

lanta, Chicago and Washington, DC, metropolitan areas. 866-300-2900, Kidneyfund.org (click on Prevention).

ASTHMA

•**American College of Allergy, Asthma & Immunology** sponsors free asthma screenings, mostly done in May, in more than 250 locations across the US as part of National Asthma and Allergy Awareness Month. ACAAI.org (search "free screenings").

MEMORY

•**National Memory Screening Day.** On the third Tuesday in November, the Alzheimer's Foundation of America offers free, confidential memory screenings. 866-232-8484, NationalMemoryScreening.org.

VISION

•**Prevent Blindness America** offers free vision screenings in 24 states and the District of Columbia. 800-331-2020, PreventBlindness.org.

MENTAL HEALTH

•**National Depression Screening Day.** Screening for Mental Health Inc. offers free confidential screenings nationwide for depression, suicide risk, bipolar disorder, chronic anxiety and posttraumatic stress disorder, usually first week of October. MentalHealthScreening.org.

STDS

Most health departments and many hospitals and other health-care facilities provide free or low-cost screenings for HIV, AIDS and other sexually transmitted diseases. 800-458-5231, HIVtest.org.

FREE SCREENINGS FROM PHARMACIES

•**CVS Project Health.** National retail pharmacy chain CVS offers free screenings, including blood pressure, glucose, BMI and total cholesterol, at their Project-Health special events held at CVS locations in major US cities and Puerto Rico. Visit CVS.com/project-health to find an event near you.

•**Sam's Club Free Screenings.** Warehouse club retailer Sam's Club offers free screenings on specific days in the year. Go to SamsClub.com, click on "Shop by department," then "Health Screenings." Membership not required, but availability varies by state and club. The screenings include choles-terol…blood pressure…glucose levels…body mass index…vision and hearing.

How to Repair Broken Eyeglasses

Neil Hounchell, owner of National Eyewear Repair, a Phoe-nix-based company that offers a repair-by-mail service for eyeglass wearers outside the Phoenix area. NationalEyewear Repair.com

Many eyeglass repairs are best left to op-tometrists or other eyeglass-repair profes-sionals, but some can be tackled quickly and cheaply on one's own…

•**Loose hinges.** Eyeglass hinges often become stretched out over time. When that happens, the eyeglass arms no longer fit snugly against the tem-ples, and the glasses become prone to sliding down the nose or falling off entirely.

What to do: Though this may be a temporary measure until you can get to an optometrist, many people find it works so well that they don't bother seeing a professional. Take a pair of very small rubber bands, and slide one up each arm of the glasses until the rubber bands rest in the V-shaped gaps formed between the frame and arm when the arms are not fully extended. (Crafts stores often sell very small rubber bands.)

These rubber bands will serve as springs, pushing the arms of the glasses tighter against the temples. If you don't like the way they look on your glasses, use a marker that matches the color of the eyeglass frame to color the rubber bands before sliding them into place. They might not be noticeable at all.

•**Lost screw for the hinge.** The tiny screws that hold eyeglass hinges together occasionally fall out—and they're so small that they often get lost.

What to do: The eyeglass repair kits sold in dol-lar stores, discount stores and elsewhere typically contain a small screwdriver and an assortment of tiny replacement screws. But there's no guaran-tee that any of these screws will be the right size

for your glasses. If you use one, check it each day for the first week or so to confirm that it has not started to come loose. If this tiny screw is even a fraction of a millimeter narrower than the original one, it could fall out, too.

If you don't have a screw of the appropriate size, a paper clip can serve as a temporary substitute. Feed one end of the paper clip through the hinge, then use a pair of needle-nose pliers to bend it just above and below the hinge so that it can't fall out. Use a wire cutter (often built into the same needle-nose pliers) to trim off the excess paper clip metal.

•**Lens that pops out of rimless or semi-rimless frames.** Rimless and semi-rimless frames typically use a thin monofilament—essentially a piece of fish-ing line—to hold lenses in place.

What to do: After a lens pops out, loop a piece of ribbon around the monofilament, then use this ribbon to gently pull the monofilament aside so that you can slip the lens partially into place in the frame. Next, slide the ribbon down the length of the mono-filament, gently tugging the monofilament into the groove on the edge of the lens as you do so. When the monofilament is completely in the grove, pull the ribbon free. If the ribbon is too tightly trapped between the monofilament and the lens to remove it without popping the lens back out, use scissors to cut the ribbon near where it passes between the mono-filament and lens to make it easier to work free.

Two repairs NOT to do…

•**Do NOT use superglue on broken plastic frames.** Mainstream glues generally will not repair a plastic eyeglass frame for long, and the residue this glue leaves behind will make it harder for a professional to later repair the glasses.

•**Do NOT use lens-scratch repair kits.** There are products available that claim to remove eyeglass lens scratches. But they will either do a poor job removing scratches or will distort your vision when you look through the lens.

How to Get Good Dental Care for Lots Less

Jim Miller, an advocate for older Americans, writes "Savvy Senior," a weekly information column syndicated in more than 400 newspapers nationwide. Based in Norman, Oklahoma, he also offers a free senior e-news service at SavvySenior.org.

Taking care of your teeth these days can take a big bite out of your budget. This is especially true for the 108 million Americans who don't have dental insurance and are stuck paying full out-of-pocket expenses every time they visit a dentist. But even many people who have dental coverage often end up paying a lot for what their insurance doesn't cover.

There are a number of strategies, resources and services that can help you reduce your dental bills or maybe even get care for free. Of course, the most obvious way to reduce costs is to simply ask for a discount—many dentists will readily shave off 10% for any uninsured customers. And if you're over age 55 or 60, it is wise to ask whether there is a senior discount program, which is quite common even though it's not usually advertised.

Here are more ways to save…

JOIN A DISCOUNT PLAN

There are various plans that provide members access to networks of dentists who have agreed to offer their services at discounted rates. You pay an annual membership fee—roughly $80 to $200 a year—in exchange for 10% to 60% discounts on cleanings, crowns, implants, root canals and other procedures from participating dentists. To locate a plan, go to *DentalPlans.com* (or call 888-632-5353), the biggest resource with more than 40 dental discount plans listed. You can search by zip code and get a breakdown of the discounts offered in your area.

Another discount option currently available only in the southern California area is Brighter. It provides free access to a network of dentists offering an average discount of 35% on services. Call 888-230-5305, or go to Brighter.com.

CONSIDER MEDICARE ADVANTAGE

If you are a Medicare beneficiary, you already may know that original Medicare (Part A and Part B) and Medigap supplemental policies do not cover most dental care—but there are some Medicare Advantage (Part C) plans that do. Many of these plans, which are sold through private insurance companies, cover routine dental care along with vision care, hearing care and prescription drugs, in addition to all of your hospital and medical insurance. To find Medicare Advantage plans in your area that offer dental care, call 800-633-4227 or go to Medicare.gov/find-a-plan.

You can switch from original Medicare to a Medicare Advantage plan each year during the open-enrollment period, which is between October 15 and December 7. Or, if you are about to enroll in Medicare for the first time, you may want to consider a Medicare Advantage plan that covers dental.

USE A DENTAL SCHOOL

To get dental care at a reduced price, find a college or university near you that has a dental school. Most of the 65 accredited dental schools in the US and Puerto Rico offer comprehensive care provided by dental students who are overseen by experienced, qualified teachers. You can expect to pay about half of what a traditional dentist would charge and still receive excellent, well-supervised care.

Or, if you want to get your teeth cleaned, you can check with local colleges that offer dental-hygiene programs. For training purposes, most of the 335 US programs provide supervised dental cleanings by their students for 50% to 75% less than you would pay at a dentist's office.

To locate dental schools or dental-hygiene programs in your area, visit ADA.org/dentalschools.

DENTAL BENEFITS FOR VETERANS

The US Department of Veterans Affairs provides free dental care to certain veterans who have a service-connected dental condition or disability…and to former prisoners of war. To learn more about this benefit and the eligibility requirements, call 877-222-8387 or visit VA.gov/dental.

If you're not eligible for its free dental care, the VA also is now offering a national VA Dental Insurance Program that gives you the option to buy dental insurance through Delta Dental (DeltaDentalVAdip.org) and MetLife (MetLife.com/vadip) at a reduced cost. To be eligible, you must be a veteran enrolled in the VA health-care program or an individual enrolled in the VA's Civilian Health and Medical Program. To find out more about these last two programs, including eligibility, call 877-222-8387 or visit VA.gov/dental.

LOW-INCOME OPTIONS

If your income is low, there are various programs and services that provide dental care at a reduced rate or for free. *Here's where to look…*

•**Medicaid & CHIP benefits.** All states provide dental-care services to children covered by Medicaid and the Children's Health Insurance Program (CHIP), but dental coverage for adults on Medicaid will vary by state. See Medicaid.gov for coverage and eligibility details.

•**State and local services.** Some state and local programs as well as local clinics offer reduced-rate or free dental care to people with low incomes—generally below 200% of the federal poverty level. To find out what's available in your area, call your state or local dental society (EBusiness.ada.org/mystate.aspx).

•**HRSA health centers.** Supported by the US Health Resources and Services Administration, there are nearly 1,300 health centers that operate more than 9,200 locations around the US that provide discounted or free health and dental care based on financial need. To find a center near you that provides dental care, call 877-464-4772 or visit FindaHealthCenter.HRSA.gov.

•**Free health clinics.** There are around 1,200 nonprofit, privately funded, volunteer-based free clinics across the country that provide a range of medical, dental and pharmacy services to economically disadvantaged people. Call 703-647-7427, or go to NAFCClinics.org.

•**Dental Lifeline Network.** This national humanitarian organization provides free dental care to the elderly and disabled people who can't afford to pay. The program operates through a volunteer network of more than 15,000 dentists and 3,600 dental labs across the US. It also offers the Donated Orthodontic Services program in Illinois, Indiana, Kansas, New Jersey, North Carolina, Rhode Island,

Tennessee and Virginia that enables low-income children to receive orthodontic treatment for a fee of $200. Call 888-471-6334, or go to DentalLifeline.org.

•**Remote Area Medical.** This is a nonprofit, volunteer, charitable organization that provides free health, eye and dental care to people in need in certain areas of the US based on requests from local health departments and civic groups. The 2015 clinic schedule includes a total of 21 stops during the year in parts of Texas, Tennessee, California, Virginia, Illinois, Kentucky and Nevada. Call 865-579-1530, or go to RAMUSA.org.

•**Indian Health Service (IHS).** This is an agency within the US Department of Health and Human Services that provides free dental care at more than 230 IHS dental clinics across the US to American Indians and Alaska Natives who are members of federally recognized Indian tribes. Visit IHS.gov.

How to Save Big on Hearing Aids

Charles B. Inlander, consumer advocate and health-care consultant based in Fogelsville, Pennsylvania. He was the founding president of the nonprofit People's Medical Society, a consumer advocacy organization credited with key improvements in the quality of US health care, and is the author or co-author of more than 20 consumer-health books.

A friend of mine recently saved 90% on his first hearing aid!

Here's what happened: He had noticed some hearing loss in one ear, and the audiologist he visited suggested a single-ear aid. But the problem was the price. The one that was recommended cost $4,000! And Medicare and most private insurers do not cover hearing aids. Many patients would have bit the bullet and paid the $4,000…or simply gone without a hearing aid (a bad decision). But instead, with some creative shopping, this person was able to buy a good hearing aid for $400, and a local audiologist programmed and fit it for less than $100.

What my friend did: He found lots of used hearing aids online but ultimately found a one-year-old aid that his neighbor was getting rid of after purchasing a newer, more sophisticated model.

In general, prices for new, high-tech hearing aids have soared in recent years, particularly at private audiologists' offices. That's partially why only 20% of people who could benefit from a hearing aid ever use one. But there are many ways to save 50% to 90% on even the most sophisticated device.

My advice on how to save big on hearing aids...

•**Check national warehouse stores.** Costco and other warehouse stores now sell top brands of hearing aids at up to half off list prices. These aids are fully warranted (with the same warranty periods offered on hearing aids sold by audiologists), and an in-house hearing aid technician will test your hearing and fit you. Even though these technicians don't have as much training as an audiologist, they are generally qualified to do basic hearing tests and fittings. Free follow-up appointments are also provided.

•**Try a community-service organization.** Working with local audiologists, organizations such as the Lions Club and the Starkey Hearing Foundation have programs that provide refurbished or new hearing aids for people who cannot afford retail prices. The hearing aids are sold at a drastically reduced price or sometimes are free. You may be asked to show proof of your financial need—for example, a Medicaid Benefit Identification Card.

•**Look for a used hearing aid online.** Many used hearing aids are offered for sale on eBay and Craigslist. But before you tell yourself that you'd never consider buying a used version of an item that is so personalized to the user's needs, hear me out. As with any other purchase you might make on eBay or Craigslist, you must do your homework. For example, before you start shopping online, you need to get a hearing evaluation from an audiologist. This is usually covered by your insurance. Ask him/her what type of hearing aid is best for you—for example, behind the ear or open fit in the ear canal. When the audiologist recommends the type of hearing aid you need, he will likely also suggest a few good brands. You can then check for those types and brands on eBay and Craigslist. Before making a purchase, get a written agreement from the seller (it may be a private

party or a company) that the hearing aid is returnable within 30 days if any defects are found. Then, after you make the purchase, take the hearing aid to an audiologist for cleaning and reprogramming based on your specific type and degree of hearing loss. This final step should cost only about $100.

Wow! Insurance Pays for This?

Charles B. Inlander is a consumer advocate and healthcare consultant based in Fogelsville, Pennsylvania. He was the founding president of the nonprofit People's Medical Society, a consumer advocacy organization credited with key improvements in the quality of US health care, and is the author or coauthor of more than 20 consumer-health books.

My friend just received a 40% discount on a fitness watch. And after a dental procedure, he paid nothing for acupuncture to help ease the pain. His wife recently saved more than $800 on hearing aids. The surprising thing is that all these savings were benefits of their health insurance plan. Such benefits vary from state-to-state and plan-to-plan, but there are some widely used services and programs that your health plan may cover. Important: The onus is on you to find out about these programs (see below) and enroll in them. *What you should check out...*

WEIGHT-LOSS PROGRAMS, GRIEF COUNSELING AND MORE...

Are you having a hard time shedding those extra pounds? Chances are your health plan will pay all or most of the cost of a weight-loss and/or nutritional counseling program (often affiliated with a hospital and led by certified nutritionists). Your plan may also cover 10 or more sessions of grief counseling or even life coaching (which helps individuals cope with stressful work or life situations) as long as you see a licensed therapist (such as a psychiatrist, psychologist or social worker). Most health plans also offer disease/condition-management programs ranging from diabetes control to pain management. These plans often assign nurses, counselors and others to work directly with you to effectively deal with your condition. You may need a doctor's prescription or order to enroll in some of these programs—check with your insurer for details. Here's how: If you are enrolled in traditional Medicare, check with your Medicare supplemental carrier for services. If you are in a Medicare Advantage Plan, check your plan website or call for details. If your insurance plan is through your employer or a health exchange, contact the insurer.

HEALTHY LIVING PROGRAM...

Don't want to pay hefty gym membership fees? You could be in luck! Most larger health insurance carriers have healthy-living programs available through their plans.

Examples: Blue Cross Blue Shield 365...Cigna Healthy Rewards...and Humana Vitality offer a wide range of incentives to keep you active and healthy. Most pay all or part of gym membership fees for you and your family through programs such as Silver Sneakers. You may also be eligible for 10% to 50% off personal-training sessions. Other programs offer you reward points for participating in fitness activities, such as Zumba classes, swimming programs, etc. You can then "cash in" the points for rewards ranging from cameras to walking shoes. Other programs pay for smoking-cessation classes.

SAVE HUNDREDS ON THESE SPECIAL SERVICES...

Chances are your health insurer has partnered with companies offering health-related products and services at steep discounts. For example, recent offerings by some plans include a more than $800 discount on Lasik eye-correction surgery...up to 70% off teeth whitening...partial payment for massage therapy for pain management...and much more.

Beware: Discount programs change regularly, adding new or discontinuing little-used services. So check regularly with your carrier to find out what's being offered.

Guide to Health Helplines and Crisis Hotlines

Gretchen Phillips, MD, a hospitalist (specialist in in-patient medicine) and family physician at Fairview Lakes Medical Center in Wyoming, Minnesota, with long-standing expertise in urgent care and women's health. She is the host of the regional radio programs *Fairview On Call* and *WCCO Radio Check Up with Dr. Gretchen Phillips.* DoctorGretchen.com

When someone is diagnosed with a serious disease or faces a personal or mental-health crisis, help can be as close as the nearest telephone. Health helplines provide information from national organizations on specific medical conditions...give referrals to treatment facilities...and suggest coping strategies. Crisis hotlines operate around the clock, providing emotional support and step-by-step guidelines on how to handle a crisis.

More hotlines: Check the government website *HealthHotlines.nlm.nih.gov.*

CRISIS SITUATION

Domestic Violence: National Domestic Violence Hotline, 800-799-SAFE (800-799-7233), NDVH.org.

Sexual Assault: National Sexual Assault Hotline, 800-656-HOPE (800-656-4673), RAINN.org.

Suicidal Intentions: National Suicide Prevention Lifeline, 800-273-TALK (800-273-8255), SuicidePreventionLifeline.org.

GENERAL HEALTH

Arthritis: Arthritis Foundation, 800-283-7800, Arthritis.org.

Breast Cancer: Susan G. Komen for the Cure, 877-GO-KOMEN (877-465-6636), Komen.org.

Cancer: American Cancer Society, 800-ACS-2345 (800-227-2345), Cancer.org.

Diabetes: American Diabetes Association, 800-342-2383, Diabetes.org.

Headache/Migraine: American Headache Society, 856-423-0043, AmericanHeadacheSociety.org.

Heart Disease: American Heart Association, 800-AHA-USA-1 (800-242-8721), Heart.org.

Ovarian Cancer: Gilda Radner Familial Ovarian Cancer Registry, 800-OVARIAN (800-682-7426), OvarianCancer.com.

Pain: American Chronic Pain Association, 800-533-3231, TheACPA.org.

MENTAL HEALTH

Alcoholism/Drug Addiction: National Council on Alcoholism and Drug Dependence, 800-NCA-CALL (800-622-2255), NCADD.org.

Alzheimer's Disease: Alzheimer's Foundation of America, 866-AFA-8484 (866-232-8484), Alzfdn.org.

Depression/Bipolar Disorder: Depression and Bipolar Support Alliance, 800-826-3632, DBSAlliance.org.

Grief/End of Life: Caring Connections, 800-658-8898, CaringInfo.org.

CAREGIVING

Family Care Providers: National Family Caregivers Association, 800-896-3650, TheFamilyCaregiver.org.

Hospice: Hospice Education Institute, 800-331-1620, HospiceWorld.org.

Senior Care: Department of Health and Human Services Eldercare Locator, 800-677-1116, Eldercare.gov.

How to Save Big on Medications

Charles B. Inlander, health-care consultant and founding president of the People's Medical Society, a consumer advocacy organization active in the 1980s and 1990s. He is the author of 20 books, including *Take This Book to the Hospital with You: A Consumer Guide to Surviving Your Hospital Stay.*

Everyone wants to save as much money as possible on medications, but some of the best ways for doing so are not well known. *My advice…*

•**Stay up to date on generic drugs.** Generic drugs are as safe as brand-name medications and can sometimes cost 50% to 70% less. Unfortunately, most people—even many doctors—are not aware when drugs become available in generic form. The popular cholesterol-lowering drug Zocor (generic name simvastatin), the antidepressant Zoloft (*sertraline*) and the allergy-control nasal spray Flonase (*fluticasone*) became available in much less expensive generic forms.

•**Shop around for generic drugs.** Pharmacies are now in a price war over generic drugs. It started when Walmart announced that it would sell hundreds of commonly prescribed generic drugs at $4 per 30-day supply. Other chains, including Target and Kmart, and food stores, such as Wegmans and Price Cutter, have similar programs now.

Look at the generic drugs you take to see if any are on the discount list of a store near you. These lists are available on store websites or you simply can call the pharmacy. If the generic medication you take is not listed, ask your doctor if you can switch to one that is. Your savings will be significant. For example, the popular generic blood pressure drug lisinopril is $4 for 30 10-mg tablets at Walmart, compared with $13.99 at Drugstore.com and $30 at several community pharmacies I called. Even if you have medication insurance, the $4 price is probably lower than your current copayment.

•**Ask about older brand-name drugs.** Of course, not all drugs are available in generic form. More than half of all medications dispensed are brand-name drugs. But you still can save money if you ask your doctor to consider prescribing an older drug rather than one of the newer, more expensive drugs. Brand-name drugs on the market for seven or more years are often up to 40% cheaper than newer ones. Studies show that most older drugs are just as effective as new ones. It's also smart to shop around. Regardless of the drug, prices vary by up to 25% from pharmacy to pharmacy. There are even price variations within the same chain!

•**Opt for medication insurance.** If your employer offers drug coverage, get it. It will save you up to 90% in out-of-pocket expenses. When you become eligible for Medicare, unless you have private insurance from a previous employer, sign up for one of the many Medicare drug programs available in your state.

Warning: Even if you use no drugs at the time you sign up for Medicare, get the insurance. If you do not and decide to buy the drug insurance later, you will pay a 1% penalty on your premium for every month you were not in the program. So if you wait four years to enroll, your premium will be 48% higher than if you had enrolled when you first became eligible for Medicare.

Get Your Drugs at 50% Off—or Even Free

Edward Jardini, MD, a family physician at Twin Cities Community Hospital in Templeton, California, where he has served as chair of the pharmacy and therapeutics committee. He is the author of *How to Save on Prescription Drugs: 20 Cost-Saving Methods.*

Anyone who regularly uses prescription medication knows how pricey drugs can be. Fortunately, there are places where you can buy your drugs for less—or even get them for free. The key is knowing where to look.

Important: Although most low-cost drug programs have income eligibility requirements, do not assume that you won't be accepted into a program just because your income is officially too high. Many programs will consider applications on a case-by-case basis.

Best resources for finding low-cost or free medications...

DRUG DISCOUNT NETWORKS

Some groups connect patients with public and private assistance programs that provide discounted or free drugs to eligible patients. *These include...*

•**Partnership for Prescription Assistance** (888-477-2669 or pparx.org). This large collaborative network of professional medical organizations, including the American Academy of Family Physicians, and private groups links patients with more than 475 public and private patient assistance programs that offer more than 2,500 drugs at reduced cost or no charge. Income qualifications vary by state.

PHARMACEUTICAL PATIENT-ASSISTANCE PROGRAMS

Major pharmaceutical companies have their own patient-assistance programs that provide many—though not all—drugs for a discount, or even for free, to people who cannot afford them. Eligibility requirements vary—even families earning up to $70,000 a year can qualify. Some companies evaluate the applications on a case-by-case basis.

For a comprehensive directory of patient assistance programs, visit pparx.org or call 888-477-2669. To determine the manufacturer of a particular drug, ask your pharmacist or go online. *Among the pharmaceutical companies with programs...*

•**AstraZeneca's AZ&Me Prescription Savings Program** (800-292-6363, AZandMeapp.com).

•**GlaxoSmithKline** (888-825-5249, GSKforyou.com).

•**Lilly TruAssist Patient Assistance Program (Eli Lilly)** (855-559-8783, LillyTruassist.com).

•**Merck Patient Assistance Program** (800-727-5400, MerckHelps.com).

•**Novartis Patient Assistance Foundation** (888-669-6682, Pharma.us.novartis.com).

•**Pfizer Helpful Answers** (866-706-2400, Pfizer RxPathways.com).

Some pharmaceutical companies also offer coupons that can be printed from their websites, as well as discount card programs offering savings on some products. Check the drug manufacturer's website for details.

Are Bargain Medicines Really Safe?

Jack Rosenberg, PharmD, PhD, professor of pharmacy practice and pharmacology, International Drug Information Center, Long Island University, New York.

It is a painful reality in America—health care and prescription medications cost a bundle. Many Americans—especially seniors who take multiple medications—are tempted to buy cheap prescription medications in Canada or over the Internet. But are these drugs safe?

The answer depends upon whom you ask.

THE OFFICIAL POINT OF VIEW

Under a law passed in 1987, it generally is illegal for anyone other than the manufacturer to import drugs into the US. The US Food and Drug Administration (FDA) warns that imported medication may be outdated, contaminated, counterfeit or contain too much or too little of the active ingredient.

Not surprisingly, pharmaceutical companies agree with this official point of view. Ironically, however, the fact is that we already import a huge quantity of drugs from other countries. While drug manufacturers publicly worry about the safety of medications from abroad, they have quietly relocated many of their own factories to foreign shores to take advantage of cheaper labor costs. The difference is that these plants are considered safe because they are inspected by the FDA.

PLAYING WITH FIRE

While everyone agrees that we want safe drugs, problems arise because of the pharmaceutical industry's unbalanced pricing structure. American consumers currently pay the world's highest prices for drugs, while price controls and shrewd bargaining compel manufacturers to sell the same drugs for far less money in foreign markets. This makes imported drugs a great bargain.

Unfortunately, when you buy imported drugs that have not been inspected by the FDA, you're playing with fire. Ten percent of drugs worldwide may be counterfeit, according to the World Health Organization (WHO). Without FDA inspection, there is usually no way to tell whether a drug is real or fake.

There also is no way to know how imported drugs have been stored. It was reported that in one sting operation, the FDA discovered that a Canadian supplier mistakenly shipped insulin, which requires refrigeration, at room temperature.

CONSUMERS SEEK A
MORE ECONOMICAL ALTERNATIVE

Safe or not, legal or not, seniors in border states from Maine to Washington organize regular bus trips to Canada to purchase prescription medica-tions. In just one trip, they collectively save thousands of dollars. Moreover, American consumers tend to trust the safety of Canadian drugs, which are regulated much like the drugs in our own country. (This is clearly not the case with all imported medications.) If you are set on visiting a Canadian pharmacy, you can first check to see if it is accredited at NAPRA.org, Canada's National Association of Pharmacy Regulatory Authorities.

In a new trend that extends beyond individuals, several cities and states around the country also have expressed interest in buying drugs from abroad. In open defiance of the FDA, the city of Springfield, Massachusetts, imported drugs from Canada for its workers and retirees, and at least two states—Illinois and California—considered the possibility of doing so as well.

EXERCISE CARE ON THE INTERNET

Another tempting alternative is shopping on the Internet. Both domestic and imported drugs are available on line. If you spend much time on the Web, chances are you are already bombarded with e-mail opportunities to buy prescription drugs.

On the Internet, it's "buyer beware." Although it's very tempting when you see an ad for a drug you're taking at a significant discount, you must be careful.

Which sites are safe? *The FDA offers the following suggestions...*

•**Check with the Verified Internet Pharmacy Practice Sites (VIPPS)** (VIPPS.nabp.net/verify.asp) to determine whether the website is a licensed pharmacy in good standing.

•**Don't use sites that offer to prescribe a prescription drug for the first time** without verification that you have had a physical exam or that will sell a prescription drug without a prescription.

•**Avoid sites that do not provide a US address and phone number to contact if there is a problem.**

•**Steer clear of foreign sites, sites that advertise "new cures" or "amazing results"** and sites that claim the government or researchers have conspired to suppress a product.

SAFER ALTERNATIVES

Many states offer discounted-drug plans to seniors with limited incomes. Call your local office for the aging to inquire about your particular state's policies. There are also options that guarantee health insurance to all children of low-income parents. Contact your local or state authorities for details. Finally, if you are having difficulty with prescription bills, talk to your doctor. Most pharmaceutical companies offer discounts to those who can't otherwise afford their medications.

Trick to Save Big on Prescriptions

Randall S. Stafford, MD, PhD, associate professor of medicine, Stanford Prevention Research Center, Stanford School of Medicine, Stanford, California. His study was published in *The American Journal of Managed Care.* AJMC.com

Reduce your medication costs by asking your doctor to prescribe twice your usual drug dosage. Cut the pills in half using a pill splitter, sold in most drugstores. Take one-half of a pill as your normal dosage. Because a double dosage of a prescription drug usually costs only slightly more than the prescribed amount, this practice can reduce the price of some medications by up to 50%.

Important: Not all drugs can be safely halved. Ask your pharmacist for advice. *Here are 11 commonly used medications that can be split…*

Brand Drug	Name	Estimated Condition	Savings
Atorvastatin	Lipitor	High cholesterol	49%
Pravastatin	Pravachol	High cholesterol	23%
Doxazosin	Cardura	Hypertension, prostate enlargement	46%
Lisinopril	Zestril	Congestive heart failure, hypertension	38%
Sildenafil	Viagra	Impotence	50%
Citalopram	Celexa	Depression	46%
Paroxetine	Paxil	Depression, anxiety	46%
Sertraline	Zoloft	Depression	46%
Olanzapine	Zyprexa	Schizophrenia, bipolar disorder	31%
Clonazepam	Klonopin	Panic disorder, epilepsy	41%

Avoid These Medicare Mistakes

Philip Moeller, author of *Get What's Yours for Medicare.* He is a research fellow at Sloan Center on Aging & Work at Boston College and writes a column at PBS.org called "Ask Phil, the Medicare Maven." GetWhatsYours.org

Medicare beneficiaries often make costly mistakes during the annual year-end "open enrollment" period during which they are allowed to make adjustments for the following year of coverage. *Common mistakes…*

Mistake: Assuming that the options that were best for you in the past are still best for you for the coming year. Medicare beneficiaries often stick with the same selections for many years simply because reevaluating their earlier selections would be time-consuming and confusing. But if your health-care needs have changed, those earlier selections might no longer be good options—the expensive prescription drugs you now require might be better covered by a different Part D prescription drug plan, for example.

In fact, your current Medicare selections might no longer be good options even if your medical needs have not changed—your Part D plan or Medicare Advantage (private Medicare-approved coverage) plan might have changed. Many Part D plans recently have reduced or eliminated their coverage of certain drugs due to sudden spikes in the prices of those drugs, for example…and many Medicare Advantage plans have been making substantial changes to their provider networks, meaning that your health-care providers might no longer be in-network.

What to do: Ideally, you would use Medicare's online "Plan Finder" tool to reanalyze your Medicare options each year (on Medicare.gov, click the green "Find Health & Drug Plans" tab). But if you don't do that this year, at least…

Read the *Plan Annual Notice of Change (ANOC)* sent to you by your current Medicare Part D plan and/or Medicare Advantage plan each September. This notice will lay out any changes made to the plan from the prior year in relatively easy-to-understand language. Look for changes that will affect you, such as a drug you take being dropped from coverage or made available only in certain situations...or increases to premiums, deductibles and/or co-pays.

Call your health-care providers, and ask them to confirm that they will still be "in network" for your Medicare Advantage plan (or for original Medicare) in 2017.

Mistake: Assuming that you can easily make changes with Medigap plans during open enrollment. Open enrollment is a great opportunity to change Medicare Advantage plans and/or Part D plans, but that isn't true with Medigap plans—and that limitation means that it sometimes isn't wise to make other Medicare coverage changes, either.

A Medigap plan is supplemental insurance that covers certain out-of-pocket costs not covered by original Medicare.

Example: Medicare Part B, which covers medical services such as doctor visits and surgeries, typically pays 80% of incurred costs, leaving patients to pay 20% out of pocket. A Medigap plan could cover much or all of that remaining 20% in exchange for your paying a monthly premium. (Medigap plans are not used with Medicare Advantage plans.)

But many Medicare recipients do not realize that the companies that sell Medigap coverage are required to sell these plans at their standard rates only during the first six months that the recipient is Medigap eligible. After that, these companies might charge prohibitive premiums or deny coverage entirely.

So while you could switch from a Medicare Advantage Plan to original Medicare during open enrollment, you might not be able to add a Medigap plan to supplement that original Medicare at a decent price. And while you could switch from original Medicare and a Medigap plan to a Medicare Advantage plan during open enrollment, you might not be able to reenroll in that Medigap plan at a reasonable price during a future open enrollment if you change your mind.

Medigap plans are regulated by states, however, and there might be rules in your state that mean you do still have access to some or all Medigap options at a reasonable price after your initial six-month eligibility even if you have preexisting health conditions. Search online for your state's State Health Insurance Assistance Program for details.

Mistake: Choosing a Medigap plan based on its issuer. Medigap plans are offered by many different insurance companies in most states, but any plan, regardless of issuer, will carry one of 10 "letter codes"—A, B, C, D, F, G, K, L, M or N. Every plan with a particular letter code is required to offer exactly the same coverage as every other plan available in that state with the same letter code. Any plan with a code of F or C will cover your entire Medicare Part B and Part A deductibles, for example, along with a preset list of other expenses. (In certain cases, plans with a certain letter code might be offered with either a low or high deductible. Plan options and rules are different in Massachusetts, Minnesota and Wisconsin.)

If you choose to pay for a Medigap plan in addition to original Medicare, just pick the Medigap letter code that makes the most sense for you and then buy it from the insurer that offers you the lowest price.

Mistake: Expecting too much from Medicare Advantage dental, vision and hearing coverage. Companies that sell Medicare Advantage plans often heavily promote the fact that their plans include dental, vision and hearing coverage—all things that original Medicare does not cover except in very limited circumstances. But participants still end up paying most of these costs out of pocket.

If dental, vision and hearing costs are a big part of the reason that you are considering a Medicare Advantage plan, take the time to carefully read the section of the contract that lays out the details of this coverage before signing up. What types of services are covered? What are the annual coverage maximums? Do not assume that the coverage fits your needs because the marketing materials imply this is so.

If you have major upcoming dental costs, for example, a stand-alone dental insurance plan might be the better choice. AARP offers dental insurance, for instance...and some retirees can obtain dental insurance through a former employer's retiree benefits package.

Brain-Boosting Secrets Every Senior Should Know

The Groundbreaking Alzheimer's Prevention Diet

Richard S. Isaacson, MD, director of the Alzheimer's Prevention Clinic, Weill Cornell Memory Disorders Program at Weill Cornell Medicine and NewYork-Presbyterian, where he is an associate professor of neurology and director of the neurology residency training program, New York City. He is coauthor of *The Alzheimer's Prevention & Treatment Diet: Using Nutrition to Combat the Effects of Alzheimer's Disease.*

As head of the renowned Alzheimer's Prevention Clinic at Weill Cornell Medicine and NewYork-Presbyterian, Richard S. Isaacson, MD, is on top of the latest research on Alzheimer's disease. Groundbreaking studies show that proper diet can make a real difference not only in slowing the progression of the disease but also in preventing it.

Here, Dr. Isaacson explains how we can change our eating habits to fight Alzheimer's. His recommendations are not specifically designed for weight loss, but most overweight people who follow this eating plan will lose weight—important because obesity more than triples the risk for Alzheimer's.

FEWER CALORIES

The Okinawa Centenarian Study (an ongoing study of centenarians in the Japanese prefecture of Okinawa) found that these long-lived people typically consume fewer calories (up to 1,900 calories a day) than the average American (up to 2,600 calories).

Lowering calorie intake appears to reduce beta-amyloid, particles of protein that form brain plaques—the hallmark of Alzheimer's disease. A 2012 study at the Mayo Clinic found that people who overate had twice the risk for memory loss... and those who consumed more than 2,142 calories a day were more likely to have cognitive impairment.

I generally advise my patients to try to have fewer than 2,100 calories a day. I can't give an exact number because calorie requirements depend on body type, activity level, etc. Many of my patients tend to consume less than 1,800 calories a day, which may be even more protective.

Bonus: Calorie restriction also lowers insulin, body fat, inflammation and blood pressure, all of which can reduce the risk for cognitive impairment. It even improves neurogenesis, the formation of new brain cells.

LESS CARBS, MORE KETONES

Glucose from the breakdown of carbohydrates is the fuel that keeps the body running. But you don't need a lot of carbs. Ketones, another source of fuel, are healthier for the brain.

When you restrict carbohydrates, the body manufactures ketones from stored fat. On occasion, a "ketogenic diet" is recommended for some patients with Alzheimer's disease because ketones produce fewer wastes and put less stress on damaged brain cells. There's some evidence that this diet improves mild cognitive impairment symptoms (and theoretically may slow further damage).

We previously found in our clinic that patients consumed an average of 278 grams of carbohydrates daily before their first visits. We recommend reducing that slowly over the nine weeks of the diet plan to 100 to 120 grams of carbohydrates daily. (One sweet potato has about 23 grams.) The USDA SuperTracker website (SuperTracker.USDA.gov) gives carbohydrate amounts and other nutritional information for specific foods. Eat healthful carbohydrates such as beans and whole grains in moderation. Unlike refined carbs, they are high in fiber and can help to reduce insulin resistance and improve blood sugar control—which reduces risk for Alzheimer's.

FASTING

Some trendy diets recommend extreme fasts. With the Alzheimer's prevention diet, you'll fast—but mainly when you wouldn't be eating anyway, during sleep!

Several times a week, you'll go without food (particularly carbohydrates) for more than 12 hours. After 12 hours, the body starts making ketones. This type of fast, known as time-restricted eating, reduces inflammation, improves metabolic efficiency and improves insulin levels, insulin sensitivity and brain health.

How to do it: Eat an early supper—say, at about 5 pm. You won't eat again until after 5 am the next day. Your eventual goal will be to fast for 12 to 14 hours five nights a week.

MORE PROTEIN

The Institute of Medicine recommends getting 10% to 35% of calories from protein—go for the higher end. On a 2,000-calorie diet, that's about 175 grams. (Five ounces of cooked salmon has about 36 grams of protein.)

The amino acids in protein are important for memory and other brain functions. Protein-rich foods often are high in B vitamins, including folic acid and vitamins B-6 and B-12. The Bs are critical because they reduce homocysteine, an amino acid linked to poor brain performance and an increased Alzheimer's risk.

Which protein: Chicken, fish, nuts, legumes and eggs all are good choices. I recommend limiting red meat to one weekly serving because of potential associated health risks, including an increased risk for certain cancers…and because too much saturated fat (see below) can be a problem.

Helpful: Aim for four to eight eggs a week. They're high in selenium, lutein, zeaxanthin and other brain-healthy antioxidants.

LIMIT SATURATED FAT

A large study found that people who eat a lot of foods high in saturated fat—rich desserts, red meat, fast food, etc.—may be up to 2.4 times more likely to develop Alzheimer's disease.

Saturated fat limits the body's ability to "clear" beta-amyloid deposits from the brain. It also raises cholesterol and increases the risk for cardiovascular diseases—and what's bad for the heart also is bad for the brain.

Consuming some saturated fat is healthful—it's only in excess that it causes problems. The American Heart Association advises limiting it to about 5% to 6% of total calories. I recommend a little more—up to 10% of your daily calories. On a 2,000-calorie diet, the upper limit would be about 20 grams. (One ounce of cheese can have as much as eight grams.)

FISH, TURMERIC AND COCOA

Studies have shown that a few specific foods can fight Alzheimer's…

•**Fish.** A UCLA study found that adults who regularly ate foods high in omega-3 fatty acids (the healthful fats in fish) had a lower risk for mental decline. Other research has shown that low blood levels of DHA (a type of omega-3) are linked to smaller brain volume and lower scores on cognitive tests.

My advice: Eat one serving of fatty fish (such as wild salmon, mackerel and sardines) at least twice a week.

•**Turmeric.** In India, where people use the spice turmeric frequently, the risk for Alzheimer's is lower than in the US. This doesn't prove that turmeric is responsible (genetic factors, for example, also could be involved), but other evidence suggests that it's protective. Turmeric contains the compound curcumin, which has potent antioxidant and anti-inflammatory effects.

My advice: Use the spice in recipes—don't depend on supplements—because curcumin is fat-soluble and absorption is enhanced by the fat in foods.

•**Cocoa.** The flavanols in cocoa improve memory and other cognitive functions. They also have been linked to reduced blood pressure and improved insulin resistance.

My advice: Buy chocolate bars or cocoa powder that lists purified cocoa flavanols on the label.

How a Harvard Brain Specialist Keeps Her Own Brain Healthy

Marie Pasinski, MD, a memory specialist and neurologist who is on the faculty of Harvard Medical School and a staff neurologist at Massachusetts General Hospital, both in Boston. She is author, with Liz Neporent, of *Chicken Soup for the Soul: Boost Your Brain Power!*

Scientists used to believe that memory and other mental abilities inevitably declined with age. Not anymore. We now know that the brain has the ability to form new neurons and create new neural pathways throughout life. This means that your ability to remember and learn actually can get better as you age.

It doesn't take hard work—or complicated mental "workouts"—to improve mental agility. *Here's what Marie Pasinski, MD, a memory specialist at Harvard Medical School, does to keep her own brain healthy…*

HANG OUT WITH FRIENDS

Close relationships are good for the brain. We have found that people who have supportive friends (or spouses) and rich social networks have better cognitive function and lower rates of dementia than those who spend more time alone.

When I take a break during my workday to go for a walk, I like to find someone to go with me. Exercising with friends is ideal because you can catch up on one another's lives while you get in shape.

It's not entirely clear why friendships are so important. One reason is purely mental—the brain is stimulated when you share ideas with other people. Mental stimulation increases the number of neurons and the connections among neurons. Social engagement lowers levels of stress hormones, which appear to be toxic to the neurons in the hippocampus—the brain's memory center. It also appears to lower blood pressure and reduce the risk for stroke.

Spend as much time as you can with people you care about—getting together with one close friend can be just as beneficial as hanging out with a group. Meeting new people is beneficial because it adds an extra jolt of stimulation. You can broaden your social network by volunteering or joining community groups.

DON'T LIVE ON AUTOPILOT

Routine is seductive. People like going to the same restaurants or taking the same route to work. The problem with routine is that it literally creates mental ruts—the brain uses only preexisting pathways and neural connections to complete familiar tasks. It stops growing and improving.

By embracing new experiences, you stimulate your brain to create neurons and forge additional neural pathways. This happens every time you extend your scope of experience and think in new ways. The more you challenge your brain—even when the "challenge" is as simple as looking at unfamiliar scenery—the more its functions improve.

For me, writing is a new experience. I can't spell to save my life. My worst course in college was English 101. When a friend suggested that I write a book about memory, I immediately dismissed the idea. Then, a few weeks later, I learned that Harvard was offering a course on publishing. I decided to take it. Now I've completed two books.

For me, shifting attention from medicine to writing was a radical change. But any change, even a small one, can help boost memory and thinking. If you take a new route to work, you will see different buildings. You will have to think about where you're going. This alone is enough to stimulate the brain's circuitry.

WORK BOTH SIDES OF THE BRAIN

A lot of my patients love to do crossword or other puzzles. They enjoy the challenge, and they've heard that mental activities improve memory. They're right—but only up to a point.

The improvements that you get from mental challenges quickly level off as you gain expertise.

Better: In addition to taking on new challenges, do things that work the underused side of your brain. If you're an accountant who crunches numbers all day, you're drawing heavily on the logical left side of the brain. Take up a hobby that works the right side, the imaginative side, such as painting or making pottery.

For me, playing the piano is a creative and welcome distraction from my work in medicine. I tried to learn to play when I was young, but my teacher was awful! I took it up again later in life. This time, I got to choose my own teacher, who has since become a close friend.

HAVE FUN

People who enjoy what they're doing get a mental boost. "Forcing" yourself to do things that aren't fun won't be anywhere near as good for your brain as activities that you genuinely enjoy. Also, enjoyment triggers the release of dopamine, a neurotransmitter that enhances learning and retention of new material.

I often ask patients to describe some of the things that they would like to do but have never done. Some would like to learn a new language. Others want to take up a new hobby, such as bird-watching or playing a sport. Ideally, whatever you choose will be both unfamiliar and fun.

I've tried all sorts of things in recent years, from joining Facebook and taking improv classes to competing in triathlons and gardening.

MOVE!

I do something physical every day. I enjoy biking, running, swimming, tennis and skiing. I also take jazz-dance classes.

Exercise triggers the release of brain-derived neurotrophic factor, a growth factor that promotes the formation of new synapses in the brain—the connections among brain cells that are critical for memory and other cognitive functions.

Exercise also increases the size of the brain. In one study, nonexercisers were given MRI scans to measure their brain volume. Then they were instructed to walk for 60 minutes, three days a week. After six months, they were given another MRI. The scans showed that they had an increase in the size of the prefrontal cortex, the part of the brain that is involved in reasoning, problem-solving and other "executive" functions.

Exercise also increases the size of the hippocampus, the area of the brain that is closely involved with memory. It improves circulation and helps prevent hypertension and other conditions that increase the risk for dementia.

Even if you don't enjoy "formal" exercise, you can get similar benefits just by moving more. I spend a lot of time at my computer, but I take a break every hour or so just to move around.

EAT BRAIN FOOD

A Mediterranean-style diet, with relatively little red meat and lots of fish, vegetables and whole grains, is the best diet for brain health. People who follow this diet have less atherosclerosis, hypertension and diabetes, conditions that cause inflammation and other brain changes that impair thinking and memory. *Fish and olive oil, two staples of the Mediterranean diet, are particularly good for the brain...*

●**Fish and omega-3s.** About two-thirds of the brain consists of fat. When you eat salmon, sardines or other cold-water fish, the omega-3s from the fish are incorporated into brain tissue. A study published in *American Journal of Clinical Nutrition*, which looked at more than 2,000 men and women ages 70 to 74, found that those who ate, on average, one-third of an ounce or more of fish daily did better on cognitive tests than those who ate less.

I try to eat fish at least a few days a week. If you're not fond of fish, you can get some of the same benefits from eggs or milk that is fortified with omega-3s. Other less potent sources of omega-3s include walnuts, pumpkin seeds and soybeans. You also can take fish-oil supplements. The usual dose is 1,000 milligrams (mg) to 2,000 mg daily. Because the supplements can have a blood-thinning effect and/or interact with some medications, check with your doctor before taking them.

•**Olive oil.** It's a healthy fat that reduces inflammation, improves cholesterol and helps reduce the risk for stroke. I use it for cooking almost every day. People who use olive oil regularly tend to have lower rates of dementia and better cognitive function.

Probiotics for Brainpower

Mahmoud Salami, PhD, professor of neurophysiology, Kashan University of Medical Sciences and Health Services, Iran.

When 52 patients with Alzheimer's disease took a probiotic supplement containing four billion units of Lactobacillus and Bifidobacterium, they showed improvement in memory and other cognitive test scores after 12 weeks.

Possible explanation: These probiotics may decrease inflammation in the brain.

If a loved one has Alzheimer's disease: Talk to his/her doctor about a probiotic supplement.

2 Tasty Spices for Brain Health

Janet Bond Brill, PhD, RDN, FAND, is a registered dietitian nutritionist, a fellow of the Academy of Nutrition and Dietetics and a nationally recognized nutrition, health and fitness expert who specializes in cardiovascular disease prevention. Based in Allentown, Pennsylvania, Dr. Brill is the author of *Blood Pressure DOWN, Cholesterol DOWN and Prevent a Second Heart Attack.* DrJanet.com

When you think of turmeric and saffron, delicious and flavorful Indian and Spanish dishes probably come to mind. A special perk: These two super spices have been recently proven to have excellent brain health benefits.

Turmeric, the main ingredient in curry powder, has been shown to reduce risk for Alzheimer's disease and brain cancer. And exotic saffron has been shown to have an antidepressant effect and to help fight off brain disease such as Alzheimer's and dementia.

Here's some additional information on these powerful spices—as well as easy and tasty ways to use them in your cooking to boost your brain health…

•**Saffron.** Saffron threads are actually the dried stigmas (the part of the flower that traps pollen) of a particular variety of blue flowering crocus (crocus sativus). Commonly used in the cuisines of India, the Middle East, Spain and Portugal, saffron is the spice that gives dishes from these regions their golden-yellow hue. Also known as "red gold" or the "king of spices," saffron beats out truffles as the most expensive food in the entire world. (Premium saffron sells for approximately $130 per ounce!) Luckily, you need only a few threads of this powerful spice to color and flavor an entire dish. Saffron is available in gourmet food markets and online—1 g costs about $12.

Brain-health benefits: The reddish golden color of saffron indicates that it contains carotenoids—plant pigments such as beta-carotene. These powerful antioxidants help the body fight off brain disease, such as Alzheimer's and dementia, boost immune function and lower inflammation. Other studies suggest that this spice can have an antidepressant effect.

How to use it: Saffron works well in rice dishes…seafood recipes such as paella and bouillabaisse…chicken dishes…and even in some desserts, including cakes and puddings.

Remember: The tiniest bit of saffron goes a long way. There's an old saying among chefs that if you can taste the saffron, you've used too much. And just two threads (about 10 mg) have been shown to provide health benefits.

•**Turmeric.** The plant turmeric, or Curcuma longa, is also known as Indian saffron and is a member of the ginger family. Curcumin is the compound in turmeric that's responsible for its health effects and its yellow-orange color.

Turmeric is the primary ingredient of curry powder (other spices in curry powder can include chili powder, coriander, ginger and cumin). Turmeric and curry powder are widely available in grocery stores, but for the greatest brain health benefit, opt for turmeric by itself—a 0.95-ounce bottle of ground turmeric costs about $2.*

Brain-health benefits: Rich in antioxidants and dietary fiber, turmeric is high in pyridoxine, a B vitamin, as well as potassium and manganese. It has been scientifically shown to disrupt the brain plaques that are the hallmark of Alzheimer's disease and to inhibit the growth of malignant brain tumor cells.

How to use it: Toss a little turmeric into smoothies to add a pop of color and an exotic taste…add a pinch to any soup recipe or roasted vegetables… sprinkle onto scrambled eggs…or add to any rice or chicken dish during cooking. Just a dash is all you need. Investigators have found that consuming curry just a few times monthly is linked to improved cognitive function.

*Lead contamination has been found in a few turmeric products. To avoid such possible contaminants, buy spices from large, reputable companies such as McCormick and Spice Islands.

Does Fish Protect the Brain—or Poison It with Mercury?

Study titled "Association of Seafood Consumption, Brain Mercury Level, and APOE ε4 Status with Brain Neuropathology in Older Adults" by researchers at Rush University Medical Center, Chicago, Missouri University Researcher Reactor, Columbia, and Wageningen University, the Netherlands, published in *JAMA*.

When it comes to preventing dementia, eating seafood is a double-edged sword. On the one hand, it's high in mercury, a neurotoxin. Bad for the brain. On the other hand, it's high in omega-3 fatty acids, which support nerve functioning. Good for the brain.

So what happens to people who eat seafood regularly, compared with those who eat little or none?

They're less likely to get dementia. All those omega-3s protect the brain even with the extra mercury.

This is something of a breakthrough finding. While earlier population studies had suggested that the cardiovascular and other benefits of eating seafood outweighed the risks of consuming contaminants, doubts remained. In a new study, researchers at Rush University Medical Center in Chicago looked at what you might call hard evidence—autopsies of 286 men and women (average age 90). They had already been studying these people when they were alive, so they knew how much seafood they were eating, and now they could look directly at their body tissues and inside their brains to see if there was accumulation of mercury—and neurological evidence of Alzheimer's disease.

The surprise answer was that while the seafood eaters did have higher levels of mercury, there was no increased incidence of Alzheimer's. That's true even for those who had the highest levels of mercury.

While mercury didn't harm, however, seafood protected those at the highest risk. These are the estimated about one-quarter of the population who carry a gene variant (apolipoprotein E4) that triples Alzheimer's risk. Seafood didn't protect everyone, but in this group, those who ate seafood regularly, compared with those who rarely or never ate it, were 47% less likely to show the brain pathology that defines Alzheimer's disease.

Bottom line: By all means, choose seafood lowest in mercury—good choices include catfish, clams, flounder, salmon, sardines, scallops, shrimp, squid and light (not albacore) tuna. But don't let worry about mercury stop you from getting the brain-protective benefits of seafood.

How to Convince a Loved One to Get a Hearing Aid

Richard E. Carmen, AuD, an audiologist who practiced in Los Angeles for 20 years and in Sedona, Arizona, for 16 years. He has held several national board posts and counseled thousands of patients on the ways hearing loss affects relationships. He is editor, coauthor or author of several books, including editor of *The Consumer Handbook on Hearing Loss & Hearing Aids*, and author of *How Hearing Loss Impacts Relationships: Motivating Your Loved One.*

About 36 million Americans suffer from hearing loss—but only one in five people who would benefit from a hearing aid actually wears one.

How does untreated hearing loss affect the sufferer's loved ones? Over time, it can seriously strain—even destroy—a marriage or parent-child relationship due, for example, to misunderstandings and frayed nerves in the person who must constantly repeat himself/herself. *Fortunately, you can motivate your loved one to take action…*

MORE THAN JUST HEARING LOSS

Understanding the full extent to which hearing loss impacts your loved one will strengthen your resolve to motivate him to get treatment. The psychological effects are huge. People with untreated hearing loss tend to become withdrawn and are significantly more prone to depression and anxiety than those with adequate hearing. Anger, confusion, discouragement, loss of self-esteem and shame often occur as well.

Important recent discovery: Researchers at Johns Hopkins University and the National Institute on Aging found that even mild hearing loss was associated with twice the risk for dementia, while people with severe hearing loss were five times more likely to develop the condition—a link that gives sufferers yet another reason to consider getting hearing aids.

BREAKING THROUGH DENIAL

More than two-thirds of people who refuse hearing aids do so because they think "my hearing isn't bad enough," according to research conducted by the National Council on Aging. It is also easy for the person with hearing loss to blame other people ("you're just mumbling").

The most direct way to respond to this situation is to use "tough love." This means that you must stop being your loved one's ears. Take sensible steps to optimize communication—for example, speak clearly and face to face, not from another room. However, do not repeat yourself every time your loved one asks what you said and don't shout yourself hoarse just so he can hear. If you stop filling in the information that your loved one isn't hearing, he will be more likely to get treated.

Helpful: Tell your loved one that you're going to begin this practice out of love and concern and to make both your lives better. It is not a step that you're taking out of anger or vindictiveness.

If it feels too extreme to stop helping your loved one when he doesn't hear something, try this: Keep repeating yourself and/or conveying what others are saying, but preface it each time with the phrase "hearing help." This reminds your loved one of the hearing problem without cutting off communication.

Important: If you can't bear to try one of these approaches with your loved one, take an honest look at your own feelings about the situation. Is it possible that you find some degree of satisfaction in being your spouse's or parent's link to the world and having that person depend on you so much? Wanting to help is a wonderful human trait, but when you need to help your loved one, it locks you both into a pattern of codependence. If you suspect that you're caught in such a cycle, seeing a therapist can help—even in just a session or two.

KNOWLEDGE IS POWER

If your loved one recognizes his hearing problem but still won't get treated, here are some possible reasons why—and how to respond…

●**Vanity.** Research shows that 20% of those who refuse to have their hearing corrected said the following about using a hearing aid: "It makes me feel old"…"I'm too embarrassed to wear one"…or "I don't like what others will think of me."

What to do: Tell your loved one that the inability to hear is far more noticeable than a hearing aid and may well be interpreted as a cognitive problem or other illness. Then ask your loved one if he is familiar with modern hearing devices, which are much smaller and far less intrusive than those used years ago.

●**Expense.** Even many people who can well afford the cost of a hearing aid use price as an excuse to avoid treatment.

What to do: Ask if your loved one knows exactly how much hearing aids cost. Mention that many different devices are available and that costs vary widely.

Then remind your loved one how hearing loss impacts his life, yours and other family members'—and ask, "What's it worth for you to keep these relationships intact?"

●**Inferior equipment.** Many people say, "I've been told that hearing aids don't work so well."

What to do: Ask for the source of your loved one's information to determine how reliable it is. Then ask whether he's willing to take a 30-day trial to test the effectiveness of hearing aids. Most state laws mandate a trial period. Check local laws by contacting your state's Department of Consumer Affairs. If your state does not require a 30-day trial, ask that it be written into any hearing-aid sales agreement—reputable sellers will agree to this.

If a loved one says, "I tried hearing aids and they didn't work," find out when and where the devices were purchased and suggest that he go to another audiologist. To find one near you, check with the American Academy of Audiology, Audiology.org.

STRONG MEDICINE

If you try these approaches and your loved one still won't address his hearing loss, even stronger actions may be necessary. Be sure to consider your loved one's personality—can he deal with more direct confrontation, even if done in a gentle, loving way?

If so, you might try…

●**Videotape.** Make a videotape of your loved one in a situation where he struggles to hear, such as a family get-together. Then sit down and view the tape with him privately to prevent embarrassment.

●**Intervention.** Without prior warning to the loved one, family members meet with him for 10 to 15 minutes to talk about how the problem has affected them. The overall message of the meeting should be how much the family members care… and want a higher quality of life for the person with hearing loss (and for themselves).

How Healing Hands Provide Sleep for Dementia Patients

Michael Reed Gach, PhD, founder of Acupressure.com. He is based in Kihei, Hawaii, and is the author of seven books and numerous self-healing CDs on the topic of acupressure and health, including the fully guided *CD Sleep Better.*

I f you live with someone who has Alzheimer's disease or another type of dementia, he or she may be keeping you up at night—even keeping you up all night—with restlessness just as a newborn baby would. But the feeling of dealing with an Alzheimer's patient overnight is worlds apart from that of dealing with a beautiful new baby's nighttime fussing. In fact, it can be maddening, exhausting and frustrating for caregivers.

Difficulty falling or staying asleep as well as "sundowning" (becoming agitated in the late afternoon or early evening) are common among people with dementia. Although medication can help calm agitation in a person with dementia, it won't necessarily improve his or her sleep quality. In fact, medication for sleep can make patients drowsy at the wrong times and unsteady on their feet, causing falls. It also can increase confusion and reduce a patient's self-care abilities. But there is a safe, effective non-drug technique that can relieve dementia-related sleep problems—acupressure. And if you are a caregiver, you can easily learn it and do it at home.

Acupressure is based on the same principles as acupuncture—but no needles are used. Acupressure simply involves using the fingers and hands to press certain parts of a person's body. The pressure is applied to meridian points, a highway of human energy flow, explained Michael Reed Gach, PhD, acupressure educator and founder of Acupressure. com, an online hub for self-healing. Acupressure can release stress and tension, increase circulation and reduce pain—all of which leads, as you might imagine, to better sleep.

PROVEN TO IMPROVE SLEEP

Acupressure was recently shown, in a scientific study from Turin, Italy, to relieve sleep problems in nursing home residents who had insomnia and either Alzheimer's disease or mild cognitive impairment (a mild form of dementia that may or may not worsen to full-blown dementia). The study included 129 people between the ages of 69 and 96 who received acupressure on a pressure point called HT7 every day for eight weeks. (To find HT7, follow a line on the palm side of the hand from the space between the little finger and ring finger to the crease where the hand and wrist meet.) Residents were much better able to fall asleep and stay asleep and also got more overall hours of sleep when they had acupressure treatment. Plus, the need to use sedative drugs for sleep among these residents decreased.

ACUPRESSURE TECHNIQUES FOR YOU

Although having some formal training in acupressure is ideal, anyone can learn the basics of this hands-on therapy to help another person—including a person with dementia. *Here is some guidance from Dr. Gach to improve sleep…*

When the person with dementia is in bed and ready for sleep, sit beside him or her and…

• **Locate the two main acupressure points for relief of agitation, anxiety and sleep problems.** These are HT7 (the spot on the wrist in line with the space between the little finger and ring finger) and a spot on the forearm, called P6, that's in line with the middle finger but about two inches (three fingers' width) below the wrist.

• **Apply firm, steady pressure to each point, one after the other** (which point is first doesn't matter), using a finger, thumb or, if you have arthritis that makes this uncomfortable, a knuckle. For P6, Dr. Gach suggests clasping the person's forearm so that you press your thumb on the P6 point while pressing your fingertips into the corresponding spot on the other side of the arm.

How much pressure to apply? It should be the kind that "hurts good," similar to the kind of smarting relief you feel from a nice massage of sore mus-

cles. Although it mildly hurts, it also feels good. So when doing acupressure on a person with dementia, you will have to carefully observe and patiently ask the person about his or her comfort level and not go beyond it. (Explaining that this "massage" will help with sleep can be a good strategy, too.)

• **Hold the pressure for two to three minutes on each spot,** and, if possible, encourage the patient to breathe slowly and deeply. "But even if the patient doesn't understand what acupressure is or why you are doing it, it will still have the desired effect," said Dr. Gach. "The body will respond even if the brain doesn't fully comprehend the purpose of it."

Also, although you might think anxiety and aggression are symptoms that might get in the way of giving acupressure to a person with dementia, studies have shown that acupressure and similar hands-on healing techniques, such as massage therapy, are well-tolerated and symptom-relieving solutions for people with dementia. In addition to improving sleep, acupressure relieves anxiety and agitation and decreases aggression and combativeness.

EMPOWER YOURSELF

Of course, you can use these acupressure techniques on anyone, including yourself, to help the body naturally fall asleep and sleep well. But these techniques are particularly empowering for caregivers of people with dementia, who may feel helpless in the face of a disease that can only get worse, said Dr. Gach. "Even if you can't stop the disease or reverse it, you can at least be empowered to help with the symptoms."

Better Depression-Fighting Regimen

Brandon Alderman, PhD, assistant professor of exercise science, Rutgers, The State University of New Jersey, New Brunswick.

Depressed adults who completed 30 minutes of meditation followed by a half-hour of moderate-intensity exercise twice a week (on a treadmill, stationary bike or elliptical machine) lowered depressive symptoms by an average of 40% after two months—regardless of whether they were taking an antidepressant. Researchers theorize that the combination of meditation and exercise may result in brain changes that reduce negative feelings.

Hours of Power…Use the Science of Chronobiology to Harness Your Peak Times

Michael Breus, PhD, board-certified sleep specialist, Manhattan Beach, California, and author of *The Power of When: Discover Your Chronotype—and the Best Time to Eat Lunch, Ask for a Raise, Have Sex, Write a Novel, Take Your Meds, and More*. TheSleepDoctor.com

Imagine what your day would be like if you did everything at the best time—when your body clock is naturally most in tune with what each kind of activity requires and rewards. The reality is, the way you feel and function changes throughout the day, hour by hour, based on your body's daily (circadian) rhythms. These physiologic ups and downs are orchestrated by 24-hour fluctuations in hormones (such as serotonin, cortisol, dopamine and melatonin), blood pressure and body temperature.

The trick is to match each activity to your appropriate biological peak. Then you'll find the best time to eat, think, exercise, daydream, talk to friends—even see your dentist—for you. "There's a never-ending set of peaks, depending on what you want to accomplish. It's all about riding the wave and jumping from one peak to another.

DOLPHINS, LIONS, BEARS AND WOLVES

The "power of when" works whether you're an early-morning lark or a night owl—it's just that your peaks will come at a different times of the day for you. Most of us are one of four "chronotypes.

The following "best time to" routine is based on the chronotype called "Bears." It's the most common one, describing about 50% of the population. Bears tend to wake up in a daze after hitting the snooze button once or twice, start to feel tired by

mid-to-late afternoon and sleep deeply but not as long as they'd like.

To adjust to an earlier schedule or later schedule, just shift the numbers to be closer to your starting wake and sleep times.

THE BEST ACTIVITY TO PLAN WHEN THE CLOCK SAYS…

You won't be able to do each of these activities every day—after all, if you have a job, shopping and napping in the afternoon aren't daily options! Yes, there's no TV time here, either, but then there's no ideal time to watch—although there's an ideal time not to watch (right before bedtime). So don't consider this an actual schedule. *Rather, it's a guide to the best times to do these activities…*

●**7:00-8:00 am, Wake up—and have sex.** While many people have sex before bedtime, sexual desire actually peaks in the morning for most people. That's when testosterone, which affects sex drive in both men and women, is at its highest. Plus, having sex in the morning, which can put you in a good mood and flood your brain with feel-good hormones such as oxytocin (the "love hormone"), is a great way to start your day.

●**8:00-9:00 am, If you need to schedule something that's uncomfortable, do it now.** On most days, you'd eat a hearty breakfast about now, but if you need to have a tooth drilled or get a mammogram, now's the best time. Pain tolerance peaks in the early morning—no one knows exactly why, but it may be related to the lingering analgesic effects of cortisol, which tends to rise just after you wake up. So if you have any kind of physically uncomfortable or potentially painful event to schedule, get it over with early in the day.

●**9:00-9:30 am, Organize your day.** Alertness and attention build slowly after you wake up and tend to be at a high level by mid-morning—which makes this the perfect time to map out what you plan to accomplish for the rest of the day. Instead of just jumping into the routine task that you didn't finish yesterday—something you may be able to do when you're less primed for alertness—step back and think strategically. It's a great time to make lists.

• **9:30-11:30 am, Tackle your hardest work problems now.** During this window of opportunity, your intellectual capabilities are the highest they'll be all day. This is an ideal time to learn new information or work through a complicated project.

• **11:30 am-1:00 pm, Get aerobic exercise such as a walk or do yoga—and then have lunch.** If you exercise first before you eat, you'll speed up your metabolism—and decrease your appetite at the same time. Plus, it's a great way to stave off that afternoon lull. Your core body temperature dips between 1:00 and 3:00 pms—that may make you feel a little sleepy, but getting a little exercise beforehand can rejuvenate you.

• **1:00-3:00 pm, Do chores—especially shopping.** You're less susceptible to overspending now. Why? Chances are you're not hungry and your energy is slightly low. Shopping in this state, can help you avoid impulse purchases—which are more common when adrenalin levels are up.

• **2:30 pm, Take a (short) power nap.** A 20-minute nap can restore your energy and alertness. Set an alarm so you don't sleep longer than that—or else you could wake up with a case of sleep inertia (aka, brain fog).

• **3:00-5:00 pm, Make important decisions.** Your alertness picks up again in the later afternoon. Now you'll be better able to make logical, less risky decisions rather than being emotionally reactive when faced with choices. If you're a little hungry, have a light snack—no more than 250 calories—with some protein, since eating too much can dampen your alertness.

Examples: An apple with a tablespoon of almond butter…or a handful of whole-grain crackers with an ounce of cheese.

• **5:00-7:00 pm, Didn't exercise at lunch?** Go now! Consider a run, a bike ride, lifting weights—or playing a team sport. Why? Your body temperature is higher in the early evening, which means your strength, hand-eye coordination and aerobic capacity are at their peak. This is a great time to get physical.

• **7:00-8 pm, Eat dinner.** Make it the smallest meal of your day—a vegetable-rich stew and a salad, for example—so your body isn't overwhelmed with digestion when you need to start winding down. You'll want to finish eating at least three hours before your bedtime.

• **8:00-9:00 pm, Call a friend or brainstorm.** Your alertness and concentration now start to wane, but that means creativity starts to peak. Now is also a good time to play games. So now's your best time to come up with innovative ideas or have fun conversations with friends and family.

• **9:00-10:00 pm, Power down.** Create a "digital sunset"—power off all screens—at least one hour before bed to help you get in the mood to snooze. This way, the blue light from your screens won't interfere with the release of melatonin, which helps you fall asleep.

• **9:00-11:00 pm, Read for pleasure, not purpose.** As you power down, reading an engrossing or comforting book lowers your cortisol level—reducing stress—and your heart rate, which helps relax your body and mind. Your mind will wander a bit and bring the imagery of a book to life. That'll put you in a great state for drifting off to sleep.

• **10:00-11:00 pm, Go to bed.** Your pillow unlocks your potential. If you know when the right time to sleep is, everything else falls into place. Try to keep your bedtime and wake-up time fairly consistent to anchor your body's rhythms and help you enjoy these hours of power, day after day.

Want to Boost Learning and Memory? Time Your Exercise

Study titled "Physical Exercise Performed Four Hours After Learning Improves Memory Retention and Increases Hippocampal Pattern Similarity During Retrieval," by researchers at the Radboud University Medical Center in the Netherlands, published in Current Biology.

Cynthia Green, PhD, president and CEO of Total Brain Health and TBH Brands, LLC, Montclair, New Jersey, and founding director of the Memory Enhancement Program at the Icahn School of Medicine at Mount Sinai, New York City.

You already know that exercise is great for your mind as well as your body. Now brain researchers are uncovering exactly how exercise helps our brains learn and, more importantly, how best to retain what we've learned.

Exercise is key. But it's all in the timing.

To evaluate the new research, we spoke with cognitive health expert and frequent *Bottom Line* contributor Cynthia Green, PhD, president and CEO of Total Brain Health and TBH Brands.

LEARNING + TIME + EXERCISE = KNOWLEDGE

Researchers in the Netherlands asked 72 volunteers to learn 90 picture-location associations in a 40-minute exercise. The researchers did noninvasive brain scans to see how the different parts of the brains lit up.

Then the researchers asked about one-third of the volunteers to exercise immediately afterward… another third to exercise four hours later…and a third group to not exercise at all. The exercise was a garden-variety aerobic workout—35 minutes of interval training on an exercise bike, at an intensity of up to 80% of maximum recommended heart rate for each individual.

Then, two days later, all the volunteers were asked to repeat the task to see how well they retained what they had learned. They repeated the brain scans, too.

Results: Exercising immediately after didn't help—those folks didn't retain knowledge any better than those who didn't exercise at all. But the ones who exercised four hours later did significantly better than everyone else at retaining what they'd learned.

What happened inside their brains was even more interesting. For those who delayed exercise for four hours, the hippocampus—a part of the brain crucial to long-term memory—looked remarkably similar during the initial learning task and the one repeated two days later when they got correct answers. It lit up in the same pattern. For the other volunteers, not so much—when confronted with the same task again, they had to, in essence, relearn much of what they had learned earlier.

While this experiment didn't examine physiology directly, the researchers note that other studies have found that exercise boosts brain chemicals known as catecholamines, including dopamine and norepinephrine, which are key to memory and learning. Still, they're not sure why waiting four hours made a big difference. That's where future research will go. The study also didn't look at what happens if you exercise, say, two or three hours after learning something—or five. For now, all they know is that getting some aerobic exercise about four hours later helps you remember.

EXERCISE AND YOUR BRAIN

Dr. Green is all for using the new research to help you consolidate learning. The next time you need to make sure new information sticks—when you've just immersed yourself in a big new work project—try heading to the gym or lace on your running shoes and go out for a job four hours later, she suggests.

But Dr. Green also wants us to see the big picture when it comes to exercise and our brains. "We know exercise overall is one of the best things we can do for our brains, and studies have repeatedly demonstrated that aerobic activity benefits cognition," she said. Regular aerobic exercise—a rough total target of 150 minutes a week—is also key to maintaining cognitive health as you age, and it helps prevent dementia. But there's also growing evidence that strength training is also important for maintaining cognitive performance.

In other words, even if you don't care how buff you look, if you value your brain, when it comes to exercise—just do it. And to learn more ways to stay sharp, see Dr. Green's suggestions on the best ways to keep your brain buff.

Early Alzheimer's Sign

Mark Albers, MD, PhD, assistant professor of neurology, Harvard Medical School, Boston.

Difficulty identifying certain smells, such as lemon or smoke, could signal Alzheimer's disease 10 years before the onset of memory loss, according to a new study of older adults.

Why: Alzheimer's can cause brain circuits to lose memory of certain smells.

Self-defense: If you or a loved one has difficulty identifying familiar smells, talk to your doctor about screening for Alzheimer's disease.

Think Fast! Can a Brain Game Prevent Dementia?

Cynthia R. Green, PhD, a practicing clinical psychologist and founder and president of Total Brain Health and TBH Brands, LLC, a brain-health and memory fitness consulting service in Montclair, New Jersey. She is also founding director of The Memory Enhancement Program at Mount Sinai School of Medicine in New York City. Her most recent book is *Your Best Brain Ever: A Complete Guide & Workout.* TotalBrainHealth.com

Paper based on "Advanced Cognitive Training for Independent and Vital Elderly" (ACTIVE) study, presented at the Alzheimer's Association International Conference 2016.

If the latest news about "brain games" and dementia makes your head spin, that's understandable. Claims and refutations have made this field an intellectual roller coaster.

Not long ago, ads implying that online games designed to sharpen cognitive skills can help prevent dementia flooded the Internet, radio and TV. Then the Federal Trade Commission ruled that these claims were essentially bogus.

Now a new study claims that a certain kind of brain game is, in fact, associated with a reduced risk of developing Alzheimer's. It's been touted as a significant finding in The New Yorker, and Time ran an article with the headline "The Best Way to Delay Dementia Without Drugs."

A little investigation, however, made us skeptical. Is it really time to invest your time—and money—in these programs to protect yourself from dementia?

TEASING OUT AN ALZHEIMER'S LINK

To get to the bottom of this mystery, we turned to Cynthia R. Green, PhD, founder of the brain-health consulting service Total Brain Health in Montclair, New Jersey, founding director of the Memory Enhancement Program at Mount Sinai School of Medicine in New York City and frequent Bottom Line contributor. We weren't surprised to learn that she's already looked closely at the matter.

The new research, presented at the Alzheimer's Association International Conference, provided a new analysis of data from University of South Florida, Indiana University and The Pennsylvania State University based on an ongoing study called "Advanced Cognitive Training for Independent and Vital Elderly" (ACTIVE). That study looked at men and women over age 65 who showed no evidence of dementia when they enrolled.

One kind of brain game stood out, researchers found. Over the course of 10 years, the men and women who had training in something called "speed of processing" were about one-third less likely to develop cognitive impairment or dementia compared with those who didn't have this kind of training. Since there was no actual measurement of dementia in the study, researchers used a statistical analysis to indirectly pick up evidence of dementia.

Here's what speed-of-processing games train you to do: Process visual information faster. For example, you may be asked to click on an icon of a bird in a flock that looks different from the other birds—and then do so faster and faster while the background gets more and more complicated. The goal is to speed up your brain's ability to process information.

A one-third reduction in dementia risk is an exciting finding, right? Yes…but it's too soon to conclude that think-fast brain games are proven dementia protectors, says Dr. Green. As she explains in her blog post, "Think Fast! Should Processing Speed Challenges Be Part of Your Brain Health Plan?," the study hasn't been subject to peer review in a medical journal yet and wasn't even designed to study dementia—the goal of the study was to determine whether cognitive interventions (e.g. "brain games") can help adults keep their cognitive skills as they age. That's actually a different thing from identifying who is going to get Alzheimer's or another form of dementia. According to an article published in *MedPage Today*, "Watch Out for Brain Training Claims" (free subscription required), there may also be a conflict-of-interest issue because a close colleague of one of the study authors has had financial links to the company, Posit Science, that developed the speed-of-processing test that was studied.

Even so, Dr. Green is decidedly enthusiastic about training our brains to think and act faster. She believes that learning new ways to speed up the brain's processing ability is an important tool in your brain-training toolbox. Why? Because there is growing evidence that this kind of practice can help you stay sharper as you age—it's a core skill that enables many other mental abilities, including memory and learning. "The rate at which we 'think through' information is critical to everyday intellectual performance," she writes. Games and activities that teach you to process information against the clock, she writes, "may help us maintain our processing speed as we grow older." Honing visual speed-of-processing skills is also key to being able to drive safely as you get older, which helps you stay independent longer.

Those are all good things—even if they don't prevent dementia.

HOW TO THINK FASTER

Dr. Green has several suggestions to enhance your ability to think faster…

•**Play games against the clock.** They can be board games, electronic games—anything that you time. Now try to do it faster!

•**Play online games with friends, such as Word Streak with Friends** (free, available for both iOS and Google Play), which challenges everyone playing to make as many words as possible with a set amount of letters before the time runs out.

•**Do anything faster.** Whether it's prepping vegetables for dinner, folding the laundry or doing new dance steps—try timing yourself and see how you can improve your time.

Dr. Green has nothing against "Double Decision," the speed-of-processing game developed by Posit Science's program that is available along with other games by subscribing to BrainHQ, which is a version of the computer program used in the ACTIVE study. You may decide that it's worth $96 a year.

But there are many ways to learn how to think faster every day, for free—and doing so is only part of an overall lifestyle that's good for brain health.

A healthy diet matters, too, especially these 10 foods that nourish your brain.

Finally…There's a Way to Connect with a Loved One Who Has Dementia

Tom Brenner, MA, cofounder, with his wife, **Karen Brenner, MA,** of Brenner Pathways, a consulting and educational company in Chicago that specializes in the Montessori Method for Positive Dementia Care, BrennerPathways.org. He and his wife are also coauthors of *You Say Goodbye and We Say Hello: The Montessori Method for Positive Dementia Care* (Brenner Pathways). A researcher for the State of Illinois Department on Aging, Brenner trains caregivers and case managers through the Illinois Community Care Program.

Henry had been diagnosed with early-onset Alzheimer's and was quiet and withdrawn. When he was younger, he had collected vintage cars, so his caregiver gave him some old hubcaps and polish. After 30 minutes of polishing, Henry began talking with a great deal of emotion about his time as a soldier. Perhaps the process of polishing the hubcaps reminded him of polishing his boots, and an important memory was triggered. This activity enabled Henry and his caregiver to connect, even if only for a short time.

One of the most heartbreaking and frustrating aspects of caring for a loved one with dementia is the loss of meaningful interaction.

But there's good news on this front: The Montessori Method for Positive Dementia Care, a non-drug approach (often used in combination with medication), is now being used by some caregivers in home-care settings and nursing homes with dramatic results.

Through basic Montessori principles (see below), this method offers ways to be in the moment with a dementia patient and possibly have a deep connection. Patients become more secure, confident and calm. And caregivers are less likely to get frustrated and burn out.

Recent research: In a study involving nine residential facilities in Melbourne, Australia, dementia patients were two times more actively engaged when participating in Montessori-based activities than when they were not doing these activities.

Background: Developed more than 100 years ago as a method of teaching "unreachable" children with learning disabilities, the Montessori approach encourages the use of all five senses to stimulate different areas of the brain and the use of "muscle memory"* to develop small-muscle coordination and promote confidence. The Montessori method also advocates an environment that meets the specific physical and emotional needs of those using it.

Montessori classrooms for children are uncluttered but homey and filled with natural light and materials to promote use of the senses. Students are free to move about and engage in activities that appeal most to them. This sets the stage for focused and calm activity. Research has shown that Montessori pupils learn to excel at problem solving, adapting to change and social skills—all areas that are difficult for adults with dementia.

Key Montessori tenets and how they can help dementia patients…

●**Emphasis on environment.** The surroundings of the dementia patient should be familiar and comforting and designed to foster as much independence as possible. For example, the layout of a facility, or your home if a loved one is living with you, should be uncomplicated so there is less potential for confusion. Visual cues, such as large-print labeling indicating what can be found in drawers, are also very helpful. Clutter should be minimized, but the use of natural elements—such as plants, pictures of nature, natural lighting, etc.—can induce a feeling of calm.

●**Muscle memory stimulation.** While the mind of a dementia patient might be faltering, the muscles often "remember" how to do an activity that was done repetitively and enjoyably in the past. The key is to discover a patient's unique strengths, passions and interests—not only tapping muscle memory but strong emotions as well. Focusing on a physical task and having success helps dementia patients feel more secure and confident and less angry and agitated.

A caregiver might take a former golfer to the driving range to jump-start his/her muscle memory. Or a long-retired handyman might be given a toolbox

*Sometimes called procedural memory, this involves physical movements fixed into memory through repetition (think of riding a bike or playing a musical instrument).

with a tape measure, paintbrushes and a level so that he can tinker.

These activities also build muscle coordination and can simply make life more pleasant and enriching for a dementia patient.

●**Sharing stories.** This is one of the most effective tools for helping dementia sufferers stay connected. Moments when patients share their stories, even if the time is fleeting, can enable the patient and caregiver to feel a deep connection, boosting the patient's sense of security.

To encourage a patient to share a story: A caregiver might give him a meaningful object to hold—something important from the patient's life or an object from nature. This simple act can help spark a memory and get the patient talking.

●**Art therapy.** Painting, singing and playing an instrument can provide patients new avenues of self-expression and strengthen their spirits. These activities also can give patients the opportunity to engage their senses.

Good activity: Flower arranging. Patients are encouraged to feel and smell the flowers, cut stems and pour water. This exercise calls on small motor skills, essential for independence and range of motion. Key areas of the brain are also exercised when deciding how to arrange the flowers.

●**The Knobbed Cylinder.** This classic Montessori tool—a long wooden block with 10 different-sized holes in which the user places matching cylinders—builds focus and small-muscle coordination. Dementia patients might be asked to fill only two holes—the point is for the patient to feel success and build confidence through this activity.

●**Finish a phrase.** Old sayings may never leave our minds. With this technique, the caregiver holds up the first half of a statement on a piece of paper ("The whole nine…") and asks the patient to finish the saying ("…yards"). It's astonishing to see dementia sufferers suddenly become very vocal and involved.

Benefits for the caregivers: The Montessori method gives the caregiver more tools to care for a dementia patient. It encourages the caregiver to use his imagination and allows him to act more like a guide than a director. Plus, patients are less agitated and aggressive, so they are easier to be with. All this helps minimize caregiver burnout and frustration.

Try out a few of these exercises with your loved one. To find a facility that offers this specific approach, you'll need to ask the director of the center you are considering.

Too Busy? It's Good for Your Brain!

Study titled "The Busier the Better: Greater Busyness Is Associated with Better Cognition," by Sara B. Festini, PhD, Denise C. Park, PhD, and Ian M. McDonough, PhD, The University of Texas at Dallas, The University of Alabama, Tuscaloosa, published in *Frontiers in Aging Neuroscience*.

When you have too much to do, you might dream of spending time up a lazy river. But if you want to keep your brain sharp and your memory strong, you're better off staying busy.

Really busy—so busy that you feel like you have so many things to do that you can't possibly get them all done. So busy that you wish the day were longer. So busy that you sometimes stay up later than you want to in order to get everything done.

That's the surprising conclusion of a new study of men and women ages 50 to 89. Researchers at the University of Texas at Dallas studied 330 participants who filled out a "busyness" questionnaire and then measured that against memory and brain function scores. *Results…*

●**The busiest ones processed information faster,** reasoned better, could remember more at one time and had a better recall of important moments in their own lives.

●**The strongest association was for "episodic" memory**—remembering specific times and places.

●**While participants in their 50s and 60s tended to be busier than those in their 70s and 80s,** the cognitive benefits of busyness remained a strong association at any age. "Our findings," the authors conclude, "offer encouragement to maintain active, busy lifestyles throughout middle and late adulthood."

It's an observational study, to be sure, so it doesn't prove cause and effect. Plus, the researchers note, it's well-established that chronic high stress levels can impair cognitive function, including memory—so there's no point to being so busy that you want to tear your hair out.

But it may be time to stop envying the lucky old sun, who keeps rolling around heaven all day. It's good to stay busy—at any age.

Shakespeare's Memory Booster Works Well Today

Mark Moss, PhD, head of psychology, Northumbria University, Newcastle upon Tyne, UK.

Need to remember to make a phone call or take your medication? A whiff of rosemary oil could help.

New study: 150 people over age 65 performed memory tasks either in a rosemary-scented room or in a room without scent. The aroma of rosemary significantly improved both mood and prospective memory (the ability to remember planned events and tasks).

Why: The herb contains compounds that boost the area of the brain involved in memory.

Don't Let Your Home Kill You!

House Noises You Should Never Ignore

Danny Lipford, who has been a remodeling contractor for more than 30 years. He is based in Mobile, Alabama, and is host of the nationally syndicated TV program *Today's Homeowner with Danny Lipford.* TodaysHomeowner.com

Young children are not the only ones frightened by things that go bump in the night. Fully grown home owners often become terrified when they hear bumps, bangs or other noises emanating from their houses—that's because these unfamiliar noises might mean steep home-repair bills. Although some house noises do indeed mean that it's time to call in a pro, others point to simple problems that home owners can fix on their own…and certain sounds can be ignored entirely. *Here's what home owners need to know about 11 worry-inducing types of house sounds…*

HEATING AND AC NOISES

Heating and air-conditioning can make any number of noises…

•**Pings and dings from ducts and radiators** are perfectly normal and can be safely ignored—they're just metal expanding and contracting due to temperature changes.

•**High-pitched squeals** or a grinding noise from a furnace or an air conditioner could mean that a moving part is not moving the way it should and requires quick action. Immediately shut off the system, then wait a few moments and turn it back on. (If the troubling sound is a whine, replace the unit's filter before turning it back on—the restricted air flow caused by a dirty filter could be the cause.) If the sound returns, shut down the system again and leave it off until a heating, ventilation and air-conditioning (HVAC) professional can take a look unless temperatures are so extreme that you have no choice but to use it. The problem could be something simple such as a worn bearing or belt that an HVAC pro can replace for just $100 to $150.* But the longer you allow the unit to make the sound, the greater the odds that the small problem will cause a larger one as parts strain or overheat, and then a motor or pump may have to be replaced.

•**Frequent clicking sounds from a furnace or air conditioner often mean an electrical relay is malfunctioning.** This, too, requires a call to an HVAC pro, but the repair bill shouldn't be much greater than the basic service call rate, usually less than $100.

*All repair prices cited include parts and labor and are based on typical component and service rates. Prices may vary by region.

ELECTRICAL HUMMING

Humming or buzzing sounds from an outlet or switch usually mean that a wire has come loose. (Dimmer switches can hum for other reasons—see below.) If so, the switch or outlet might be warm to the touch as well—although not necessarily. A loose wire is a fire hazard, so call an electrician right away to check out the humming or buzzing. If it is just a loose wire, fixing it should cost no more than the basic service call rate, typically less than $100.

Humming or buzzing noises from a lighting fixture could point to a loose wire as well—but with lights, there's a good chance that something else is to blame. If the humming light is on a dimmer switch (or the dimmer switch itself is humming), replace the bulb with a different type of bulb or one made by a different company. Some bulbs mention on their packaging that they are designed to work well with dimmers. If that doesn't end the sound, replace the dimmer. If a fluorescent bulb is making the noise, the fixture's "ballast" might need to be replaced (the ballast is the part of the fixture that controls voltage to the bulb).

WALL OR ATTIC SOUNDS

Scratching or scurrying from within a wall or ceiling. You can probably guess what this means—a rodent (or some other small animal) has gotten into your house. Get it out as soon as possible. The longer this uninvited houseguest lingers, the greater the odds that it will chew through wiring… die in your walls, causing an unpleasant lingering odor…or give birth to babies.

A pest-control professional should be able to solve the problem for between $100 and $300 (potentially more with major infestations or in expensive areas). Or purchase and set traps—avoid poisons, which could be consumed by your pets or result in the pests dying and rotting inside your walls.

Do not just evict the pest—also search for and seal the opening that it used to get into your home so that other animals can't get in. Expanding spray sealants are a simple and effective way to fill small gaps

One spot to check: If you have a crawl space under your house, look under tubs and showers—

builders often fail to properly seal off the openings beneath drain assemblies.

•**Dripping.** A water leak inside a wall can destroy wallboard and insulation and lead to mold or mildew problems. Fortunately, not every water sound signals a problem—sometimes the water is safely inside pipes.

First, check your basement or crawl space below the spot where you hear the water sound. If there is a water leak, that water likely would find its way down there. If you see water or water damage, call a plumber immediately (or a roofer if the water dripping sounds occur only when it is raining and/or when there is ice or snow on the roof). If you do not find water beneath the location of the dripping sound but the troubling water sound persists, conduct a water-loss test. Stop all water use in your home for 30 minutes—instruct family members to refrain from flushing the toilet and using the sink, tub, shower, dishwasher and washing machine during this time…and turn off the ice maker, sprinkler system and any other systems in the home that use water on their own.

Note the exact reading on your water meter at the beginning and end of this half hour. If this reading has not changed, it's unlikely that you have a leaky pipe. If it has changed even slightly, shut off the water to your toilets and redo the test—leaky toilets are the most common source of phantom water use. If this second test still shows water use, consider replacing the toilet's flapper valve or call a plumber.

Alternative: If you have a heating system that uses hot water or steam, the leak could be from there. Monitor the boiler's pressure gauge—if the system is leaking, this is likely to show a loss of pressure over time.

If you have a well: You won't have a water meter to check, so instead, stop all water use and then stand near your water pump for 30 minutes. If you hear clicking sounds from the pump, that could mean you have a water leak.

BANGING OR THUMPING PIPES

This is called "water hammer" and is caused by water changing direction or being brought to a sudden halt in pipes. Water hammer almost never

Don't Let Your Home Kill You!

causes any problems for the home, but the noise can be annoying. If you want it to stop, install "water heater arrestors" in the waterline near appliances and fixtures that tend to trigger the noise. These cost just $10 to $15 at home centers and provide a cushion of air that absorbs the force of the water, greatly reducing the noise. If you call in a plumber, it should not cost much more than $100 (you can save $85 by doing it yourself).

WATER-HEATER NOISE

Water heaters fueled by natural gas or oil make a subtle "poof" noise when the gas ignites at the start of a heating cycle. Other than that, water heaters should operate almost silently. If you hear gurgling or popping noises coming from your water heater, that means it's struggling to operate and might soon fail, most likely because sediment has built up around its coils. You might be able to save the water heater by draining it to flush away this sediment. Check your heater's manual for specific instructions, but typically the procedure involves shutting off the water and electricity to the water heater, attaching a hose to its drain spigot near the base, running the other end of the hose to a drain, then opening the drain valve. After the water heater has drained, close the drain valve and turn on the electricity and water to the tank. Do this every year.

WELL PUMP CLICKS

Occasional clicks from a well pump are normal—it just means that the pump is working. Frequent clicks when no water is being used in the house suggest that either an electrical relay in the pump is faulty or that there is a water leak in the house. Use the leak-check procedure described in the water-dripping section on the previous page. If that does not turn up a problem, call in a well professional to see if there's a faulty relay switch. Replacing the switch shouldn't cost more than $100. Don't let this problem linger—until it is fixed, your well pump is under unnecessary strain, which could shorten its life.

FIREPLACE DRIPPING SOUNDS

If you hear dripping from your fireplace when it rains, it could mean that rain is finding its way down your chimney. You need to put a stop to this or the metal firebox inside your fireplace could rust, creating a fire risk. The source of the problem could be as simple as loose flashing or a dislodged chimney cap. If so, a roofer probably can correct it for less than $100. You even might be able to solve this yourself, perhaps using caulk to seal gaps between the flashing and the chimney if you are comfortable walking on your roof. If bricks are coming loose, you might need a brick mason, which could cost hundreds or thousands of dollars depending on what's needed.

---

6 Surprising Places Where Mold Lurks

Martin J. Blaser, MD, the Muriel G. and George W. Singer Professor of Translational Medicine and director of the Human Microbiome Program in the departments of medicine and microbiology at New York University School of Medicine, New York City. He has served as chair of medicine at NYU and president of the Infectious Diseases Society of America. He is author of *Missing Microbes: How the Overuse of Antibiotics Is Fueling Our Modern Plagues.*

We all know that mold thrives in obvious places such as damp basements, steamy bathrooms and storage areas with piles of old books and/or clothing. But there are plenty of other spots you'd never suspect that also can harbor these nasty fungal spores.

For the 10% to 15% of Americans who are allergic to mold, inhaling (or ingesting) the spores can trigger symptoms such as sneezing, runny nose, swollen eyelids, an itchy throat and wheezing.

Six surprising mold hot spots…

HOT SPOT #1: **Your coffeemaker.** In one study, mold was found in the water reservoirs of about half of the tested drip-type coffeemakers.

What to do: Once a month, fill your coffeemaker's reservoir with a 50/50 mixture of water and white vinegar. Turn the coffeemaker on, just as you would if you were brewing a pot of coffee. When the reservoir is half emptied, turn off the coffeemaker. Wait 30 minutes and then finish the brewing cycle. Rinse the machine by running plain, cool water through the cycle twice (or check manufacturer's instructions). When you finish your coffee each day, allow the reservoir to dry completely by leaving the lid open.

HOT SPOT #2: **Your washing machine.** Mold has no problem growing inside the rubber gaskets on the doors of front-loading machines. Those gaskets prevent water from pouring through the door, but water is often trapped inside the rubber folds. In all kinds of machines, detergent trays can stay damp between cycles, and the agitators of top-loading machines can be an area for mold growth, too.

What to do: Keep the door and detergent tray open when you're not using the washing machine. For front-loaders, wipe the inside of the gasket bottom with a rag or paper towel to dry it if no more loads will be done that day.

If you think you have mold, run an empty cycle with the machine on its hottest setting, using a mixture of one cup of baking soda, one cup of bleach and one-half cup of powdered dishwasher detergent. Some front-loading washers have a separate cycle for washing the inside of the machine. If a top-loading washer smells musty, the agitator may have to be removed and the shaft and agitator cleaned.

HOT SPOT #3: **Under your refrigerator.** Keep an eye on frost-free refrigerators and freezers.

Here's why: Your freezer section isn't actually frost-free. Frost is automatically melted during a heating cycle, and then the water accumulates in a pan at the bottom. The heat released from the condenser coils is supposed to speed up this evaporation, but often there is standing water in the pan. This water allows bacteria, yeast and mold to grow in the dust in the pan, and air movement can disperse these organisms into your kitchen.

What to do: Keep the condenser coils on your refrigerator clean by removing the grille at the bottom or back of the appliance and vacuuming the dust from the coils. A 36-inch Flexible Crevice Tool is available at Amazon.com for $12.99. Cleaning the coils once a year improves the efficiency of the refrigerator and can eliminate dust-containing pollen, mold spores and pet dander.

Cleaning the drip pan might not be as easy—with some refrigerator models, the pan is accessible only from the back of the fridge and/or may be attached to the condenser. Check the refrigerator manufacturer's instructions for proper cleaning of the condenser coils and drip pan.

HOT SPOT #4: **The underside of the toilet tank.** You probably don't look, but moisture often lingers here—and so does mold.

What to do: If it's easy enough, get on the floor (otherwise, use a mirror and flashlight) and take a look at the underside of each toilet tank in your home. If there's mold, mix one cup of bleach with one gallon of water, open a window or door for ventilation and scrub the moldy areas with gloved hands. Clean these areas with a nonabrasive bathroom cleanser once a month during times of high outdoor humidity.

Also helpful: Use a squeegee (found at home-supply stores) to remove moisture from the shower walls. A ceiling fan or oscillating fan that directs air at the shower walls will also help dry surfaces and reduce the threat of mold. Generally, small exhaust fans commonly used in bathrooms do not effectively remove moisture—but they do help, so if you have one, use it when showering and for about an hour afterward.

HOT SPOT #5: **Your Waterpik and toothbrush.** The water reservoir of your Waterpik or other water-jet appliance may not dry out between uses, and mold may grow on rubber gaskets and/or the water reservoir. Toothbrushes generally dry too fast for mold to grow, but it can grow inside the hollow heads of electric toothbrushes.

What to do: After each use of your Waterpik, remove the water reservoir, invert it and let it dry. To drain the pump, lower the sprayer in the sink so that it is below the level of the pump. Gravity will allow the water to drain. To clean electric toothbrush heads, soak in diluted bleach, 3% hydrogen peroxide or vinegar for a few minutes once a month.

HOT SPOT #6: **Your dehumidifier.** Dehumidifiers are designed to remove moisture and help prevent mold. But condensed water accumulates on cooling coils and can lead to mold growth in any dust trapped on the cooling-coil fins.

What to do: Empty the water basin at least weekly. During hot, humid weather, empty it daily. A few times a year, wash the plastic filter in a sink, scrub the inside of the bucket with nonabrasive cleanser (use diluted bleach if it is moldy) and spray any dust off the fins with water. Before storing the dehumidifier when it's not in use, wash and dry all of the parts carefully. Follow the manufacturer's instructions for cleaning the machine.

Lead: The Dangers No One Is Talking About

Hyla Cass, MD, a psychiatrist and integrative medicine practitioner located in Southern California. Dr. Cass is also the author of numerous articles and books, most recently *The Addicted Brain and How to Break Free.* CassMD.com

It started with Flint, Michigan, where outraged parents complained of toxic concentrations of lead in their drinking water. But anyone who reads newspapers, watches TV or goes online knows that lead continues to be a national problem.

A hidden danger: While attention has largely focused on the potential harms to children (including lasting damage to their developing brains and lowered IQs), adults are not immune to lead toxicity. *Here's how to protect yourself—and your family…*

HOW DAMAGE OCCURS

Lead poisons mitochondria (energy-producing structures within each cell), potentially harming your body in several ways. It blocks the production of glutathione, a naturally occurring antioxidant that keeps free radicals (implicated in a host of age-related chronic diseases) in check. The metal also interferes with the production of nitric oxide, a natural vasodilator that keeps blood flowing normally and blood pressure at proper levels.

As with children, high lead levels in adults can impair brain function, leading to memory problems, depression, anxiety, irritability and trouble concentrating. Headaches, insomnia and poor co-ordination are frequent, as are digestive difficulties such as constipation. Reduced sex drive in adults also can result.

When elevated lead levels persist over a period of years, high blood pressure can develop. Deaths due to cardiovascular disease become 50% more common as blood levels of lead rise, according to research published in the journal *Circulation*.

Even more concerning: The increased heart and stroke risks in this research occurred with blood lead concentrations of 2 micrograms per deciliter (mcg/dL)—less than half the level considered harmful by the CDC and EPA. Lead reaches or exceeds this level in almost 40% of American adults, according to data from the National Health and Nutrition Examination Survey.

SHOULD YOU BE TESTED?

Given the prevalence of lead toxicity, you might consider testing if you have one or more of the symptoms mentioned earlier. Age is a factor, too. As bones thin and break down with age, they release lead that may have been stored for decades in the skeleton.

Blood testing is simple and relatively inexpensive but won't tell the whole story—blood lead levels indicate exposures to the metal only during the past 35 days…and a low reading may mask high levels of lead stored in the bones.

Best test for lead: A "provocation test" in which you are given a dose of prescription medication to help release lead from tissues and bones. Then your body's lead level can be determined by checking for it in the urine collected in the next few hours.

No matter which test you use, the result can best be interpreted by an integrative medicine doctor, a doctor of osteopathy or a naturopathic doctor—all of whom are typically knowledgeable about lead toxicity. To find one near you, consult the American College for Advancement in Medicine (ACAM. org)…the American Academy of Environmental Medicine (AAEMonline.org)…or The Institute for Functional Medicine (FunctionalMedicine.org).

Many integrative practitioners are well versed in treatments, such as chelation therapy. This involves a series of IV injections of a chemical that binds to molecules of lead and other heavy metals for excretion in the urine. Since the body stores are generally so high, the course will likely need repeating as lead continues to be released. The treatment is generally not covered by insurance and costs about $75 to $125 per session.

Certain supplements can also be used to help fight lead toxicity, most of which boost glutathione, the body's master antioxidant. These include vitamin C, N-acetyl cysteine (NAC), quercetin, alpha-lipoic acid and cilantro. Discuss such therapy with your physicians first.

HOW TO PROTECT YOURSELF

Whether or not you already have elevated levels of lead in your body, we're all at risk and should try to limit exposure. *My advice…*

•**Test your water.** This is crucial if you live in a home built before 1986—but lead may also be found in newer homes. Until two years ago, the legal limit for "lead-free" pipes was up to 8% lead. If any questions have been raised about your municipal water supply, get an analysis from your water district. For your own home's supply, online kits are available or call a professional. The EPA supplies a list of certified labs in your area at EPA.gov/dwlabcert.

If there's any appreciable amount of lead (or other contaminants such as PCBs) in your water, get a kitchen filter (carbon or reverse osmosis) to remove them. You may also want to consider a whole-house filtration system.

•**Limit lead dust.** If your home was built before 1978 (when lead paint was banned), have all air ducts thoroughly cleaned to remove lead dust. When stripping paint, use a respirator and protective clothing and scrupulously remove paint chips.

Best option: Hire a professional who is EPA-certified in lead paint removal.

To find such a professional, go to: EPA.gov/lead.

Lead can also be found in the soil, particularly if you live anywhere near a highway or busy street—particles may have settled there from the exhaust of cars using leaded gasoline, which was banned years ago. To avoid tracking lead-containing particulates into your home, remove your shoes before entering. Also test your soil before planting a vegetable garden.

•**Avoid lead-containing products.** Ceramic dishes and cookware should be made with lead-free glazes. Most US-manufactured items are safe, but there may be lead in imported products. When buying such items, you can check them by using the First Alert lead-testing kit that identifies the presence (not the amount) of lead on dishes, toys and other household items. It is available online and at home-improvement stores for about $17.

To confirm that lipstick and other cosmetics are free from lead and other toxins, consult the Environmental Working Group's database (EWG.org).

•**Watch your supplements.** Especially with herbs, which can be contaminated with lead, buy only from highly reputable manufacturers that can certify their purity. Look for brands that have been certified by NSF International or The US Pharmacopeia (USP).

After a Bone Fracture, Check Your Meds

Study titled "Patterns of Prescription Drug Use Before and After Fragility Fracture" by Jeffrey C. Munson, MD, Geisel School of Medicine, Dartmouth College, Lebanon, New Hampshire, and colleagues, published in *JAMA Internal Medicine*.

A broken bone can have devastating consequences for an older person. It can lead to functional decline and loss of independence—even increased risk for death. One of the biggest post-fracture health risks is getting another fracture. But few patients get the right care after a fracture to help them prevent future fractures, a new study finds—and lots of people keep taking meds that increase fracture risk!

THE DRUG CONNECTION

It's not a secret that many drugs for conditions such as diabetes, depression, high blood pressure, insomnia and even GERD can contribute to increased fracture risk. But breaking a bone should be a loud wake-up call for doctors to reevaluate the meds a patient is taking.

Unfortunately, that isn't happening. A recent study from the Geisel School of Medicine at Dartmouth College looked at 168,000 Medicare recipients who had had bone fractures and found that four months after their fractures, more than 80% of them were still taking at least one medication known to increase risk for fracture. Even more alarming—more patients increased use of fracture-promoting drugs than decreased such use after their breaks!

The list of drugs most associated with fracture risk in the study included…

- **Oral steroids**
- **Proton pump inhibitors** (for peptic ulcers, GERD)
- **Thiazolidinediones** (a class of diabetes drug)
- **Diuretics** (for high blood pressure)
- **Hypnotics (for insomnia)**
- **Selective serotonin reuptake inhibitors** (antidepressants)
- **Antipsychotics**

Some of these drugs increase fracture risk because they increase the risk of falling—for example, hypnotics, antidepressants and even diuretics can make people dizzy. Others, such as proton pump inhibitors, decrease bone density—weakening bones.

Bottom line: If you have had a fracture, be sure to discuss with your doctor whether any of the medications you are taking might either weaken your bones or make falls more likely. You may be able to take a different class of medication to accomplish the same purpose. You may also want to discuss whether you should take medications for osteoporosis, suggest the study authors.

You can also take steps—literally—to strengthen your bones and help keep you steady on your feet. Weight-bearing exercises, such as walking and lifting weights, can help strengthen your bones, while yoga and tai chi help improve balance—and prevent falls.

Do-It-Yourself Dangers

The late **Richard O'Brien, MD,** associate professor of emergency medicine at The Commonwealth Medical College of Pennsylvania in Scranton. Dr. O'Brien, who died in 2015, was also a spokesperson for the American College of Emergency Physicians, ACEP.org, and a recipient of the group's Communications Lifetime Achievement Award.

I t may be cheaper to do home maintenance and repairs yourself than to call a professional, but don't let the economic downturn trump your common sense. Emergency rooms have seen an uptick in do-it-yourself (DIY) injuries as home owners attempt their own repairs—sometimes with disastrous results. And autumn is a particularly dangerous time as people ready their homes for winter.

Some of the most common DIY injuries—and how to prevent them…

- **Antenna installations.** This year, I noticed an increase in patients who had fallen off their roofs. They were trying to save money by giving up cable television and installing rooftop antennas. Instead, they wound up in the emergency room.

Self-defense: Make sure that your ladder is in good shape and set up properly (see page 00). Use a ladder made of fiberglass or wood if you're working near power lines. Every year, I see patients who get zapped when a metal ladder touches a power source. In rare cases, people are electrocuted. More often, they're "sucker punched" by the surprise of the electrical jolt, lose their footing and fall off the ladder.

Also, protect your hands. Most antennas are fastened to chimneys or other upright supports with metal bands. The bands can have knife-sharp edges. If you don't wear heavy gloves, you may end up needing a surgeon.

- **Gutter cuts.** Roof gutters, even those made of vinyl, have extremely sharp edges. So do the guards that fit on top to keep out leaves. Cuts from roof gutters typically are jagged and very dirty—so there's a high risk for infection.

Self-defense: Always wear sturdy work gloves when repairing or cleaning gutters. If you cut yourself, rinse the cut with running water for at least five minutes to wash out debris and germs.

If the bleeding doesn't stop within a few minutes, go to the emergency room. These cuts are very painful and can be slow to heal. The doctor will numb the area with lidocaine and clean the wound more thoroughly than you can at home—and medical treatment may reduce scarring.

Important: Never go out in the rain on a ladder or on a wet roof to clean a clogged gutter—you're much more likely to slip and fall.

●**"Welder's Eye."** The Home Depot and other home-improvement centers now sell inexpensive welding gear. People without a lot of training or safety knowledge are doing their own welding.

Main risk: Corneal burn. The ultraviolet light emitted by welding torches can scorch the cornea. You won't feel the injury right away, but about two or three hours later, you'll have the most excruciating pain imaginable. Corneal burns usually heal on their own within a few days, but see a doctor as soon as possible.

Self-defense: Put on protective eyewear intended for welders before you light the torch.

●**Insulation installation.** A lot of people are insulating their basements and attics to save money on heating bills. Insulating walls is relatively easy—injuries usually occur when people are standing on ladders to install ceiling insulation.

Self-defense: Measure and cut the insulation before getting on the ladder. A lot of falls happen when people are standing on a ladder and trying to juggle a tape measure, a utility knife and a staple gun. Wear gloves and protective goggles.

●**Hard plastic packaging.** Everything from a spark plug to a screwdriver set now is packaged in tough, hard-to-open plastic shells. We see patients all the time in the ER who have sliced themselves with utility knives or even butcher knives while trying to open those things. Also, the sharp plastic edges of the opened container can cut you as deeply as a knife.

Self-defense: Buy heavy scissors or utility shears to open the packaging. And wear gloves.

●**Lawn mower burns.** One study reported an average of 74,000 emergency visits for lawn mower injuries annually in the US. Most lawn mower injuries involve flying debris, but muffler burns also are common. And late in the season, people who have been mowing their lawns all summer tend to feel confident in their handling of the machines—sometimes overly confident.

What happens: People decide to repair the mower or change the oil while the machine is hot. Touching the muffler, even for a fraction of a second, can cause a second-degree burn. Also dangerous is filling the gas tank while the machine is hot. Spilled gasoline that vaporizes is highly combustible.

●**Lawn tractors.** They're designed not to tip over, but it happens. Manufacturers include safety mechanisms that stop the blades if the machine tips, but the blades don't stop instantly. I've seen patients who lost fingers or toes when the machines they were riding tipped over.

Self-defense: Study the instruction manual thoroughly. No one should get on a lawn tractor without knowing exactly what he's doing. Also important: Know where the cutting blades are located. Different models have different blade configurations. I have a picture of a dog that now has only three legs because his owner didn't realize the dog was in the danger zone.

DIY SAFETY

●**Position a ladder correctly.** The ladder should be at a 75° angle from the ground or floor. That means about one foot between the bottom of the wall and the base of the ladder for every four feet of ladder height.

Also: Reposition your ladder rather than lean or reach far to one side.

If you use your ladder to climb onto a roof: The top of the ladder should extend at least three feet beyond the roof's edge. You don't want to have to stand on the ladder's top two rungs, because you will be too close to the wall to maintain your balance.

●**Protect your hands.** Every home owner should own one or two pairs of heavy cloth or leather gloves.

Helpful: Hand injuries that occur during home repairs often involve the nondominant hand. We would see fewer patients in the ER if, for example, right-handed people would keep their left hands out of the way when using power tools.

●**Wear special protective eyewear whenever you're using a tool that could send debris into your eye.**

●**Read the manual.** Know how your tools work before plugging them in.

●**Never work in a risky location when you're alone.** If you're on the roof or in a difficult-to-negotiate attic, you could fall, get seriously injured and need someone to help. At the very least, carry a portable phone in your pocket in case you need to call for help.

●**Turn off the main power when working with electricity.** Don't just turn off a switch—someone could flip it on when you aren't looking.

●**Wear appropriate footwear, such as boots or sneakers.** No sandals.

Beware: New Dangers from the Chemicals All Around Us

David O. Carpenter, MD, professor of environmental health in the School of Public Health, and director of the Institute for Health and the Environment at the University at Albany, State University of New York.

Until recently, the health risks associated with exposure to toxic chemicals were thought to be limited to serious ills such as lung disease and cancer.

Now: The dangers, which few people (including most doctors) are aware of, are even more far-reaching than previously thought. Certain synthetic chemicals—such as those that pervade our food, water, air and many of the products and items we use and live with at home and at work—are now being linked to a much wider array of health problems, including diabetes, stroke, heart disease and other chronic conditions.

A surprising finding: Even though diabetes has traditionally been linked to poor lifestyle habits, such as an unhealthy diet and lack of physi-

cal activity, epidemiological studies conducted in Sweden recently found that reducing exposure to certain synthetic chemicals, including polychlorinated biphenyls (PCBs) and phthalates, by 25% lowered the rate of diabetes by 13%.

Here are synthetic chemicals you should know about...*

●**PCBs.** Before these 200 or so man-made chemicals were banned in the US in 1979, hundreds of millions of pounds of PCBs were produced—and used as flame retardants in electrical devices such as transformers…as solvents in paint and caulking…in carbonless copy paper…and in plastics.

Those PCBs accumulated in the soil, in the water and sediment of lakes and rivers, and in the ocean. They continue to "volatilize" into the air, forming harmful gases. In short, we eat, drink and breathe PCBs.

PCBs have long been associated with increased risks for cancer, suppression of the immune system, damage to bones and joints, lower testosterone levels and negative effects on the brain, such as reduced cognitive function and focus.

However, an increasing body of recent evidence in both animals and humans shows that these chemicals also increase risk for diabetes, heart disease and stroke.

In fact, my research has shown that high levels of PCBs in the blood are a stronger risk factor for the development of high blood pressure—itself a risk factor for heart attack and stroke—than any other factor, except for age.

To minimize exposure: PCBs are stored in animal fat—such as red meat, poultry, fish and dairy products. To reduce PCB exposure, minimize fatty cuts of red meat and emphasize lean cuts, such as round roast and top sirloin steak. For poultry, remove the skin and opt for white meat. For dairy, minimize full-fat products such as cream.

For fish, minimize fatty fish high on the food chain, such as tuna. Atlantic and farmed salmon are also typically loaded with PCBs, as are farmed carp and catfish. Fish low in PCBs and other contami-

*Because researchers have not yet determined the level of exposure tied to health risks, it's wise to avoid these chemicals whenever possible.

nants include wild-caught Alaskan salmon and Pacific sardines. For a reliable guide to other low-PCB fish and seafood: Visit the website of the Monterey Bay Aquarium Seafood Watch (SeafoodWatch.org).

Note: Fish oil supplements typically have fewer PCBs than fish because the manufacturing process used to minimize the fishy taste and smell helps remove some of the PCBs.

•**Phthalates and bisphenol A (BPA).** Phthalates (also called plasticizers) are used to make plastic more flexible, transparent and durable. Phthalate-containing products include adhesives, scented products, printed store receipts, plastic clothes such as raincoats (vinyl is loaded with phthalates), synthetic leather used in clothing and furniture, sunglasses and eyeglasses with plastic lenses and contact lenses, dental fillings and sealants, DVDs and CDs, and personal-care products such as soaps, shampoos, moisturizers, hair sprays and nail polish. Phthalates are also prevalent in plastic food containers and plastic kitchen utensils.

•**Phthalates are endocrine-disrupting chemicals (EDCs).** They mimic or interfere with the endocrine system, which manufactures hormones—chemical messengers that regulate every system, organ, tissue and cell in your body. That's why EDCs increase the risk for almost every chronic disease, ranging from diabetes and cardiovascular disorders to learning disabilities and attention deficit hyperactivity disorder. Phthalates also mimic the female sex hormone estrogen, increasing risk for breast cancer.

Another endocrine-disrupting chemical: BPA, which is found in the linings of many canned food products and beverages. In adults, BPA has been linked to diabetes, heart disease, breast cancer, infertility and erectile dysfunction.

Important: Because of consumer demand, many manufacturers have switched from BPA to BPS (bisphenol S), but there's no proof that it's less toxic. It is just less studied.

To minimize exposure to phthalates and BPA: Don't believe that there are "safe" plastics. Never microwave food in plastic—not even plastic that is labeled "microwave safe." Avoid drinking wa-

ter or any beverage that is bottled in disposable plastic—even if the bottle is labeled "BPA-free." Don't store food in plastic—use glass, ceramic or stainless steel containers. In a study in the journal Environmental Health Perspectives, scientists tested more than 455 plastic products and found that almost all of them leached EDCs.

•**Minimize canned food and beverages**—many linings contain BPA.

•**Don't use scented candles or air fresheners.** (Beeswax candles do not contain phthalates.) Don't use scented detergents and dryer sheets.

•**Avoid personal-care products that list "parfum" or "fragrance" as an ingredient**—a sure sign of the presence of phthalates.

•**Don't use vinyl,** which is loaded with phthalates.

Example: Trade in your vinyl shower curtain for fabric. Also, avoid clothes and accessories made with polyvinyl chloride (PVC), such as coats, shoes and bags.

Note: It's helpful to check product labels for phthalates, but phthalates can be present even when not listed on the label.

To find phthalate-free personal-care products: Consult the Environmental Working Group (at EWG.org, click on "EWG's Skin Deep Guide to Cosmetics").

•**PFCs (perfluorinated compounds).** PFCs are found in food packaging, in Teflon and other nonstick cookware, in waterproof or rainproof jackets, in stain-resistant brands and treatments and in many furniture fabrics and carpets. They are also widely used in pesticides, and in the automobile, electronics and aerospace industries.

According to human and animal studies, PFCs are not only linked to increased risk for diabetes but also contribute to a host of other health issues, such as cardiovascular disease, cancer, a weakened immune system, thyroid disease, obesity and problems with fertility in both women and men.

To minimize exposure: Don't buy or use Teflon and other nonstick pans. If you already own nonstick cookware, do your best to avoid scratching or chipping it, which releases PFCs, and cook on low heat to minimize release of PFCs into food and as vapors. When you're ready to buy new cookware, choose stainless steel, cast iron or glass.

•**Nonstick chemicals are also used in some personal-care products**—don't buy anything that has an ingredient starting with "perfluoro-."

•**Avoid microwave popcorn or pizza**—the coating of the interior packaging may contain PFCs. For other microwavable frozen foods, be sure to remove the food from the packaging before microwaving.

•**PFCs are also found in many fish**—follow the same guidelines as those listed for PCBs.

•**Don't use clothing or furniture labeled stain resistant, or clothing labeled water resistant**—most of these items contain PFCs.

•**Use a carbon filter** to reduce exposure to PFCs and other synthetic chemicals in your drinking water.

•**PFCs, phthalates and other disease-causing synthetic chemicals can also end up in household dust**—and in your lungs. Vacuum regularly, using a vacuum with a chemical-catching HEPA filter—they're available from brands such as Hoover, Eureka, Bissell and Dyson.

Hidden Poisons in Your Clothes…and in Your Mattress, Mouthwash, More

Myron W. Wentz, PhD, a microbiologist based in Salt Lake City, who founded Gull Laboratories and developed the first commercially available diagnostic test for the Epstein-Barr virus. Later, he founded USANA Health Sciences, headquartered in Salt Lake City, and Sanoviv Medical Institute in National City, California. He is coauthor of *The Healthy Home: Simple Truths to Protect Your Family from Hidden Household Dangers*. His website is MyHealthyHome.com.

Dangerous chemicals are all around us—even in everyday items that we think of as safe. *Some of the most common dangers—and what to do…*

WRINKLE-FREE FABRICS

Perfluorochemicals (PFCs) are added to fabrics for durability, stain resistance and wrinkle resistance. Clothing labeled "no iron," "permanent press" and "wrinkle-free" often contain PFCs. PFCs are extremely long-lasting in the body because they cannot be broken down and eliminated. They accumulate in the body's cells and have been linked to reproductive and developmental toxicity, as well as cancers of the liver and bladder.

The chemicals in clothing may be absorbed through the skin or inhaled when they outgas from the fabrics. Numerous cycles through the washer may release some, but not all, of the PFC coating from the fabrics.

In addition, synthetic fibers, including polyester and nylon, may contain substances such as polyvinyl chloride, a known carcinogen, and phthalates, a group of chemicals that disrupts hormones.

What to use instead: Clothes made from 100% natural fibers, such as cotton, linen, wool and cashmere and that are not labeled "wrinkle-free," "stain resistant," "static resistant," etc.

DRY CLEANING

A chemical cleaning solution, usually perchloroethylene (perc), is used to saturate clothing and remove dirt and stains. Unfortunately, plenty of the solution remains in clothing fibers after the cleaning is done.

Exposure to perc has been linked to kidney and liver damage. It causes cancer in laboratory animals. Even short-term exposure can result in dizziness, headaches and a rapid heart rate. One study that looked at air samples found elevated levels of perc for up to 48 hours after dry-cleaned fabrics were brought into the home.

California and other states have mandated that dry cleaners stop using perc by the year 2023. *In the meantime, you can…*

•**Air it out.** Remove the plastic from dry-cleaned fabrics and hang them outdoors or in a garage or other well-ventilated area for one to two days. If they still have a chemical smell, air them out for another day or two.

●**Use a barrier layer.** Wear a T-shirt or tank top underneath a jacket or other clothing that has been dry-cleaned.

●**Find a "green" dry cleaner.** Look for one that uses liquid carbon dioxide. To find a green cleaner, go to GreenCleanersCouncil.com.

MATTRESSES

Most innerspring and foam mattresses are made with polyurethane, a product so flammable that it is known as "solid gasoline." To counteract that, manufacturers are required to add chemicals with flame-retardant properties. Before 2005, these included highly toxic *polybrominated diphenyl ethers*. Since then, to combat flammability, manufacturers have added the dangerous heavy metal antimony… and brominated fire retardants, which can disrupt hormone activity and may interfere with normal brain functions.

If you're sleeping on a mattress made prior to 2005, consider replacing it. A good choice is an organic mattress. These usually use natural latex (from rubber trees) and/or naturally flame-resistant wool.

If you do buy a synthetic mattress, remove it from the packaging and let it outgas in the garage or outdoors for several days before sleeping on it.

Also helpful: A natural latex mattress topper or an organic cotton or wool mattress protector can provide a barrier between you and the flame-retardant materials.

LIGHT AT NIGHT

Most people don't think of light as a "toxin," but when it comes at the wrong time, it can have toxic effects. Humans evolved to be exposed to light during the day, not at night, but since the invention of electric lights, we rarely experience a completely dark night.

The risk: Even a blink of light at night signals the body's pineal gland to curtail the production of melatonin, frequently known as the "hormone of darkness." Low levels of melatonin can reduce immunity…increase the oxidation that can lead to degenerative diseases such as heart disease…and impair our natural sleep-wake cycles.

●**Keep your bedroom dark.** Make sure that drapes and blinds fit snugly to block out all external light at night.

●**Opt for red light.** Use electronic devices, including night-lights, that are illuminated with red light. Melatonin appears to be more sensitive to blue lights, such as those commonly used on alarm clocks, DVD players, etc.

MOUTHWASHES AND ANTIPERSPIRANTS

Antiperspirants contain aluminum compounds, which in high doses can increase the risk for cancer and neurological conditions such as Parkinson's and Alzheimer's diseases.

Most mouthwashes contain the germ killers phenol, cresol and ethanol that are used in bathroom disinfectants, though in lower concentrations. These ingredients and others such as formaldehyde can be harmful when absorbed by soft tissue and/or swallowed. *Instead…*

●**Freshen your breath by using a tongue scraper** (available at drugstores) rather than a chemical-filled mouthwash…brush your teeth with baking soda.

●**Avoid using antiperspirants,** especially during the cooler months or on weekends when it may not matter so much if you sweat a little. Deodorant (without an antiperspirant) is an option for people concerned about odor.

DRYER SHEETS, DETERGENTS AND FABRIC SOFTENERS

If a product smells "clean," it's probably bad for your health. The National Academy of Sciences reports that up to 95% of the substances used to make fragrances in detergents, dryer sheets and fabric softeners are petroleum-based synthetic chemicals that can trigger asthma, damage the lungs and nervous system and cause cancer.

Luckily, your laundry is one everyday part of life in which you can easily eliminate unnecessary chemicals…

●**Opt for nontoxic natural detergents.** These are readily available in many supermarkets. Good brands include Seventh Generation, Method and Nellie's.

Ask yourself if you really need dryer sheets or fabric softeners. If you feel that you must use such products, you can find reusable cloth dryer sheets online. These dryer sheets are not coated with chemicals, unlike disposable dryer sheets, and they contain carbon fiber that helps eliminate static electricity in the dryer.

Or you can try one-half cup of white vinegar in place of fabric softener in the washer to reduce static cling and soften clothing.

Warning: Never combine vinegar and bleach in the same load—toxic fumes could result.

How to Prevent and Kill Bedbugs

Jerome Goddard, PhD, associate extension professor, medical and veterinary entomology, department of entomology and plant pathology, Mississippi State University, Starkville, and clinical assistant professor of preventive medicine, The University of Mississippi Medical Center, Jacksonville.

Good night, sleep tight, don't let the bedbugs bite…the bedtime nursery rhyme you may remember from your childhood could now be keeping you awake at night—bedbug infestations are all over the headlines!

Because the powerful pesticide DDT so effectively eradicated them decades ago, bed bugs hadn't been much of a problem here in the US until recently. But now that DDT (and other pesticides like it) are no longer used and travelers are bringing bedbugs back from areas where these pests remain common, bedbugs are back. A joint study by the National Pest Management Association (NPMA) and the University of Kentucky found that 95% of pest-management professionals have been called in for at least one bedbug infestation in the past few years compared with just 25% 10 years ago.

BEDBUG BASICS

We should start with a bit of bedbug biology. Each of these tiny critters is about the size and color of an apple seed. They feed on blood, typically at night, while the unknowing "host" is asleep. Their bites are painless, and most people don't even know they've been bitten. But others have an allergic reaction that leads to itchy red welts (similar to mosquito bites) that arise a day or so later.

The one bit of good news about bedbugs is that their bites are only annoying. They don't transmit disease. Bedbugs are nuisance biters that suck blood, although there is a health hazard when a person scratches the bites, breaking the skin, which can lead to infection. (Instead of scratching, soothe the itch with an anti-itch hydrocortisone cream.)

The obvious best bedbug advice is to avoid them. While news reports tell of bedbugs in clothing stores, movie theaters and office buildings, the truth is that for the vast majority of people, the likeliest exposure is still hotels and motels. When traveling, take a few minutes (it doesn't take much more than that) to check accommodations before you settle in and get comfortable.

WHAT TO DO

Place your luggage on a hard surface, away from the bed and any upholstered furniture. *Luggage stands and tabletops are good choices, as is the bathroom…*

●**Unmake the bed.** Strip off the blankets, sheets and pillowcases so that you can check the mattress and box spring. Examine the crease along the cords that run around the top and bottom of the mattress. Look not only for bugs but also for black specks (signs of their droppings) or reddish-brown ones (signs of blood from engorged insects). These can vary in size and shape, from a pencil tip to a large smear (a sign of a major infestation).

●**Do a visual check of the room,** again looking not only for the bugs but the black or blood-colored evidence that signals their presence. Since most infestations begin within 10 feet of the bed, examine that area especially closely (paying particular attention around and behind the headboard) but also look at baseboards and carpeted areas.

Ask for a different room if you find any signs of bedbugs. Do not accept the room next door because bedbugs are able to travel through unseen openings between rooms.

If your inspection doesn't turn up any signs of an infestation, you're probably safe.

WHAT'S WORSE: THE PROBLEM OR THE SOLUTION?

If you or another family member has brought bedbugs home, roll up your sleeves. You've got work to do, and it's best to use a professional exterminator with experience with bedbugs to help. It's not a do-it-yourself project—but it's not one that you can totally outsource either.

What you need to do: Minimize hiding places. Laundry and soft goods, such as stuffed toys and pillows, should be put into plastic containers that can be sealed. After your home is exterminated, you will need to run these items through a dryer set on high (over 120°F) for 20 minutes, which will kill the bugs. The clothes do not need to be washed first.

Depending on the treatment, you may need to throw out and replace mattresses, box springs and upholstered furniture. Ask your exterminator whether pesticide can be used on your items.

Once you've performed this initial cleanup, the exterminator will come to spray your home (usually several times over a few weeks) with pesticide such as pyrethrins or organic phosphates. While these are all EPA-approved, it's important to realize that these are toxic chemicals that can negatively impact human health in a number of ways.

Example: Pyrethrins can cause coughing, wheezing, shortness of breath, runny or stuffy nose, chest pain, difficulty breathing, rash, itching or blisters. To learn more about general and specific dangers of pesticides, contact the EPA's National Pesticide Information Center, NPIC.orst.edu or 800-858-7378.

Be prepared for the most painful part: The typical price for the pesticide treatment is about $1,200 for the first two visits—often more visits are required.

NONTOXIC OPTION

There is a non toxic treatment—but it is more expensive ($1,500 and up), less effective and, frankly, in most cases, impractical. It involves sealing your entire home (doors, windows and any cracks to the outside) and then quickly heating up the entire living space and all its contents to 120° F or higher.

Problem: As soon as the bedbugs feel the heat, they'll decamp to pockets where the temperature stays cooler than 120° within the house, and it is extremely difficult to eliminate all such pockets. Also items that can't tolerate extreme heat (framed photos and artwork) have to be removed—and these can harbor hidden bugs.

FOR MORE INFORMATION

Visit the entomology website of the University of Kentucky (Entomology.ca.uky.edu) to learn more. It features detailed images of bedbugs and helpful information on detecting signs of infestation. It's not exactly bedtime reading…but on the other hand, knowing that you've done all that you can to keep bedbugs away will help you sleep all the more soundly, no matter where you are bedding down for the night!

Caregiver Confidential: How to Take Care of Yourself While Taking Care of Others

DICE Promises to Improve Life for Dementia Patients and Caregivers

Helen C. Kales, MD, professor of psychiatry, director, section of geriatric psychiatry and Program for Positive Aging, University of Michigan, Ann Arbor. Her study appeared in the *Journal of the American Geriatrics Society.*

Although we casually think of Alzheimer's as memory loss, any caregiver will tell you that it's far more than that—depression, anxiety, agitation, delusions, hallucinations and apathy are all symptoms, and they all can take a great toll on the caregiver. How to cope with this often martyring challenge?

A strategy that goes by the acronym DICE and is forged by a partnership between patient, caregiver and health-care provider has gotten a lot of buzz in the health-care community. The Centers for Medicare and Medicaid Services will include DICE in their training and resource modules for health-care providers. If you are the caregiver of someone with dementia, DICE really can improve life for you and the person you care for.

FOUR STEPS TO WORK IT OUT

DICE is a four-step process in which the patient, caregiver and a health-care provider—it could be a geriatrician, geriatric psychiatrist, nurse practitioner or physician assistant, social worker or similar professional trained in dementia care—work as a team to identify the real causes of a patient's "bad behavior" in any given situation and come up with solutions.

The four steps are…

●**D…escribe.** Encouraged by the health-care provider, the caregiver describes a specific event that exemplifies the patient's behavior problems to the health-care provider in a way that gets the caregiver to relive the episode with all its details and feelings. One way of doing this is to describe the event as if it were a movie scene. This conversation may take place in person or over the phone, and the patient may also be present. The caregiver may be encouraged to record episodes of problem behavior in a journal so that one or another episode can be easily remembered and discussed when meeting with the health-care provider. Unless dementia in the person being cared for is so severe that he or she can't communicate anymore, the health-care provider also gets that person's version of the story. The provider then helps the caregiver think about what led up to the event being discussed and its aftermath to get insight about the context and patterns underlying it.

●**I…nvestigate.** The health-care provider then investigates the cause of the problem. Issues to be probed include whether another medical or psychiatric condition is at play, whether the patient's behavior is related to side effects of medications, whether he or she is in pain or not getting enough sleep or is frightened, depressed, bored, etc. or whether the dementia is simply getting worse. Much of this can be learned from a physical and psychiatric exam. Followup laboratory work may also help shed light on underlying causes (such as a urinary tract infection). The caregiver's expectations and any social or cultural issues, such as economic status, education level, ethnic traditions and religious beliefs, of the caregiver and patient might also be examined.

•**C…reate.** Together, the caregiver and health-care provider—with participation from the patient, if possible—create a plan for positive change. The plan begins with the health-care provider addressing problems discovered during the investigation. For example, a medication might be discontinued if it is thought to be causing a behavioral side effect…pain management might be started if pain is the issue…more intensive psychiatric care might begin and any other newly discovered health need of the patient will be attended to.

The caregiver will be directed toward education resources and support groups, and the caregiver and health-care provider will work together to improve communication with the patient, simplify caregiver tasks, create structured routines and establish meaningful activities for the patient (such as revival of a hobby or participation in an adult daycare program) to help minimize his or her boredom, frustration, fear or other difficult emotions.

•**E…valuate.** The health-care provider then evaluates the plan as time goes by. Is the caregiver using it? Is it working? If so, great! If not, a reassessment takes place to tweak and optimize the plan.

A SIMPLE EXAMPLE IN PRACTICE

This example illustrates a problem situation that DICE is meant to address.

Imagine that you're the caregiver of a relative—maybe your mom—with Alzheimer's disease. You're preparing to bathe her and think you are being gentle as you lower her into a tub, but she physically and verbally lashes out at you, exclaiming that she's in pain. Well, you've been through this before with her and think that she's intentionally giving you a hard time. How could she possibly be in pain? You were handling her with kid gloves!

These misunderstood problem behaviors also referred to as noncognitive neuropsychiatric symptoms, are often so stressful for caregivers that families sometimes put loved ones in nursing homes much sooner than they really want to.

With the DICE approach, you would relate the event in detail during an appointment with a specialist trained in dementia care. The specialist would get you thinking about what might be causing this repeated problem and would also get your mother's take on the situation. The specialist would arrange for Mom's physical and psychiatric evaluation and, in examining her living space, might question you about whether the tub has grab bars, nonslip mats or other fixtures that would make bathing less stressful for her.

Suppose that, during the physical examination, it's discovered that your mother has arthritis but isn't on medication for it. The specialist explains that Mom means it when she says she's in pain. Pain medication is prescribed, and your mother is referred for physical therapy. Meanwhile, you get to work outfitting the bathroom and other parts of the home to make them more user friendly for your mother. The specialist also provides you with educational counseling, reading material and referrals to support resources to help you better understand what your mother is going through…and to help you feel less alone.

PLAYING WITH THE DICE APPROACH

The DICE approach is only recently being rolled out in a formal way. Its real value and feasibility won't be fully known until its use becomes more widespread and clinical trials are completed to scientifically prove its value, ease of use and cost effectiveness. If you would like to try the DICE approach, start by asking your loved one's health-care providers whether they are familiar with it—they may be able to refer you to a specialist or a practice that provides a similar service. Also contact a geriatric psychiatrist, whose training makes it more likely that he or she will apply an approach similar to DICE when working with dementia patients and their caregivers. You might even find that some or all of this is covered by insurance, depending on your loved one's coverage.

Caregiver Dilemma

Joanne Koenig Coste, Alzheimer's family therapist in private practice in Framingham, Massachusetts, and the author of *Learning to Speak Alzheimer's*.

"My father-in-law has dementia and keeps talking about his ex-wife, whom he divorced decades ago. Should we tell him that she is no longer his wife?"

Your question is one of the most frequently asked in caregiver support groups across the country. The dilemma for you (and other family members and caregivers in this situation) is whether to remind your father-in-law of his present life, correct him or try reasoning with him. None of these options will change the scenario and may cause frustration for you, the caregiver, and agitation for your father-in-law.

His ability to reason has most likely diminished or is nonexistent as a result of his dementia. You cannot reason with someone who has lost the ability to reason! His short-term memory is slowly being lost, and memories linger of his younger days, including times spent with his ex-wife. Again, reasoning will not help to orient him. When he is focused on these earlier times, try to redirect him…a favorite snack may work well or a change of scenery.

How to Make Caregiving Much Easier

Walter St. John, EdD, a former professor of communications and an administrator at Keene State College in New Hampshire. He is the author of *Solace: How Caregivers and Others Can Relate, Listen and Respond Effectively to a Chronically Ill Person.*

No one has to tell the more than 65 million Americans who provide unpaid care to loved ones with chronic illness that their job is difficult, stressful and exhausting—physically and emotionally.

Nor do caregivers (full or part time) need to hear yet again that they must build a support system so they can take breaks to pamper themselves from time to time. What caregivers need most are methods for making the day-to-day act of caregiving a little less exhausting.

What often gets overlooked: With the grueling demands of caregiving—whether it's shopping, handling a loved one's finances or helping with bathing and dressing—it's easy to overlook the critical aspect of effective communication.

So often, it's the misunderstandings, hurt feelings and unspoken expectations that drain precious energy from the caregiver at the very time he/she needs it most. *Here are eight secrets to help caregivers…**

SECRET #1: **Set the ground rules.** It's common for caregiving to begin with a general intention of "helping out." However, the needs of your loved one are bound to grow over time. That's why it is crucial for every caregiving arrangement (even with a spouse) to have a written agreement, initiated by the caregiver with input and consent from the loved one. What are you, as the caregiver, able and willing to do? How much time can you realistically commit to providing care? When creating the agreement, which can be reviewed and changed periodically, remind the ill person that it will help protect the relationship and prevent misunderstandings.

SECRET #2: **Don't give in.** Whether it's eating a food that's not on his diet or stopping physical therapy, it's tempting to allow a chronically ill person to have his way just to keep the peace. Do not do it. Instead, try to figure out the reason for the request. Listen closely and then repeat the request, so the person knows you're paying attention. Take some time to consider the request, even when you know the answer is no.

When you do tell the person no, be firm but explain your reasons so you don't come across as arbitrary. Try to find another way to address the

---

*These recommendations are not necessarily effective for people with dementia—seek the advice of a geriatric psychologist if you are caregiving for someone affected by this disorder, which may affect his/her ability to communicate effectively.

request in a safer and/or more appropriate way. If the person is, say, asking to eat spicy foods that you know upset his stomach, offer to contact a nutritionist for advice on what else he can eat.

SECRET #3: **Pay attention to body language.** In many cases, a person may say one thing but really be feeling something else. For example, your loved one may say that he likes the meal you've prepared, but his fidgeting at the table most likely indicates that he feels frustrated with the food choice or perhaps the table setup. Or your loved one may say that he feels comfortable taking a walk in the backyard, but if he's looking down when he makes the statement he may, in fact, feel unsafe. Be attuned to these signals, and you'll be better able to meet that person's real needs.

SECRET #4: **Practice listening.** Many chronically ill people are angry about what they're experiencing and need to vent. As the caregiver, one of your primary roles is to simply listen. (If you are a family member, it may be appropriate for you to help find a solution or look for someone who can.)

Let your loved one know that you're willing to listen, as long as he's not hurting or attacking you. If you get frustrated, say, "OK, I need to leave now. But I'll be back in a while." By saying you'll be back, you let the person know you're still in a relationship with him.

SECRET #5: **Apologize if you're wrong.** If you're spending a lot of time with a loved one, chances are you'll forget to follow through on a request, act irritated when you should not or do something else at some point that will offend or hurt that person. If this occurs, give the person an opportunity to air his grievance. Never interrupt. After hearing out the person, repeat what he has said back to him. If it's obvious that you offended your loved one, apologize immediately and sincerely.

If your fault is less obvious, offer to think about what your loved one has said and let him know that you'll discuss it further the next day. When the time comes, explain what you think happened and let the person know that you didn't intend to hurt him. Sometimes, the person may simply be looking to vent his feelings and not even expect an apology.

SECRET #6: **Use the power of touch.** Day-to-day caregiving can easily focus so much on the chores that need to be done that the relationship you have with the ill person gets somewhat neglected. In these cases, touch can be a powerful antidote. Simply holding someone's hand can ease sadness. A peck on the cheek shows you're happy to see your loved one. Touching shows acceptance, compassion and caring—and the result is a stronger bond between you and your loved one. Make sure the touch is appropriate to your relationship, and avoid touching anyone who dislikes physical contact.

SECRET #7: **Let your loved one cry.** Crying is a normal reaction to the sadness and suffering that often result from chronic illness. Even men need to cry. When someone cries, don't interrupt him with, "Why are you crying?" or "Don't cry." Simply sit silently and look empathetic. Interrupt only if you're handing the person a tissue.

When the tears stop, wait awhile and then say, "I can see you're very disturbed, and this makes me feel for you." While leaning forward with an expectant look on your face, say, "Is there anything you'd like to talk about?" Don't force your loved one to explain the tears. Often, a good cry is all it takes to ease distressful feelings.

SECRET #8: **Avoid confrontation.** Do your best to avoid clashes, especially over minor issues. Use phrases such as, "As I see it…" or "In my opinion…" to suggest that you are giving your opinion, not hard facts. If you do have an argument, stay calm. Allow the other person to talk—or show anger as long as it isn't excessive or abusive—uninterrupted. When he finishes, calmly explain your position. If the conversation is still heated, suggest that you save the discussion for later when he calms down.

What No One Tells You About Caregiving: How to Protect Your Own Health

Vicki Rackner, MD, a board-certified surgeon based on Mercer Island, Washington, and founder of the Caregiver Club (TheCaregiverClub.com), an Internet-based community for caregivers and their loved ones. She is the author of *Caregiving Without Regrets*.

I f you've ever taken care of a person who is seriously ill, you know how stressful it can be.

What you may not know: There are greater risks to the caregiver's health than previously recognized.

Troubling research finding: Caregivers are 63% more likely to die within a four-year period than people without this extra burden, according to a study published in the *Journal of the American Medical Association*.

Compared with non-caregivers, people who provide care to a loved one tend to exercise less and eat less nutritiously and are at much higher risk for physical exhaustion and depression.

CARING FOR TWO

Family members are responsible for about 80% of the elder care in the US. To meet this challenge, caregivers must care not only for a loved one (and, in many cases, other members of their family), but also maintain their own physical and emotional well-being...

•**Know what you can—and can't—change.** Every caregiver wants to create a different reality and to "fix" things. If you're caring for a stroke patient or someone with Alzheimer's disease, for example, some part of you will think that you can prevent the person from getting worse just by working harder. That's simply not true.

There are some things that we can't change. People who think that they can change the natural course of aging or disease are the ones who are most vulnerable to depression, self-recrimination and even alcoholism or drug addiction. You can make a loved one happier by engaging him/her in conversation or planning activities he enjoys—but remember that you cannot change the overall course of his disease.

My advice: Understand that caregiving is usually a long-term process and identify not only what's important, but what's possible.

Example: Suppose you're caring for someone who is disabled by rheumatoid arthritis. He won't care if the house is perfectly clean. What's likely to matter are the more personal things, such as preparing a favorite food or giving an affectionate touch. You've fulfilled your job every time you create one of these special moments.

•**Get—and give—help.** A lot of caregivers don't realize that accepting help from others is one of the best gifts you can give those who are closest to you.

For people who feel guilty accepting help without returning the favor, bartering is a great solution. We all have activities that we enjoy and activities that we don't. Suppose you hate doing laundry but love walking the dog—and one of your friends is great with laundry but dreads going for walks. You can help each other.

My advice: Consider forming a caregivers' bartering community. It might include neighbors or people from your church or synagogue. Or you could post an announcement on the bulletin board at your local health-food store or doctor's office to recruit people in similar situations who will trade chores, such as yard work or grocery shopping.

It's easier to ask for help if you know that you'll pay back the favor in your own way—especially if it's an activity you enjoy.

Many hospitals offer support groups for caregivers, widows and widowers, and programs sometimes include group or individual therapy. Contact hospitals near you. Plus, websites such as CareGiver.com provide lists of support groups in each state.

How to Care for Mom and Dad When They Live Many Miles Away

Penelope S. Tzougros, PhD, ChFC, CLU, principal at Wealthy Choices LLC, a financial planning firm in Waltham, Massachusetts. WealthyChoices.com

A doctor phones to say that your father, who lives in Arizona, has fallen and fractured his hip. The doctor wants to know your plan for when your father gets out of the hospital.

You visit your mother in Florida, and she appears very thin. She admits that she sometimes forgets to eat.

About seven million American adult children face such scenarios as they try to provide care for elderly parents who live far away. As a financial and estate-planning specialist for 20 years, I have helped hundreds of families manage long-distance caregiving. The key? *Devise a plan before a crisis arises…*

ACTIONS TO TAKE NOW

•**Keep medical, financial and legal information at hand.** For example, it is helpful to have the names and phone numbers of your parent's physician, pharmacy and health-care plan, including member ID number. Also, prepare a list of medications, supplements and dosages. Update it frequently.

Download a checklist of vital information at AARP.org/families (click on "locate valuable documents").

•**Set up automatic deposit to a checking or savings account** for checks from the Social Security Administration, the Veterans Administration and/or your parent's pension plan administrator.

Or: Become a "representative payee" who is authorized to receive your parent's monthly benefits.

•**Arrange automatic payment for recurring bills.** Ask your parent to share passwords and account numbers with you so that you can arrange for payments.

•**Ask your parent to make you an "interested party" on his/her investment accounts** so that you can get copies of monthly statements.

•**Consider asking your parent to give you power of attorney to handle financial matters.**

•**If your parent needs help writing checks and managing household accounts,** you may want to hire a third party to handle the recordkeeping and check signing. The responsibility is time-consuming, and you'll need to keep careful records. Such services are provided by American Association of Daily Money Managers (814-238-2401, AADMM.com).

Cost: $25 to $100 an hour. Expect it to take two to 10 hours or more a month.

Important: Don't become a joint owner of your parent's accounts. Many caregivers find this convenient because they can pay bills or prevent scammers from coaxing money from Mom—but it's risky. If you are sued or go through a divorce, assets in a joint account are legally considered yours—and, therefore, fair game.

•**If your parent lives alone, subscribe to a personal emergency response system (PERS).** The emergency response center will provide a radio transmitter (a help button carried or worn by your parent) and a console connected to the phone. Your parent can summon help 24 hours a day.

Cost: Monitoring fees usually range from $30 to $60 a month, depending on the services. Equipment is usually included. (Cost may be covered by insurance.) For more information and reviews of providers, contact a hospital social worker or TheSeniorList.com. For financial help, visit PayingforSeniorCare.com/medicaid-waivers/adult-day-care.html (or call 641-715-3900, ext. 606151#).

•**When you visit your parents,** assess their needs and gather information.

•**Take home the local phone book and Yellow Pages,** or order copies from the phone company.

•**Do a home-safety inspection.** Check that smoke detectors work, and change the batteries. Look for potential accident zones—loose rugs, exposed extension cords, excess clutter on the floor, unstable banisters and furniture, needed items on high shelves. Replace regular lightbulbs with the long-life kind. Check the refrigerator for expired foods.

Resource: Get a free home-safety checklist for seniors from the US Consumer Product Safety Commission (800-638-2772, CPSC.gov).

•**Check your parent's car and assess his driving skills.** Ask a mechanic to check the oil, brakes and tires and do a general inspection. Ask your parent to drive you to the service station so that you can assess his driving skills. If you are worried, encourage him to take a driving test—these are offered by senior centers. If you think he poses a danger to himself or others, ask his doctor to evaluate his reflexes, vision and cognition.

•**Evaluate the need for in-home help.**

Signs that your parent may require help daily or periodically: A breakdown in personal appearance and cleanliness…unusually messy or disorderly surroundings…outside doors left unlocked…food left cooking on the stove unattended…short-term memory failure, including the inability to recount daily activities or carry out necessary tasks such as bill-paying…inappropriate food choices or failure to eat regularly…failure to take prescribed medicines.

Signs that a parent may no longer be able to live on his own: Failure to perform daily activities without help, including moving from a bed to a chair, dressing, bathing, eating and toileting.

Resource: For a checklist of trouble signs, go to Aging-parents-and-elder-care.com.

WHEN A PARENT NEEDS MORE HELP

•**Assemble a "care team" of people to check in with him regularly.** Get your parent's approval first. Enlist trusted observers who are willing to call you when problems arise. Some churches and synagogues have volunteers who do this. *Also consider…*

•**Neighbors.** Give a neighbor a key to your parent's house or apartment. Ask him/her to drop by once a day. Offer to pay him a small monthly stipend.

•**Mail carrier.** He/she will know if the mail is piling up.

•**Clergyman or spiritual adviser.**

•**Gardener/handyman.**

•**Physician who makes house calls.** To locate one, contact the American Academy of Home Care Physicians (410-676-7966, AAHCP.org). The doctor can coordinate care with your parent's primary physician. Ask your parent if he will sign a release so that the doctors can discuss health issues with you.

Resource: For free guides on caregiving a loved one, visit the Family Caregiver Alliance website at Caregiver.org (click on "Caregiver Education," then "Fact and Tip Sheets") or call 800-445-8106.

•**Identify community services.** There are many free or low-cost resources for seniors, such as adult day-care centers, transportation and activities.

Resource: The Eldercare Locator at Eldercare. gov is a public service of the U.S. Administration on Aging connecting you to local services for older adults and their families. You can also call 800-677-1116.

IF PROFESSIONAL CARE IS NEEDED

Ask your parent's doctor or a social worker at the local hospital to recommend a local home-care agency.

Cost: $50/hour and up—it may be covered if your parent has long-term-care insurance or qualifies for Medicaid. Going through a reputable private agency is more expensive than hiring someone directly, but it can save you headaches. Agency aides are bonded (insured against theft, loss and injury in a home), you don't have to pay their taxes as an employer, and the agency provides replacement workers quickly, if necessary.

Also: Retain a geriatric care manager. These licensed social workers and/or nurses can recommend solutions to short-term problems or develop long-term-care plans for your parent. For example, one can act as the family's advocate with hospitals and physicians, fill out the proper forms for benefits programs and help smooth your parent's transition to an institutional setting.

Cost: $300 to $800 for an initial assessment, $75 to $150/hour after that. To locate a professional in your area, contact Aging Life Care Association (520-881-8008, AgingLifeCare.org).

TAX BREAKS FOR CAREGIVING

If you support one or more of your parents financially, no matter how far apart you live, the IRS may allow you to claim him as a dependent and save on your taxes.

To qualify: You must pay more than 50% of his expenses. For more information, see *IRS Publication 17, Your Federal Income Tax, Table 3-1.*

Avoid Triggering Medicaid Limits

Robert Mauterstock, CFP, CLU, ChFC, a financial adviser with Parent Care Planning, LLC, based in Brewster, Massachusetts. He specializes in helping families address the financial needs of aging parents. He is author of *Can We Talk? A Financial Guide for Baby Boomers Assisting Their Elderly Parents.*

When helping a parent financially, be careful not to let his/her assets grow to the point that they could disqualify him/her from Medicaid health coverage in the future. Generally, having total countable assets (including cash and investments, but typically not personal possessions) that exceed a limit of $2,000 disqualifies a person (figure varies per state). (For more information, go to ElderLawAnswers.com.)

How to Hire a Home Health Aide for an Aging Relative

Lee A. Lindquist, MD, MPH, associate professor of medicine, general internal medicine and geriatrics, Northwestern University Feinberg School of Medicine, Chicago.

A new study suggests that agencies that hire out home health aides are shockingly careless, and even unscrupulous, when it comes to choosing their employees—which means that you're going to want to choose your aide very carefully.

AGENCIES ARE MORE LAX THAN YOU THINK

The report on home health aides, done by Lee A. Lindquist, MD, MPH, associate professor of medicine, general internal medicine and geriatrics at the Northwestern University Feinberg School of Medicine in Chicago and her colleagues, uncovered some disturbing facts.

Researchers posing as consumers contacted 180 caregiving agencies in seven states (Arizona, California, Colorado, Florida, Illinois, Indiana and Wisconsin). *What they discovered...*

●**69% of the agencies said that they do not screen for illegal drug use before hiring caregivers.**

●**58% of agencies said that they assess skills just by asking applicants what they can do.** Only 35% said that they follow up by actually testing the caregivers' skills.

●**Just 15% of agencies said that they give on-site training or supervision while the aide is on the job at a patient's home.**

●**38% said that they do not check job applicants' references.**

"Many caregiving agencies come across as professional, but a number of them are just trying to take advantage of consumers," said Dr. Lindquist.

HOW IS THIS LEGAL?

You might be thinking, There ought to be a law. But there isn't. Agencies that provide medical care are regulated and have to be licensed. Home health aides, however, aren't supposed to provide medical care.

They may help with laundry, bathing, cooking and getting their clients in and out of bed...they may remind them to take their medications...but none of this is considered medical care. In terms of what sort of training is required, it varies from state to state, and the guidelines are loose. For example, in Illinois, an aide needs to have eight hours of training, but there are no guidelines that specify what the training should consist of, so it could entail reading a handbook over eight hours. Other states, on the other hand, require zero hours of training.

In fact, in the eyes of the law, as Dr. Lindquist puts it, home health aides are "like nannies or babysitters for seniors."

The scary part is, with such careless screening, seniors are vulnerable to abuse, neglect and even financial fraud (some caregivers are given access to the client's checkbook to pay bills for him or her).

QUESTIONS TO ASK

If you have a loved one in need of a home health aide, do your homework! Here are questions from Dr. Lindquist to ask the agency. *If any agency refuses to answer a question (or dances around it), go to another one…*

●**How do you evaluate a candidate's skills before hiring him or her?** The agency should tell you in detail how it tests each candidate's skills. If the agency doesn't do any testing whatsoever, don't use the agency.

●**How do you supervise?** Does someone come out to the house to actually watch the caregiver perform? The agency should provide home supervision at least once a month. If it doesn't, don't use the agency.

●**If a caregiver is unable to come on a given date, do you send a replacement?** The answer should be "yes." If it isn't, don't use the agency.

●**May I please see references for each candidate?** If the agency doesn't have any, don't use the agency. If the agency provides them, read them carefully before choosing one (or, ideally, a few) candidates to interview, so you can weed out anyone who seems inexperienced or untrustworthy.

●**Do you do federal and state criminal background checks and drug screening?** If the agency doesn't, then don't use the agency. If the agency does, insist on seeing the reports.

PROTECT YOUR LOVED ONE

Once you've hired a home health aide, drop by occasionally for surprise visits to evaluate him or her, said Dr. Lindquist. Is your loved one still in bed at 2:00 pm? Has your loved one showered? Eaten breakfast and lunch? Taken the correct dosages of the correct medications? You might even want to go through credit card bills and checkbooks to make sure that the bills are paid and that there are no missing checks or unusual payments with the credit card. These drop-ins are extra important when your loved one is mentally incapacitated, since he or she may not be able to explain to you later what went wrong.

How to Talk to Those with Dementia so They Can Hear You

Kristine N. Williams, RN, PhD, associate professor, University of Kansas School of Nursing, Kansas City, Kansas.

Have you noticed how loudly some people talk when attempting to communicate with a person who doesn't speak English? They seem to think turning up the volume will bridge the language gap. Similarly it is common for many, including trained professional caregivers, to use "elderspeak" with people who are old and infirm. It sounds a lot like baby talk, with simplified grammar and vocabulary and liberal use of terms of endearment, such as honey, sweetie and dearie. Though it may be done with the best intentions, a new study finds that when elderly patients are spoken to in this way, they often become angry, less responsive and harder to care for.

The study, led by researcher Kristine N. Williams, RN, PhD, an associate professor at the University of Kansas School of Nursing, videotaped interactions between caregivers (nursing assistants, nurses, therapists and social workers) and 20 nursing home residents with moderate dementia. Using a measure called the "Resistiveness to Care Scale" to quantify the intensity of care-disrupting behaviors (acts of withdrawal or aggression, such as grabbing onto a person or pulling one's own limbs tightly into the body, hitting, crying and kicking), researchers reviewed the tapes. When they witnessed such episodes, they rewound the tapes to see what kind of communications occurred in the preceding seven seconds. Often (55% of the time), it turned out that the caregivers had been using "elderspeak," compared with the 26% of the time these behaviors arose when caregivers used normal adult communication. It seemed that the elders objected to being talked to in this child-like way. The researchers hypothesized that this form of communication sends a negative message of incompetence, which ends up irritating rather than soothing listeners.

RESPECT YOUR ELDERS

The National Institute on Aging and Dr. Williams offer these tips for communicating with those who have Alzheimer's disease or dementia…

• **Before speaking, gain the person's full attention.** Use his/her name.

• **While interacting, turn off distractions such as the TV or radio.**

• **Speak in a tone that is calm and gentle, without infantilizing.** Dr. Williams also points out that nonverbal cues such as establishing eye contact convey your focus and willingness to communicate.

• **Use simple words and short, clear sentences.** If someone is having trouble finding the right words, it's fine to help him/her out by gently making suggestions.

• **Be patient, providing ample time to think and respond.** It is important to give people with dementia time to compose and communicate their thoughts, says Dr. Williams. When you are patient, it shows you believe that what they have to say is important and that you are paying attention to them.

• **Do not talk about a person with AD or dementia in front of him/her as if he/she was not present.**

It's not so hard, actually—doesn't it really come down to using the same good manners we should be using anyway?

Music and Cooking Help Behavioral Problems in Alzheimer's Patients

Pauline Narme, MD, Neuropsychology of Aging, Paris Descartes University, Boulogne-Billancourt, in collaboration with the University of Lille and the University Medical Center of Reims, all in France. This study was published in the *Journal of Alzheimer's Disease.*

Dealing with a loved one who is agitated and aggressive is never easy—but it's especially tough when that person has Alzheimer's disease and can no longer understand what is "appropriate" behavior and what isn't. Such behavioral issues are very common in Alzheimer's patients… and medication helps little while potentially causing side effects.

MUSIC TO THEIR EARS

According to the Alzheimer's Foundation of America, music has the power to improve patients' mood and cognitive function and to stimulate positive interaction because the part of the brain that responds to auditory cues requires little cognitive functioning. That's why, even in advanced dementia, the ability to engage in music by singing along may remain intact.

Although a recent study showed greater benefits from music than from cooking, the benefits from the cooking were significant…and it's possible that a patient who had a lifelong interest in cooking would respond more positively to a cooking activity than to a music activity.

Advice for caregivers: The supervisors who led the study were not professional music therapists or chefs—and in fact, one of the researchers' goals was to look for nonmedical care strategies that could easily be adapted for use at home by family caregivers. So why not try re-creating positive effects yourself through music or cookin when you're with the Alzheimer's patient you care for?

For instance, play some CDs when you're together, choosing a style of music that is familiar and soothing, and encouraging your loved one to sing, clap or drum along to the tune. Or spend time together in the kitchen, preparing a simple recipe (such as pancakes) and inviting your loved one to handle safe and easy tasks, such as measuring, mixing and pouring. You might include other family members, too, to more closely duplicate the social aspect of the study's group activities. You may end up doing everyone involved a world of good.

Financial Aid and Tax Breaks for Caregiving

Jim Miller, an advocate for older Americans, who writes "Savvy Senior," a weekly information column syndicated in more than 400 newspapers nationwide. Based in Norman, Oklahoma, he offers a free senior news service at Savvy Senior.org.

If you're hiring someone to take care of an elderly family member—or even doing it yourself—you may be in a precarious position. For many families, caregiving can quickly grow into a heavy financial burden, especially if you've had to quit your job to provide care. However, there are a number of government programs and tax breaks that can help you financially. *Here are some options to explore…*

●**State assistance.** Many states help low-income seniors pay for in-home care services, including paying family members for care. These programs—which go by various names such as "cash and counseling" or "consumer-directed"—vary greatly depending on where you live and, in some states, on whether the senior is on Medicaid. To find out what's available in your state, contact your local Medicaid office.

●**Veterans benefits.** In some communities, veterans who need assistance with daily living activities can enroll in the Veteran-Directed Home and Community Based Services program. This program provides a flexible stipend, which can be used to pay family members for home caregiving. Information about these programs is available at VA.gov/geriatrics.

A VA benefit available only to wartime veterans and their spouses is Aid and Attendance, which can provide up to $2,000 per month to veterans (or about $1,000 per month to their surviving spouses) who served during wartime and now cannot afford caregiver assistance. This benefit also can be used to pay family caregivers. To be eligible, the person must need assistance with daily living activities such as bathing, dressing and going to the bathroom. And the person's annual income and assets must meet certain requirements.

To learn more about these VA benefits, go to Benefits.va.gov/pension or contact your regional VA office or your local veterans service organization.

●**Tax breaks.** If you pay more than half of your elderly relative's yearly expenses and his/ her gross income was below $4,050, not counting Social Security, you can claim him/her as a dependent on your taxes and reduce your taxable income. Check IRS.gov for yearly updates on salary limits. For more information, see *IRS Publication 501, Exemptions, Standard Deduction, and Filing Information*, at IRS.gov/publications/p501 or call 800-829-3676 to ask for a copy.

If you can't claim your relative as a dependent, you still may be able to get a tax break if you're paying more than half his living expenses, including medical and long-term-care costs, and what you're paying exceeds 10% (or 7.5% if you're 65 or older) of your adjusted gross income. You can include your own medical expenses in calculating the total. See *IRS publication 502, Medical and Dental Expenses* (IRS.gov/publications/p502) for details.

●**Long-term-care insurance.** If your relative has long-term-care insurance, check whether it covers in-home care. Some policies permit family members to be paid, although that may exclude people who live in the same household.

●**Family funds.** If your relative has savings or other assets, discuss the possibility that he could pay for his own care. If he plans to pay a family member to provide care, consult with an attorney about drafting a short written contract that details the terms of the work and payment arrangements so that everyone involved knows what to expect.

●**Other assistance.** To look for financial assistance programs that your relative or you may be eligible for, visit BenefitsCheckup.org, a free, web-based service that helps low-income seniors and their families identify federal, state and private benefits programs that can help with prescription drug costs, health care, utilities and other basic needs.

Passages of Caregiving and the Strategies for Coping

Gail Sheehy, an award-winning journalist and author of the book *Passages*, which spent more than three years on *The New York Times* best-seller list and was named one of the 10 most influential books of our time in a Library of Congress survey. Her latest book is *Passages: Predictable Crises of Adult Life*. Sheehy served as AARP's Ambassador of Caregiving in 2009. GailSheehy.com

About 65 million Americans currently serve as primary caregivers to chronically ill or disabled relatives. Few of these caregivers ever expected to become caregivers, and fewer still are prepared for the enormity of the task.

Gail Sheehy, author of the acclaimed book Passages: Predictable Crises of Adult Life, was one of those caregivers. Her husband, Clay Felker, founding editor of New York magazine, required her assistance as he battled four separate cancer diagnoses during the final 17 years of his life.

We interviewed Sheehy, who explained that the caregiving process is like a labyrinth. As endless as it can seem, there is a path through, but there also are passages, or "turns," along the way that make it difficult to see what lies ahead. *Here, the eight turns that caregivers can expect and strategies for coping with each...*

TURN 1: SHOCK AND MOBILIZATION

The call to caregiving can come out of the blue. A previously healthy relative experiences a major medical problem, and suddenly you're asked to provide not just care, but assistance sorting through treatment options. This is important and often complex, yet you are pressured to make quick decisions. Expect to feel fear and confusion.

Strategy: Seek out multiple opinions and treatment options before proceeding.

Example: When my husband's throat cancer reappeared after a period of remission, Clay's doctor said his voice box would have to be removed. Fortunately, we knew not to jump at the first treatment option suggested. We tracked down a specialist in my husband's type of tumor, and he offered a different treatment strategy that preserved Clay's ability to speak and extended his life.

Record your loved one's consultations with doctors using a small portable voice recorder. These consultations can be emotional and confusing, which makes it easy to get the facts wrong if you're working from memory. Tell the doctor that this recording will help you avoid bothering him/her with questions later.

During these initial medical consultations, ask doctors...

"Will you be the one to coordinate care?"

"Will you help us decide among treatment options?"

"Will you help address pain and other side effects of treatment?"

These questions will point you toward a "medical quarterback," a doctor who is willing to take the lead in your loved one's care.

TURN 2: THE NEW NORMAL

You have reached this turn when you realize that you are a caregiver—and that caregiving is likely to be a big part of your life for a long time. On the bright side, your sense of panic should begin to recede as you settle into this new reality.

Strategy: Do not settle into this new life alone. Seek out friends, relatives, neighbors and colleagues who are willing to help provide care and support.

Also, if the patient is elderly, hire a geriatric care manager (GCM), an expert in sorting though insurance and Medicare mazes and finding resources available to caregivers. These professionals typically charge $80 to $250 per hour and are not covered by Medicare or most insurance policies, but it's worth paying for at least a one-hour consultation even if money is tight. The Aging Life Care Association can help you find a GCM in your region (520-881-8008, AgingLifeCare.org).

TURN 3: BOOMERANG

Months have passed, perhaps years. You have settled into the routines of caregiving—and then there's another crisis. Your loved one's health has taken a turn for the worse, and you feel like you're right back at Turn 1. Only you're not—you're now much better equipped to handle these emergencies. You've become an expert on your loved one's medical condition...you're an old hand at dealing with insurance companies and Medicare…and you have a medical quarterback in place.

Strategy: The relative calm of The New Normal might have convinced you that you can handle caregiving. The emotional roller coaster of the Boomerang serves as a reminder that caregivers require care, too. If you haven't already done so, find a support network for yourself. The Well Spouse Association (800-838-0879, WellSpouse.org) directs spousal caregivers to local and online support groups. The Family Caregiver Alliance (800-445-8106, Caregiver.org) directs caregivers to a range of appropriate support groups, many associated with specific health problems.

TURN 4: PLAYING GOD

Many caregivers understandably come to see themselves as pivotal to their loved one's survival. It is perfectly fine to take pride in your caregiving efforts—but it is vital that you do not view your loved one's good days and progress as proof of your value. If you do this, you are likely to blame yourself for your loved one's bad days and setbacks — and bad days and setbacks are virtually inevitable with chronic health conditions.

Strategy: When there are changes in your loved one's condition—good or bad—remind yourself that there is a God, and it is not you. Be sure to involve family members and the patient in decision-making to protect yourself from guilt if something goes wrong.

TURN 5: "I CAN'T DO THIS ANYMORE!"

There are no weekends or vacations for many caregivers. Their responsibilities seem unending — but no one can be a caregiver every day for years. We reach the end of our rope.

Strategy: Get out of the home and away from your loved one for at least one hour each day and at least one full day every month, even if this means stretching the budget to hire a professional caregiver. If your loved one is on Medicare, contact the hospice or palliative care department (see Turns 7 and 8) of a local hospital and request a "respite." Most caregivers do not realize that Medicare often will pay most or all of the costs of having this department look after their loved ones for as long as

five days as frequently as every 90 days so that the caregiver can take a break. (Private medical insurance generally does not cover respite care.)

TURN 6: COMING BACK

You have reached this turn when you realize that your loved one is never going to fully recover. He will only become more dependent.

You have reached the center of the labyrinth, and it is time to start planning your journey back out. This is the most painful turn in the caregiving process because it forces a caregiver to acknowledge that the only way to escape the labyrinth is to start to release his/her loved one. A caregiver who can't take this step becomes indistinguishable from his loved one, so lost in another person's medical struggles that he loses his "self" and becomes a caregiver, nothing else.

Example: By the end of my husband's life, I began to doubt my ability to write, something I had been doing virtually all my life.

Strategy: Take up a challenging and fulfilling hobby that you can pursue while in the home, such as art, writing or music. Just waiting for your next caregiving task is not a life.

TURNS 7 AND 8: THE IN-BETWEEN STAGE/THE LONG GOOD-BYE

Hospitals are designed to cure medical problems, not treat patients with incurable conditions. Hospice care is intended only for patients in the final months of life. Caregivers often are at a loss for where to seek medical care when neither of these solutions fits.

Strategy: Find a local hospital that offers "palliative care" (go to GetPalliativeCare.org, then search the "Provider Directory"). Like hospice care, palliative care focuses on pain relief—but unlike hospice care, it is not just for those close to death, and it can be combined with treatments meant to address the underlying condition.

Hospice care becomes an option once a doctor has determined that the patient most likely has six months or less to live. Caregivers often receive the most cherished benefit of hospice care. They and other family members almost universally express gratitude for being guided and supported through the mysteries of the dying process. The common refrain is, "We couldn't have done it alone."

Parenting Your Parents

John Bertschler, PhD, a mediator, licensed psychologist and co-owner of Northcoast Conflict Solutions, a mediation practice based in Seven Hills, Ohio. He also trains mediators and is coauthor of *Elder Mediation: A New Solution to Age-Old Problems.* NCSMediation.com

Teenagers aren't the only ones who argue with their parents. Full-grown adults sometimes disagree with their aging parents. When these conflicts involve a parent's safety or financial security, the adult children often refuse to yield despite the parent's wishes.

These disagreements can grow so heated that it almost seems as if a referee needs to be called in to avoid ruining the relationship.

Here are ways to increase the odds of a peaceful resolution when grown children and their parents disagree...

•**Include close family members in the conversation with the parent,** and meet with those family members beforehand. Family members who are close to this parent are more likely to oppose your position if they feel excluded from the decision-making process. Also, parents are more likely to respect an opinion shared by many family members than that of just one adult child.

•**Schedule the conversation for morning or early afternoon if the parent experiences "sundowning"**—reduced mental clarity as evening approaches. People in the early stages of dementia often are mentally sharpest and best able to contribute to important conversations early in the day.

•**Have ready specific examples of why you believe something needs to be done.** Examples can increase the odds that the parent and other relatives will agree that action is required.

Example: "It's not just my opinion that your driving skills have slipped. You've had three fender benders in the past year."

•**Raise an issue by saying it might be time to discuss the available options,** not by saying it's time to take the specific action that you, personally, consider best. Pushing your opinion at the outset only increases the odds that the parent will dig in his/her heels.

Example: Say, "I think it's time we discussed what sort of help you might need in the future," rather than, "I think it's time we thought about moving you into a nursing home"—even if you think a nursing home is the best choice.

Once a parent agrees to take part in the discussion, it is more likely that he will listen when you provide evidence that the option you favor is worth a look.

•**If family discussions about elder issues become rancorous, find a mediator.** Mediators typically charge from $150 to $500 an hour, depending on the region and their experience. If this is cost prohibitive, perhaps the family can agree on a respected family member, family friend or religious counselor to serve as a mediator. Visit Long TermCareLink.net/a7mediation.htm to find a mediator near you or call 800-989-8137.

Among the issues involving elderly parents that often become sources of family strife...

HOW MUCH CARE

Conflict: Some family members believe an elderly parent needs more assistance from professional caregivers, possibly even a nursing home—but the parent disagrees.

Strategy: Cite the specific dangerous incidents that are causing your concern—falls or ovens being left on, for example. Keep the term "nursing home" out of the conversation—it carries too much negative baggage in many people's minds. Instead, explain that there are many other possible care options, ranging from having someone look in on the parent regularly...to an assisted-living facility. Say that your goal is to find the option that gets the parent the amount of assistance needed to live the life he wants.

If that fails—or if you are the elderly parent and you truly believe that your current living arrangements are appropriate—suggest that the family arrange a geriatric assessment. This provides an unbiased, informed evaluation of what level of assistance is appropriate for a senior. It is typically offered through hospitals and geriatric care centers. The parent's doctor might be able to recommend someone. If not, your state's Adult Protective Services department might be able to help you find one. (Put "Adult Protective Services" and your state's name into any search engine to find contact information for this government agency.)

SHOULD THE PARENT DRIVE?

Conflict: An aging parent's driving seems unsafe to one or more family members, but the parent won't surrender the car keys.

Strategy: Do not just ask a parent to give up the car keys—present a plan for how the parent will get around without a car. If you are the parent, explain that you might be willing to discuss giving up driving if such a plan could be arranged. Research the region's public transit, senior shuttles and taxi services. Or explore whether family members and friends who live in the region could provide rides when needed.

Example: A man agreed to sell his car when his son suggested that some of the money from this sale be put into an account with a local cab company.

If the parent still considers himself a safe driver, suggest that he retake the driving test through the state department of motor vehicles to settle the matter objectively...and/or suggest that he take driving lessons designed for aging adults given by or-

ganizations such as Keeping Us Safe (877-907-8841, KeepingUsSafe.org).

LIVING TOGETHER

Conflict: Family members may get under one another's skin when an elderly parent moves in with an adult child.

Strategy: Neither parent nor child should attempt to impose "house rules." Instead, say that everyone will have to work together to develop a system that keeps family members from annoying one another. Propose that the first month be treated as an adjustment period, and choose a date and time of month in the future for family members to discuss what policies need to be implemented.

Example: An older man often got up in the middle of the night for a snack, then left his son's kitchen a mess. During the follow-up meeting, he agreed to clean his dishes before returning to bed. He hadn't realized this was annoying because his late wife had never complained about it.

If the parent has diminished mental capacity and cannot help but do things that annoy the rest of the family, search for ways you could alter the living arrangements to minimize these annoyances. Perhaps the parent could move into a room in the basement so that his late-night noise is less disruptive. If no solution presents itself, the adult child must decide whether the behavior can be endured or whether it is so disruptive that the only solution is to find alternate living arrangements for the parent.

Deadly Medical Mistakes and How to Avoid Them

How to Leave the Hospital Alive

Jan Garavaglia, MD, chief medical examiner for the District Nine Medical Examiner's Office in Orlando, Florida. Dr. Garavaglia is host of Discovery Health channel's top-rated series *Dr. G: Medical Examiner* and is author of *How Not to Die: Surprising Lessons on Living Longer, Safer, and Healthier from America's Favorite Medical Examiner.* HowNotToDie.com).

As a medical examiner, I discover during autopsies why some people die unexpectedly. A significant number die from mistakes made in the hospital. A report from the Institute of Medicine (part of the National Academy of Sciences) found that between 44,000 and 98,000 Americans die each year from medical errors made in hospitals. Some errors are hard to prevent, but many can be avoided by alert patients or their families.

Some of the main dangers—and how to prevent them…

DRUG MISTAKES

It is estimated that up to half of adverse drug reactions are caused by errors. Sometimes it's the patient's fault, such as neglecting to inform the hospital staff about a known allergy. Sometimes doctors aren't as careful as they should be. A patient might be given a drug that is inappropriate for his/her condition—or given the right drug but the wrong dose. A "standard" dose isn't necessarily the right dose.

Example: Older adults metabolize drugs slowly. A dose that's safe for a 40-year-old might be too high for someone who is 65. A patient's size also makes a difference. A large man will generally need a larger dose than a petite woman.

My advice: Tell the hospital staff about every supplement and drug that you're taking, including over-the-counter medications. Better yet, bring a written list to the hospital.

Also, ask your doctor if drug doses should be adjusted for your body weight/metabolism. And confirm that you really need a particular drug. Sedatives, for example, frequently cause side effects, including increasing risk for falls, yet they are commonly prescribed to hospital patients who don't really need them.

In addition, ask anyone who gives you a medication or intravenous infusion what it is for. This will make him/her think twice before administering it—which helps prevent errors.

INFECTION

This is the leading cause of unexpected hospital deaths. According to the Centers for Disease Control and Prevention (CDC), 1.7 million Americans suffer a health-care–related infection each year. An extremely virulent organism—methicillin-resistant Staphylococcus aureus (MRSA)—kills up to one in five hospital patients who get it.

My advice: Ask about a surgeon's infection rates. Do this before choosing a surgeon. For "clean" procedures, such as a knee replacement, the infection rate should be 2% or less. Infection is more likely during "dirty" procedures, such as those involving the intestines. You always want the number to be as low as possible—less than 10%. *Also...*

•**Don't let the staff touch you unless you've seen them washing their hands before putting on fresh gloves.** Everyone should wash his hands as soon as he enters the room. If anyone doesn't, ask him to do so.

•**Exercise your lungs.** Bacterial pneumonia is common in hospitals. Up to 30% of patients placed on a ventilator develop pneumonia, and up to 50% of these patients die from it.

Self-defense: Ask for an incentive spirometer, a tubelike device that increases bronchial pressure. This helps remove the mucus and fluids that bacteria need to proliferate. Also, walk as soon as possible, even if it is uncomfortable.

•**Avoid urinary catheters.** They are the main cause of hospital urinary tract infections. If you can't walk to the bathroom, ask if you can use a bedpan or wear diapers. Men can request a urinal or condom catheter, which slips over the penis and doesn't require inserting a tube into the urethra.

DEEP-VEIN THROMBOSIS (DVT)

About 10% of hospital patients who stay in bed for a week and up to one-third of patients in intensive care units (ICUs) develop DVT, a life-threatening condition in which a blood clot in the leg can travel to the lungs and cause a pulmonary embolism (when an artery in the lung becomes blocked).

Immobility is the main cause of DVT. The risk is highest in hospital patients because tissue damage—either from surgery or underlying medical problems—increases the body's production of clotting factors.

My advice: Before checking into the hospital, tell your doctor that you want to move around as soon as possible after your procedure. Simply flex-

ing your legs and sitting up in bed can help prevent DVT. Walking is better—try to do it once an hour if your condition permits. Even if you're in an ICU, ask the staff to help you stand up and walk.

Also important: Ask for leg-compression devices. Known as "squeezers," they are pneumatic devices that inflate and deflate at regular intervals to help prevent clotting.

SMOKING

Anyone who smokes should quit for at least six weeks before going into the hospital. Smoking increases the risk for pneumonia. It impairs your ability to breathe on your own after being on a mechanical ventilator during surgery. It also impedes healing.

My advice: If you can't quit smoking on your own, talk to your doctor about stop-smoking aids, such as nicotine patches, or drugs, such as *varenicline* (Chantix). People who use these products have about twice the success rate of those who don't.

FALLS

They're among the leading causes of unexpected hospital deaths. The risk is higher if you're taking sedatives, have recently had anesthesia or are taking multiple drugs, including laxatives and diuretics.

My advice: Don't get out of bed without help even if you think you're well enough to do so. Wear nonskid slippers when walking around your room or down the halls.

Also important: Keep the bed rails raised and the bed low. Make sure the nurse's call light is within reach. If you need to get up, call the nurse for assistance.

WITHHOLDING INFORMATION

No one likes feeling embarrassed. Men with chest pains, for example, may hesitate to admit that they have taken Viagra—which may be dangerous when combined with nitrate drugs used to treat chest pain.

It is common for alcoholics to say that they don't drink. This is extremely risky. Alcoholics can die from withdrawal unless they're given medications to prevent it and are carefully monitored.

My advice: Be sure to tell your doctor everything. Don't withhold any information about drug use, alcohol abuse, etc.

BEWARE OF NEW DRUGS

The FDA has taken about a dozen drugs off the market in just the last 10 years. Medications that appear to be safe during the approval process can later turn out to have dangerous effects.

Example: The antibiotic *gatifloxacin* (Tequin), originally approved for respiratory infections, was later found to cause dangerous changes in blood sugar levels, resulting in the deaths of some patients. The deaths were especially tragic because most patients would have done just as well with older—and safer—drugs.

Most new drugs are tested on only a few thousand patients at most. If a drug causes a deadly reaction in, say, one in 20,000 patients, it might be years before the dangers become apparent.

Avoid any drug until it has been on the market for at least two years. That's long enough for serious dangers to surface. (Of course, some patients benefit greatly from new, breakthrough drugs, but for most conditions, older drugs with proven safety profiles are equally effective.)

Medical Errors Are Prevalent

Analysis of studies of medical death rate data from 2000 through 2008 by researchers at The Johns Hopkins University School of Medicine, Baltimore, published in *BMJ*.

Medical error is the third-leading cause of death in the US? More than 250,000 people die each year due to medical errors. Only heart disease and cancer cause more deaths annually.

Doctors Ignore Up to 90% of E-Prescription Safety Warnings

Michael Cohen, RPh, MS, ScD, president, The Institute for Safe Medication Practices, a nonprofit healthcare organization. He serves as a consultant to the FDA Drug Safety and Risk Management Committee.

Doctors and consumers alike are enthusiastic about the benefits of e-prescriptions, which add convenience and reduce potential errors—or do they? Though one of the benefits of electronic prescribing systems is that they are programmed to generate alerts about possible drug allergies or interactions, it appears that physicians override these warnings up to 90% of the time. Why, I asked Michael Cohen, RPh, MS, ScD, president of The Institute for Safe Medication Practices (ConsumerMedSafety.org), a nonprofit organization that specializes in understanding and reducing medication errors. He said that the issue isn't that the doctors are cavalier, but that kinks in the e-prescribing systems fire off too many irrelevant alerts. The problem is, the doctors may inadvertently be training themselves to ignore this important system feature.

E-PRESCRIBING SYSTEMS CRY WOLF

At Dana-Farber Cancer Institute and Beth Israel Deaconess Medical Center in Boston, doctors analyzed safety alert records generated by the e-prescribing systems of nearly 2,900 practitioners at community-based outpatient practices in Massachusetts, New Jersey and Pennsylvania. Between January 1 and September 30, 2006, clinicians wrote more than three million electronic prescriptions. Researchers discovered that 6.6% of prescriptions triggered alerts for drug interactions or allergies. Practitioners overrode 91% of drug interaction alerts and 77% of drug allergy alerts. These results were published in the February 9, 2009, issue of *Archives of Internal Medicine*.

IMPLICATIONS OF THE FINDINGS

While it sounds terrible that doctors bypass so many warnings, Dr. Cohen is quick to point out that the information is not always as helpful as it might be. Computer systems often alert physicians to drug interactions or allergies when, in fact, the information lacks clinical significance or has already been taken into account by the doctor, Dr. Cohen explains. E-prescribing software firms are working to improve their systems to decrease the high number of irrelevant alerts. In the meantime, Dr. Cohen emphasizes that consumers should not assume that e-prescriptions are free of potential errors and should continue to follow the usual advice to ensure drug safety—there really is no shortcut. *He recommends…*

•**Ask the pharmacist to do an independent screening of the medications,** herbals and nutritionals you are taking to see whether there are any potential problematic interactions.

•**If there are some that raise concern,** ask your doctor about whether it may be important.

•**Use Internet tools as well.** For example, ConsumerMedSafety.org has articles on drug interactions and a link to MedCounselor, which allows consumers to list their medications and get feedback on any potential problems. It allows you to generate a new report each time a drug gets added or removed.

•**E-prescriptions** are a move in the right direction for increasing patients' protection against drug errors, but the technology is clearly not there yet. Safety continues to depend on effective communication between you, your doctor and the pharmacist.

Check Medical Bills for Coding Mistakes

Consumer Reports Money Adviser. (Now ConsumerReports. org/money/).

Look for coding errors on medical bills. Mistakes in current procedural terminology (CPT) codes can change your diagnosis and lead to higher charges both for your insurance company and for you.

What to do: Carefully examine the explanation of benefits or Medicare summary notice you re-

ceive when bills are processed. If the charges or procedures seem wrong, call the provider or your insurer for an explanation. Check CPT codes for accuracy by searching online for theetters CPT and the code number.

When Hospitals Make Mistakes

E. Wesley Ely, MD, MPH, professor of medicine and critical care, Vanderbilt University Medical Center, Nashville. Dr. Ely is the founder of Vanderbilt's ICU Delirium and Cognitive Impairment Study Group and associate director of aging research for the VA Tennessee Valley Geriatric Research and Education Clinical Center (GRECC).

You research the pros and cons and shop around before you buy a car—so why not compare local hospitals in case you, or someone close to you, becomes ill or has an accident? Lack of accessible information may have discouraged you from taking a close look in the past, but the Centers for Medicare & Medicaid Services (CMS) now reports hospital error rates on its website. The information is right there at HospitalCompare.hhs.gov, making it easy to see how the various medical centers in your area stack up against each other. So what can you find out?

ADVERSE EVENTS: MORE COMMON THAN YOU THINK

Hospital-acquired conditions (HACs) are also called "never events"—because they are serious problems that people develop in the hospital that should seldom, if ever, happen as long as proper procedures are followed. As an example, according to the Department of Health and Human Services' Office of the Inspector General, 13.5% of hospitalized patients on Medicare experience preventable adverse events such as falls and infections. That's clearly way more than "never"…and way too many.

The CMS tracks hospitals' rates on these eight "never events"…

•**Foreign objects.** Yes, it really is true—sometimes surgeons accidentally leave a sponge or clamp in a patient's body.

•**Air embolism.** Without proper care and attention, a dangerous air bubble may develop in your bloodstream. This can happen with a central IV line and during vascular procedures.

•**Mismatched blood.** Hospitals occasionally administer the wrong type of blood in a transfusion.

•**Severe pressure sores.** If you can't move around independently and caregivers don't help you shift position frequently, you can develop painful and potentially life-threatening pressure sores, what most people call bedsores.

•**Falls and injuries.** Without proper assistance, a simple trip to the bathroom may result in a fall and a debilitating injury.

Vascular catheter-associated infection. This is a blood infection from catheters—small tubes that are used to treat heart disease or other disease and carry a risk for sepsis.

•**Catheter-associated urinary tract infections.** Catheters also are used to help patients urinate, and infections are a common complication.

•**Uncontrolled blood sugar.** Signs of poorly controlled blood sugar range from confusion, anxiety and sweating (low blood sugar or hypoglycemia) to headaches, blurred vision and fatigue (high blood sugar or hyperglycemia). This is a concern for hospital patients with diabetes and also for others—for instance, those for whom the stress of hospitalization is too much. Pregnancy can cause short-term hyperglycemia as well.

After reading through that list, are you ready to take yourself to just any old hospital? I didn't think so. It's clearly a good idea to track error rates, notes E. Wesley Ely, MD, MPH, a professor and specialist in pulmonary and critical care medicine at Vanderbilt University Medical Center—but, he adds, it's something that needs to be done very carefully for the benefit of both patients and the hospitals themselves. For example, it's reasonable and helpful to hold hospitals responsible for mistakes such as transfusing the wrong blood type or leaving a foreign object in a patient during a surgical procedure—but it's not helpful to automatically blame hospitals when patients develop delirium after surgery, as the CMS originally proposed, because delirium is not always preventable. Fortunately, the CMS reversed its position on this condition, says Dr. Ely.

WHAT YOU NEED TO KNOW BEFORE YOU GO

To increase your odds of a safe and successful hospital stay, become an educated consumer…

•**Check hospital ratings.** Visit CMS's website and read about hospital errors. You'll find the incidence rate for each of the eight HACs in the nation's 4,700 hospitals. That is how many times an HAC has occurred per 1,000 discharges. At Hospital Compare.hhs.gov, you also can learn how satisfied other people were with their hospital stays…how closely hospitals followed best practices of care… how many people died within 30 days of hospitalization for a heart attack, heart failure or pneumonia…and 30-day readmission rates for these conditions.

•**Don't pay for their mistakes.** Medicare does not pay for treatment of conditions that result from hospitals' mistakes, and you don't have to either. If you develop any of the eight above conditions in the hospital, you can't be charged for the resulting necessary treatment, according to the Deficit Reduction Act of 2005.

•**Work with caregivers as a team.** For best results, Dr. Ely urges families to communicate closely with doctors, nurses and other health-care professionals. Provide caregivers with a complete list of all prescription and over-the-counter medications and supplements that the patient takes so that nothing gets overlooked in an emergency. This is particularly important so that doctors can avoid drug interactions with new medications they might prescribe. Ask questions about the risks and potential benefits of treatment options, and speak up about any other concerns, such as a patient being sedated too deeply or for too many days. As well-meaning as most health-care professionals are, the demands of their jobs mean that a patient's quality of care isn't necessarily automatic.

•**Safer at home.** Dr. Ely also encourages you to keep talking to your hospitalized loved ones so they remain as oriented and aware as possible…so that they get out of bed sooner…recover and come back home where they belong. It's much safer there!

When Doctors Get It Wrong

Joe Graedon, MS, and **Teresa Graedon, PhD,** consumer advocates whose first book, *The People's Pharmacy*, was published in 1976. Since then, they have written *The People's Pharmacy* syndicated newspaper column, which discusses various issues related to drugs, herbs and vitamins. Their most recent book is *Top Screwups Doctors Make and How to Avoid Them.* PeoplesPharmacy.com

As an outbreak of fungal meningitis clearly revealed, certain medical conditions are notoriously difficult to diagnose. The first of these patients suffered vague symptoms—including headache, fever, nausea and stiffness of the neck—that were initially misdiagnosed. Fortunately, doctors eventually identified the tainted medication that caused the outbreak.

But mysterious symptoms are not always unraveled so quickly.

Startling statistic: Every year in the US, an estimated 40,000 to 80,000 hospital deaths are caused by diagnostic errors, according to a report in *The Journal of the American Medical Association*. When researchers use autopsies to discover discrepancies between diagnosed and actual causes of deaths, the error rate can be as high as 40%.

Conditions often misdiagnosed…

•**Alzheimer's Disease.** It's impossible to diagnose this condition with 100% certainty because the only definitive "test" is an autopsy of the patient's brain after death. Even though there are fairly accurate ways to determine that a patient might have Alzheimer's (see below), mistakes are common.

Examples: Depression is one of the most common causes of Alzheimer's-like symptoms, but doctors often fail to recognize it. Other problems, including nutritional deficiencies and medication side effects—for example, from anticholinergic drugs, such as antihistamines, incontinence medi-

cations and tricyclic antidepressants—also can cause symptoms that mimic Alzheimer's.

Surprising fact: It's estimated that 10% to 25% of patients with symptoms of dementia (such as memory problems and/or peculiar behavior) may have a non-Alzheimer's condition that could be reversed with proper treatment.

What to do: Don't accept a diagnosis of Alzheimer's disease after a single office visit or after taking a simple questionnaire. Specialists (such as neurologists) take a very detailed personal and family history…conduct neurological and mental-status tests…and order a variety of blood and imaging tests to determine whether other conditions might be involved.

•**Deep Vein Thrombosis (DVT).** A blood clot anywhere in the vascular system can be deadly. Those that form in the deep veins in the legs are particularly risky because the symptoms—if there are any—can seem minor. For that reason, some people don't even seek medical care, or doctors may assume that the symptoms are caused by a leg strain or sprain.

The risk: A clot can break free and enter a lung, creating a deadly pulmonary embolism. About 20% of DVT patients who develop pulmonary embolism will die from it.

What to do: **If you have leg pain, leg cramps or a sense of tightness in one leg** that you can't explain (discomfort in both legs probably is not caused by DVT), speak to your doctor right away. If he/she is unavailable, go to an urgent-care center or hospital emergency department. It's particularly important that you get medical attention if you have DVT symptoms and are at increased risk for the condition due to cardiovascular risk factors, such as smoking or high blood pressure.

You are also at higher risk for DVT for at least three months after knee/hip replacement or if you've recently been immobile for hours at a time, as may occur on a long airplane flight. Other DVT symptoms may include swelling, tenderness or a reddish or bluish tint on part of the leg. DVT is easy to diagnose with an ultrasound or a CT or MRI scan.

Important: Call 911 if you have any symptoms of a pulmonary embolism—such as sudden shortness of breath or sudden, sharp chest pain that may worsen when you breathe deeply or cough.

●**Hypothyroidism.** Patients who produce too little thyroid hormone (hypothyroidism) may have the condition for years before it is diagnosed because symptoms are usually vague and seemingly minor.

Common scenario: A doctor might assume that a patient who complains of fatigue, recent weight gain or apathy is suffering from stress or depression and write a prescription for an antidepressant.

What to do: **Insist on a blood test to check your thyroid hormone** levels if you have any of the above symptoms. Fatigue that's accompanied by an increased sensitivity to cold often is a sign of hypothyroidism. So is hair loss (but not that due to male-pattern baldness). For unknown reasons, thinning of the outer one-third of the eyebrows is also a red flag for hypothyroidism.

Experts disagree on the optimal range for thyroid stimulating hormone (TSH). Current guidelines suggest that it should fall somewhere between 0.45 mIU/L and 4.49 mIU/L.(The specific values will depend on the laboratory that your doctor uses.) If your TSH is normal but your symptoms persist, ask your doctor about other blood tests, such as free T3/T4 or anti-thyroglobulin. In some patients, these tests are useful in detecting hypothyroidism.

Most people do well with a thyroid replacement regimen. Some benefit from *levothyroxine* (Levoxyl, Levothroid, Synthroid, etc.), while others find that natural desiccated thyroid hormone, such as Armour Thyroid, Nature-Throid or Westhroid, provides a better balance of T3 and T4 hormones.

●**Celiac Disease.** More than three million Americans have this intestinal disease in which the immune system reacts to a protein (gluten) found in wheat, barley and rye.

Because this used to be considered a rare disease, physicians—particularly older doctors who went to medical school decades ago—don't always look for it. In addition, some of the most common symptoms, such as fatigue, abdominal pain, anemia and headaches, can be caused by dozens of other conditions.

What to do: **Get tested.** A blood test that looks for abnormal immune activity and other factors, perhaps followed by an intestinal biopsy, can detect celiac disease. If you test positive, you'll need to follow a gluten-free diet. websites such as Celiac.org list foods/products that are gluten-free. Patients who eliminate all gluten will usually make a full recovery.

Don't eliminate gluten before testing—the partial recovery of the intestinal lining will make it harder to get an accurate diagnosis.

●**Lyme Disease.** If a person has Lyme disease and it's missed, he/she may go on to develop joint inflammation, heart-rhythm disturbances and even problems with concentration and memory.

Lyme disease, the most common tick-borne disease, now has been reported in most US states, but doctors often do not look for it outside the Northeast, where the disease originated. The initial symptoms, such as muscle aches and fatigue, are often confused with the flu, particularly when patients don't even know that they were bitten.

What to do: **Look for a rash**. About three-quarters of patients will develop a "bull's eye" rash along with the flulike symptoms that last for weeks. Sadly, there are no symptoms that are especially diagnostic for Lyme if the rash is missing. In these cases, symptoms may include stiff neck, headache, swollen glands, Bell's palsy (usually temporary facial paralysis), sore throat, fever and/or tingling or numbness in the extremities.

Lyme disease can be diagnosed with a blood test. Patients who are treated with oral antibiotics at the onset of symptoms almost always make a full recovery. The longer someone goes untreated for Lyme, however, the more challenging the course of recovery may be.

What You Still Don't Know About Hospital Safety

Charles B. Inlander is a consumer advocate and health-care consultant based in Fogelsville, Pennsylvania. He was the founding president of the nonprofit People's Medical Society, a consumer health advocacy organization, and is the author of 20 books, including *Take This Book to the Hospital With You: A Consumer Guide to Surviving Your Hospital Stay*.

Since medical errors in hospitals have been widely discussed for years, you would think that things would have improved by now. Well, they haven't. In fact, a new study shows that your risk of being injured, receiving the wrong drug or acquiring an infection in the hospital is no less than it was in 1999.

Why haven't things improved? Research shows that most hospitals have not implemented key processes that are necessary to improve the safety of hospital patients, such as hand-washing protocols for staff…computerized medication-monitoring and ordering systems…and electronic medical-record systems that help alert staff to possible mistakes before they occur.

But even if all hospitals aren't yet doing things right, you can dramatically curb your chances of becoming the victim of a hospital mistake. *What to do the next time you or a loved one is hospitalized…*

•**Take control of your medications.** In the US, more than 400,000 people are seriously harmed each year by preventable hospital medication errors (such as wrong dosages and/or wrong drugs). Even though most hospitals currently check to see if you are the patient who is supposed to receive the drug and note in your file what drug is being administered, a more effective way to prevent errors is to ask the nurse to write down, on a sheet of paper that you bring and keep at your bedside, the drug being given, the time it is given and the dosage. If there are any changes, ask who ordered the change before you take the medicine.

Insider secret: You also have the right to bring your own meds from home to protect yourself against getting the wrong drug.

•**Make sure you don't get a used medical device.** Up to 10% of all hospital patients acquire in-fections during their hospital stays. That's why we've all been told to insist that no one touch us without washing his/her hands and changing gloves in our presence. However, some hospitals are also putting their patients at risk by reusing medical devices that are meant to be used only once, such as catheters, as a way to save money. Hospitals do clean these devices in between uses—but in many cases, the cleaning methods are ineffective and may result in life-threatening infections. That's why you should ask whether any device that is about to be used on you is designed for "single use." If so, insist that it be taken out of the original package in front of you.

•**Use your case manager.** Mistakes often occur because hospital patients may not see the same nurse more than once during their stays. That's why all hospitals now employ case managers (a nurse, social worker or physician's assistant) who help oversee the consistency of patient care. Ask to meet your case manager when you are admitted to the hospital. Get his direct phone number, and call whenever you have a question that is not being answered. He can be your watchdog—and a great way to get in touch with your doctor very quickly.

Before Having Surgery at the Doctor's Office…

Charles B. Inlander is a consumer advocate and health-care consultant based in Fogelsville, Pennsylvania. He was the founding president of the nonprofit People's Medical Society, a consumer health advocacy organization, and is the author of 20 books, including *Take This Book to the Hospital With You: A Consumer Guide to Surviving Your Hospital Stay*.

Just 30 years ago, more than 90% of all surgical procedures were performed in hospitals, requiring at least one night's stay. But because of advanced surgical techniques and safer, easier to administer anesthesia, one-third (about 15 million surgeries) are now performed on an outpatient basis at hospital-owned or independent surgery centers. And still another 15 million operations—everything from the removal of a skin cancer to cataract surgery and knee arthroscopy—are performed in physicians' offices.

In-hospital surgery, hospital-run outpatient centers and independently owned surgicenters are highly regulated by both federal and state governments, and most must be certified by well-respected accrediting organizations to be eligible to bill Medicare or private insurance companies. But surgical procedures performed in physicians' offices are not tightly regulated. In fact, only 25 states regulate them at all—by monitoring infection control standards, for example. *Before saying "yes" to any surgical procedure that is performed in a doctor's office, ask these questions…*

•**Does the doctor have the right credentials?** Your doctor should have privileges at a local hospital. This helps ensure that he/she is well-trained because hospitals strictly control who gets privileges.

Insider tip: Ask your doctor where he has privileges and in what specialties. Then call the hospital to double-check what you've been told. Doctors who have lost hospital privileges for safety or quality reasons have been known to continue doing surgical procedures in their offices.

Also: Check with the American Board of Medical Specialties (ABMS), ABMS.org, to ensure that your doctor is board certified in the specialty covering the procedure he is to perform. Nowadays, more doctors are attempting to bring in extra income by doing office procedures in areas in which they don't have extensive training.

•**What happens if there's an emergency?** For older adults and those of any age with a chronic medical condition, such as high blood pressure, heart disease or diabetes, an in-hospital or a hospital-operated outpatient facility may be the best choice. These facilities are equipped to handle serious problems, such as surgical errors, that can occur during surgery.

Insider tip: If you're considering an office-based surgery, ask, "Do you have an arrangement with a local hospital and ambulance service in case of emergency?" This ensures a prompter response time than simply calling 911—the approach taken by most doctors' offices.

•**How is follow-up handled?** Hospitals and outpatient surgical centers generally have doctors or nurses available to help you 24 hours a day if a problem occurs after you have gone home. Most physicians' offices do not offer that service and simply tell you to go to an emergency room.

Insider tip: Before you agree to an office procedure, ask if there are doctors or nurses on call 24 hours a day if there's a problem. If not, book your procedure at a hospital or hospital-operated facility.

Is Your Medical Record Wrong?

Charles B. Inlander is a consumer advocate and healthcare consultant based in Fogelsville, Pennsylvania. He was the founding president of the nonprofit People's Medical Society, a consumer advocacy organization credited with key improvements in the quality of US health care, and is the author or coauthor of more than 20 consumer-health books.

You've probably heard plenty about medical errors that occur when a wrong drug is prescribed or a surgeon operates on the wrong body part.

But there's another type of medical error that needs much more attention than it's getting: Errors in your medical records. More than just an administrative snafu, this type of mistake can have serious consequences—it can lead to inappropriate treatment, higher insurance premiums or even difficulty finding a doctor. And with electronic medical records that travel across computer networks in a matter of seconds, a wrong entry in your record can spread widely and be accessed by insurers, other doctors and hospitals before you even know it. *To protect yourself from such mishaps, follow these steps…*

•**Get your records.** Under both state and federal laws, you have the right to receive a copy of your medical records. Most major hospitals, medical practices and insurance networks no longer keep paper records, opting instead for electronic record keeping. And those records are usually made available to you online.

Beware: Not all doctors and hospitals share the same electronic record systems, so you may need to access several different online sources. Ask the doctors and hospitals you have used for access information. If you don't have Internet access, you can ask for paper copies of your medical records—a verbal request usually suffices, but you may need to put it in writing. You may also be asked to pay copying fees. To avoid getting overwhelmed by massive records—for example, after a lengthy hospital stay—ask for copies of reports from tests on an ongoing basis and/or request a discharge summary from the hospital.

•**Review your records carefully.** Look for gross errors such as a wrong diagnosis…medications you haven't been prescribed…and/or medical procedures you have never undergone. Also look for anything that contradicts what you may have been told during an office visit. For example, your doctor may have said that your blood pressure is under control, yet the reading listed in your record may indicate that it's not. You'd want to ask your doctor about this—you may need a different medication or change in the dose.

Also: Be sure that your records have your correct contact information and that your name and insurance information, including policy number, are accurate. Such errors could mean the difference between an insurance payment and a denial.

•**Correct errors. Under federal law,** you have the right to correct any error in your medical record. Do it in writing—by either crossing out the wrong information on a copy of the page where the error appears and writing in the correction…or by writing a more detailed explanation. Once the correction is received at the location where the record originated, the provider has 60 days to act on your request. This deadline may be extended by 30 days if the provider gives an explanation for the delay in writing. Technically, the correction is considered an "amendment" to your record—this may mean that the old, wrong information remains with the correction added. Even if your correction is denied, you can submit a letter of disagreement that must be put into your record.

Important: Double-check your record online to ensure that the correction was made, and keep a copy of the correction for yourself to take to medical appointments in case the error lingers in another provider's system.

Surprising Dangers in the Hospital

Marty Makary, MD, MPH, a surgeon and researcher at the Johns Hopkins University School of Public Health, and director, John Hopkins Pancreatic Islet Transportation Center. He was one of the researchers who helped pioneer the surgical checklists that have greatly reduced infection and other complications. He is the author of *Unaccountable: What Hospitals Won't Tell You and How Transparency Can Revolutionize Health Care.* UnaccountableBook.com

When you're admitted to a hospital, you probably don't stop and wonder what your chances are of getting out alive. But the odds are worse than you might imagine—and you can literally save your own life (or that of a loved one) by knowing how to investigate a hospital's record before you're checked in.

Frightening statistics: An estimated 98,000 hospital patients die from medical errors in the US annually. That's more than the number of Americans killed in car crashes each year. Many other hospital patients will suffer from serious—and preventable—complications.

Examples: About one of every 20 hospital patients will develop an infection…and surgeons operate on the wrong body part up to 40 times a week.

Getting the information you need: Because few hospitals publish statistics about their performance, it's difficult for patients to know which ones are worse—in some cases, much worse—than average.

For advice on avoiding the most common threats to hospital patients, we spoke to Marty Makary, MD, MPH, one of the country's leading experts on hospital safety.

WHAT YOU CAN FIND OUT

When I've asked patients why they chose a particular hospital, they typically say something like, "Because it's close to home." Others might say, "That is where my doctor has privileges." But those are bad answers. Before you get any medical care in a hospital, you should find out everything you can about the track record of the hospital. *Five clues to consider…*

CLUE #1: **Bounceback rate.** This is the term that doctors use for patients who need to be re-hospitalized within 30 days. A high bounceback rate means that you have a higher-than-average risk for postsurgery complications, such as infection or impaired wound healing. Patients also can look up bounceback rates for conditions such as heart attacks and pneumonia. The rate for a particular procedure should never be higher than the national average.

Why this matters: A high bounceback rate could indicate substandard care or even a lack of teamwork in the operating room. It could also mean that the hospital is discharging patients too soon or that patients aren't getting clear discharge instructions that tell them what to do when they get home.

What to do: Check your hospital's rating on the US Department of Health and Human Services' Web site Hospital Compare, where the majority of US hospitals are listed. You can see if the bounceback rate is better than, worse than or the same as the national average for the procedure you need.

Hospitals that are serious about reducing readmissions go the extra mile. For example, they will provide patients with detailed instructions on such issues as medication use and proper wound-cleaning procedures. Some even give patients a 24-hour hot-line number to call if they have symptoms that could indicate a problem.

CLUE #2: **Culture of safety.** My colleagues and I at Johns Hopkins recently surveyed doctors, nurses and other hospital employees at 60 reputable US hospitals and asked such questions as, "Is the teamwork good?" "Is communication strong?" "Do you feel comfortable speaking up about safety concerns?"

We found a wide variation in the "safety culture" at different hospitals—and even within different departments at the same hospital. At one-third of the hospitals, the majority of employees reported that the level of teamwork was poor. Conversely, up to 99% of the staff at some hospitals said the teamwork was good.

Why it matters: Hospitals with a poor safety culture tended to have higher infection rates and worse patient outcomes.

What to do: Few hospitals that have conducted this type of survey make the findings public. Patients have to find other ways to get similar information. To do this, I suggest that before you choose a hospital you ask employees—including nurses and lab technicians—if they'd feel comfortable getting medical care where they work. Even if some hospital employees put a positive spin on their answers, you can generally tell a lot from their demeanor and comfort level when they respond.

CLUE #3: **Use of minimally invasive procedures.** Compared with "open" surgeries, minimally invasive procedures—such as knee arthroscopy and "keyhole" gallbladder surgery—require shorter hospitalizations. They're also less painful, less likely to result in an infection and less likely to lead to the need for subsequent surgery.

In spite of this, some surgeons still prefer open procedures. During my training, for example, I worked with a surgeon who was not skilled at minimally invasive surgery. His procedures were always open and involved large incisions—his wound-infection rate was about 20%. But his colleagues, who had trained in the newer minimally invasive techniques, had infection rates that were close to zero.

Why it matters: For the reasons above, you should usually choose a minimally invasive procedure if it's appropriate for your condition.

What to do: When discussing surgery, ask your doctor if there's more than one approach…the percentage of similar procedures that are done in a minimally invasive way…and the percentage that he/she does that way versus the percentage done each way nationwide.

Important: Get a second opinion before undergoing any ongoing or extensive treatment, including surgery. About 30% of second opinions are different from the first one.

CLUE #4: **Volume of procedures.** "See one, do one, teach one" is a common expression in medical schools. The idea is that new doctors have to start somewhere to learn how to perform medical procedures. Don't let them start on you .

Why it matters: Surgical death rates are directly related to a surgeon's experience with that procedure. The death rate after pancreas surgery, for example, is 14.7% for surgeons who average fewer than two procedures a year. It is 4.6% for those who do four or more. A survey conducted by the New York State Department of Health found that hospitals with surgeons who did relatively few procedures had patient-mortality rates that were four times higher than the state average.

What to do: Ask your doctor how often he does a particular procedure. For nonsurgical care, ask how many patients with your condition he treats.

Helpful: If 50% or more of a doctor's practice is dedicated to patients with exactly your condition, he will probably be a good choice.

CLUE #5: The availability of "open notes." Doctors make detailed notes after every office visit, but many patients have never seen these notes. Hospitals may not make them easily available, or the office/hospital can make it difficult (or expensive) to get copies.

Why it matters: Transparency builds trust. Patients who know what's in their medical records will not have to wonder what the doctor is writing about them.

Patients who read the notes will remember details about treatment advice…ask questions if they are confused…and often correct errors that can make a difference in their diagnosis and/or treatment. Also, these records are needed for a second opinion.

I purposely dictate notes while my patients are still in my office sitting next to me. Once, I was corrected when I said that a prior surgery was on the left side—it was actually on the right side. Another patient corrected me when I noted a wrong medication dose. Another reminded me to mention a history of high blood pressure.

What to do: Get copies of all of your medical records, including test results. If your doctor or hospital refuses to share them, ask to speak to an administrator. The records are yours—you have a right, under federal law, to see them and get copies. Fees range from a few dollars for a few pages to hundreds of dollars for extensive records.

Before You Leave the Hospital: Do This

Elizabeth Meichsner, MD, family medicine resident, University of Minnesota Family Medicine Residency Program, Methodist Hospital, St. Louis.

After your stay at a hospital is over, there's something that you should do before you step out the door.

Talk to the hospital pharmacist—especially if you were taking multiple medications before you got to the hospital and/or you just got a few new drugs from a doctor to add to your routine.

Why is it so important to have the chat at that moment?

About 63% of medication errors in the US are due to a communication breakdown—which is particularly common at a point of transition, such as when a patient leaves the hospital—according to The Joint Commission, a nonprofit that accredits health-care organizations in the US.

A clinic in Minnesota recently conducted a study to find out whether bridging that particular communication gap might be helpful to patients.

And I know you'll be interested to find out what they discovered…

THE POWER OF COMMUNICATION

Researchers gathered hospital patients who each had at least one chronic medical condition…were currently taking at least five medications…and/or were expected to receive at least three new medications at the time of discharge. Just before each patient left the hospital, he or she had a consultation with a hospital pharmacist that lasted, on average, 20 minutes.

During the consultation between the pharmacist and the patient, the pharmacist talked with the patient about how he or she was taking each medication (such as whether he was taking the drug at a certain time of day…with a beverage and/or a meal, etc.) and asked the patient whether he had been experiencing any drug side effects. The goal was for the pharmacist to help the patient optimize dosing (so the drug is most effective)…minimize or eliminate side effects…and/or see whether the patient could stop taking certain medications. The patient was encouraged to ask the pharmacist questions and make sure that he understood the reason for taking each drug.

Researchers wanted to see whether patients found this conversation to be valuable. They also were curious to find out whether there were any recommended medication changes as a result of the consultations.

What they found: Patients felt more at ease as a result of the consults, which wasn't surprising. But here's the real stunner—nearly three-quarters of the consults resulted in the pharmacists and doctors coming together to recommend medication changes that were related to the reasons that the patients came to the hospital.

And these weren't just minor recommendations, according to Elizabeth Meichsner, MD, a study co-author. Most recommendations pertained to major, often life-saving medications, such as cardiovascular drugs, antidepressants and pulmonary drugs. The recommended changes ran the gamut—sometimes patients were told to take a drug differently…sometimes they were told to take an additional drug or take fewer drugs…and sometimes they were told to switch drugs. In other words, most patients received advice as a result of the consult that they wouldn't have otherwise received.

Now, the researchers didn't study what percentage of patients implemented the recommended changes…nor did they analyze whether the recommended changes turned out to be helpful or harmful…nor did they examine whether these consults resulted in lower hospital readmission rates. Hopefully future studies will address those issues. Still, the impact of these consults is impressive.

SPEAK UP—ASK FOR A CONSULT

It's important to note that these consults were arranged by the hospital specifically for this study—so all the pharmacists and doctors were aware of the process and on board. Unfortunately, this isn't currently a regular practice at this particular hospital, nor is it a regular practice at many hospitals in the US. But a program is now being developed at Dr. Meichsner's hospital, based on these findings, so it will soon become regular practice there. This is a relatively new concept, said Dr. Meichsner, and if this proves to reduce medication-related problems and/or save money, the hope is that more hospitals will follow suit.

But that doesn't mean that you can't be proactive and arrange this sort of consult yourself before you leave a hospital. Even if you have confidence in your doctors, it can potentially help, so why not try it? Maybe one simple recommendation from a pharmacist would help your drugs work more effectively…reduce or eliminate side effects…or help you get off a drug you're taking. To me, that's certainly worth 20 minutes!

Watch Out for Your Doctor's Smartphone

Peter J. Papadakos, MD, director of critical care medicine at the University of Rochester Medical Center and professor of anesthesiology, neurology, surgery and neurosurgery at the University of Rochester, both in Rochester, New York. Dr. Papadakos was one of the first experts to identify the potential for distraction from smartphones and to popularize the term "distracted doctoring."

If you're like most people, you love your smartphone, tablet or laptop. Doctors, nurses and other medical personnel are no different. But when they use these devices in the workplace, does that help or hurt your medical care?

It's true that smartphones, tablets and laptops allow doctors to quickly look up the newest drug information and case studies. Many hospitals and doctors' offices have invested large sums of money in smartphones, tablets and other computer devices to make staff more efficient and prevent medical errors. And it's great to be able to reach your physician in an emergency at off-hours, since doctors will sometimes share their cell-phone numbers and/or e-mail addresses with patients who require extra attention.

But there can also be dangerous downsides for the patient when medical staff has constant access to this type of technology.

To find out what patients can do to protect themselves, *Bottom Line Health* spoke to Peter J. Papadakos, MD, director of critical care medicine at the University of Rochester Medical Center and an expert on the impact of technology on medical care.

A NEW DANGER

Nearly 90% of all doctors currently use smartphones or tablets while at work. *The most significant potential dangers to patients include…*

•**Bacterial contamination.** Even though there are many nonsterile surfaces in a health-care setting, cell phones are of particular concern because they are typically handled so often. When the cell phones of orthopedic surgeons in the operating room were tested, a whopping 83% of the phones had infection-causing bacteria on them, according to a study published in *The Journal of Bone & Joint Surgery*.

Self-defense: When admitted to a hospital, ask what the guidelines are for disinfecting electronic devices, particularly any that are brought into and handled in an operating room. Some hospitals now have ultraviolet (UV) sterilizing devices that are 99.9% effective at decontaminating objects in 10 seconds.

If your doctor is holding a cell phone or other personal device, ask him/her if the device was cleaned before attending to you and make sure the doctor washes his hands as well.

Also: When visiting someone in the hospital, don't pull out your cell phone to show photos in an effort to cheer up the patient. Better yet, leave your cell phone at home or in the car. If you are a patient or visitor in the hospital and feel you need your phone, clean it regularly with sanitizing wipes (such as Wireless Wipes) or a UV sterilizing device for cell phones.

•**Interruptions to workflow and distractions.** Researchers at Oregon State University and the Oregon Health & Science University tested the impact of distractions on residents performing a simulated gallbladder surgery. When the surgeons were interrupted by a cell-phone ring, the sound of a dropped metal tray clanging or other distraction, 44% made serious errors that could have led to a fatality, including damage to organs and arteries. Only one surgeon made a mistake when there were no interruptions.

Self-defense: To protect yourself from such forms of "distracted doctoring," ask your hospital whether it has a policy on the safe use of electronic devices throughout the hospital, and ask for a copy if it does. If electronic devices are allowed in the operating room, share your concerns with your surgical team.

At the University of Rochester Medical Center, we have a "Code of eConduct" to minimize the distractions of devices such as smartphones and tablets. Guidelines include that devices must be in "silent" mode (no ringing or vibrating) when in a patient's room…work-issued devices should not be used for personal use…and all personal business must be conducted only in break rooms and out of view of patients.

•**Addiction.** Just like everyone else, many doctors and other health-care professionals do not even realize how addicted they are to their smartphones and social media.

•**iPatient.** When doctors are fixated on the computerized record of a patient, what I call an "iPatient," they miss important information such as speech patterns and body language.

Self-defense: Politely ask your doctor to put the device away for a few minutes and listen to you.

Has Your Doctor Been Sued?

Seth A. Seabury, PhD, an associate professor at the Keck School of Medicine and the Leonard D. Schaeffer Center for Health Policy & Economics at the University of Southern California in Los Angeles. His research has been published in *The New England Journal of Medicine*, *The Journal of the American Medical Association* and elsewhere.

S ome cases of medical malpractice are so egregious—and so shocking—that you have to wonder why some doctors are allowed to continue practicing medicine.

Example: A Missouri woman was permanently disabled after her surgeon mistakenly operated on the wrong side of her brain.

You can guess how you'd vote if you were on the jury. But this and other headline-making lawsuits are exceptional cases. Most malpractice lawsuits involve gray areas…honest mistakes (alleged or proven)…or legitimate disagreements about what should or should not have been done in a particular case.

Nevertheless, patients are left to wonder: What does a doctor's history of lawsuits tell about his/her ability to practice medicine? To learn more, we spoke with Seth A. Seabury, PhD, a renowned expert on medical malpractice.

How can I find out if my doctor has been sued? There are public databases, but the availability of this information varies widely from state to state. The Federation of State Medical Boards has a database, DocInfo.org, that includes disciplinary actions taken against physicians by state licensing boards. A doctor could be disciplined for egregious negligence or for unethical or even criminal behavior. You can get similar information, including payments that were made for malpractice lawsuits, from some state medical licensing boards and/or insurance departments or state or county courts.

How often do medical doctors get sued? A survey of more than 7,000 surgeons found that nearly 25% were recently involved in litigation. If you take into account all of the lawsuits that may occur in a 30- or 40-year career, the risks are much higher.

Research I conducted with colleagues from the University of Southern California and Harvard University suggests that up to 75% of physicians in lower-risk fields—pediatrics, family practice, etc.—will eventually face a malpractice claim. For those in higher-risk specialties, such as neurosurgery, lawsuits are a near certainty.

Isn't it true that bad doctors get sued more than good ones? It's true that some doctors get sued more than others. A *New England Journal of Medicine* study that appeared earlier this year found that about 1% of doctors who had previously paid two or more malpractice claims accounted for nearly one-third of all paid claims. However, while some of these doctors may indeed provide substandard care, you can't assume that a history of lawsuits/paid claims is a reliable indicator of a doctor's proficiency.

Past research had found that a bad outcome is often what drives malpractice claims. A neurosurgeon who does complicated brain surgery or a cardiac surgeon who mainly treats high-risk patients will have a higher percentage of poor outcomes than doctors who treat the easier cases. As a result, they're more likely to face multiple lawsuits during their careers.

Are these the specialties that face the most lawsuits? The study mentioned above found that four medical specialties—internal medicine, ob/gyn, surgery and general practice/family medicine—accounted for more than half of all claims.

This is partly due to volume. An internist or family practice physician sees a lot of patients. The more patients a doctor sees, the higher the risk that something will eventually go wrong. Neurosurgeons and cardiac surgeons see fewer patients, but the ones they do see have a higher-than-average risk for complications or death.

If a doctor has a terrible bedside manner, is he more likely to give substandard care—and get sued for it? I'm not aware of any evidence that a rude doctor is more likely to provide poor care than one who is warm and welcoming. However, one study did find that doctors with a more extensive history of lawsuits also had a history of dealing poorly with patients—ignoring their concerns, not communicating well, etc.

Doctors who show the most empathy—and are willing to admit to, and apologize for, mistakes—might be less vulnerable to lawsuits, but it hasn't been proven. Some states have experimented with so-called "apology laws" to protect doctors who may worry that an apology could be used later against them in court. However, there's no definitive evidence whether or not these laws reduce the number of lawsuits.

So, do most doctors—even good ones—make a lot of mistakes? Medical errors definitely happen. The Institute of Medicine estimates that tens of thousands of patients die each year due to preventable medical errors. But there is uncertainty as to how well the malpractice system does in discerning actual medical errors from just bad outcomes.

According to research, there's actually a weak relationship between medical errors and malpractice claims. A Harvard study found that about 40% of malpractice cases should never have been filed... and that many of the cases showed no evidence of mistakes or proof that patients had been harmed.

Bottom line: Malpractice law entitles patients to compensation if they were injured because their doctor was negligent, which isn't the same as being wrong or unlucky. Practicing medicine is difficult, and sometimes doctors can do everything by the book and a bad outcome can still happen. That isn't to say that malpractice doesn't occur—obviously it does—but sometimes it can be very hard to distinguish between substandard care and outcomes after the fact. That's why you have to sometimes be careful about making a judgment about quality based on the number of malpractice claims a doctor has.

Don't Forget Your Nurse

Rebecca Shannonhouse, editor, *Bottom Line/Health.*

Nurses are the health-care professionals most likely to help prevent the 44,000 to 98,000 deaths that occur in hospitals every year because of medical errors, according to the Institute of Medicine. If a doctor writes an incor-

rect drug dose or schedules you for the wrong test, nurses are in the best position to catch the mistake.

Unfortunately, heavy workloads and inadequate staffing make their jobs difficult. A survey of 2,203 nurses found that 92% say they're unable to spend enough time with patients to provide optimal care.

But patients can help nurses help them, according to Dorie Byers, RN, a clinical instructor at the Indiana University School of Nursing in Indianapolis. One important—but often overlooked—way to do this is to engage nurses. *Here's how…*

•**Get personal.** Nurses are trained to treat everyone the same, but you'll get more attentive care when you're not just another face. Introduce yourself to the nurses—and get to know them.

Also helpful: Introduce frequent visitors—your spouse, children, etc.—to the nurses. You'll get better care when everyone is working together.

•**Ask how you can help them.** Nurses love it when patients do things for themselves that their condition permits. An assertive, can-do attitude will earn respect from all the members of your health-care team.

•**Ask detailed questions about drug doses, tests, etc.** Nurses enjoy using their knowledge, particularly when it helps them catch errors that others might have missed.

Lesson: Don't be passive. Patients who take the initiative tend to have better health outcomes.

Is Your Doctor Suffering from Burnout?

Robert M. Stark, MD, a preventive cardiologist and internist in private practice in Greenwich, Connecticut. He is also an adjunct assistant professor of medicine at New York Medical College in Valhalla, New York, and medical director of the Cardiovascular Prevention Program at Greenwich Hospital.

The word "burnout" probably calls to mind air-traffic controllers, emergency room personnel and other people who work at a rapid pace under relentless pressure. But burnout also strikes people you might not expect—like your doctor. And this could be very hazardous to your health.

A MEDICAL EPIDEMIC

Exact statistics are hard to come by, but repeated studies in the US, Canada and Europe have found symptoms of burnout in 40% to 60% of doctors. And no one is exempt—the problem affects doctors who are fresh out of medical school and old-timers…generalists and specialists…men and women.

Shocking new finding: A 2011 study published in *Archives of Surgery* found that one of every 16 surgeons in the US had thought about suicide in the prior year—often due to burnout. *Burnout has three main characteristics…*

●**Emotional and physical exhaustion.** The stress of work and its demands on attention and energy leave the sufferer mentally drained and often physically fatigued.

●**Depersonalization.** Those who are approaching burnout may feel detached from themselves and others. They begin to see people less as individuals and may show a lack of enthusiasm and perform their work in a more impersonal manner.

●**Lack of a sense of achievement.** Burnout robs people of the satisfaction they need from their work. They may believe that they're doing a poor job or that their work is less meaningful than they would like.

Why has physician burnout increased so much in recent years? Many experts believe that the rapid changes in the health-care system are largely to blame.

Pressed by managed care systems to see more patients in less time, doctors are often working harder and faster—overwork is another risk factor for burnout—and are unable to practice medicine in the way they feel is best. The threat of malpractice lawsuits, pressure to rein in costs and more frequent Medicare/Medicaid audits also add to the stress.

BURNOUT TAKES ITS TOLL

Burnout doesn't affect only the doctor, it can impact the patient as well. A recent study of 188 primary care physicians published in the journal *Family Practice* found that on days when doctors felt anxious, fatigued and stressed, they wrote more prescriptions and ordered more tests (some of them unnecessary, the researchers suggested) and spent less time talking with patients. More errors in diagnosis and treatment also have been linked to physicians who suffer from burnout than among doctors who do not, according to research.

IS YOUR DOCTOR BURNED OUT?

The signs of burnout can be missed if you're not looking for them—even in a longtime family doctor whom you feel you know well. *Be alert for these red flags…*

●**Shorter office visits** could mean your doctor is under increased financial and insurance company pressure or simply overeager to get through the day.

One tip-off: If visits used to last, say, 15 minutes, but your doctor now heads for the door in five, something may be amiss.

●**An air of distraction suggests** that the doctor is having difficulty maintaining focus. This could lead to cutting corners in decision-making and making snap judgments.

One tip-off: Is your doctor quicker than he/she used to be in diagnosing your health problem?

●**Lack of empathy due to burnout** may be apparent if you tell your doctor about something that's worrying you.

One tip-off: Your doctor may fail to express concern and probe further if you reveal that you're, say, having marital difficulties. If he just goes on to the next topic—and says something like "and how is your stomach doing?"—then he may be suffering from burnout.

It's harder to recognize burnout in a specialist you're seeing for the first time, but just as important. You need him to be alert and fully involved when dealing with a problem that demands expert care.

Main clue: Does the specialist know who you are and why you're there, what tests have been done and what treatments have been tried? Your regular doctor should have sent information about you along with lab and radiology results—has the specialist taken the time to look at them?

HOW TO LOOK FOR ANSWERS

If you suspect burnout in your doctor, what should you do? There's always the option of finding another doctor. But if it's someone you've been seeing for years and know to be essentially competent and compassionate, such a switch may not be best for you or your doctor.

Ask your doctor: "How are you? Is everything OK?" You may learn that today's inattention is due to the kind of passing stress or disruption that can affect anyone, such as a poor night's sleep or an office crisis. Or you may get an inkling that problems run deeper.

At the very least, showing your concern will strengthen your relationship and may even encourage him to recognize that pressure and stress are taking their toll. This may well help to persuade him to do some introspection, consult with a colleague or seek needed help. If your visits continue to leave you dissatisfied, however, it may be time to look for a new doctor.

Medicare "Observation Status" Warning

Toby Edelman, EdM, JD, senior policy attorney with the nonprofit Center for Medicare Advocacy, Washington, DC. MedicareAdvocacy.org

When you go to the hospital as a Medicare patient with an acute condition that requires a stay of two or more nights, you are supposed to be admitted as an inpatient. However, more and more hospitals now will place you on "observation status" instead.

Warning: This seemingly innocuous designation can leave you responsible for tens of thousands of dollars in bills.

Reason: Medicare treats "observation status" the same as being an outpatient. This type of visit isn't covered under Medicare Part A, which pays for all inpatient hospital charges above your $1,184 deductible. Instead, you are billed under Medicare

Part B, so you must pay 20% of the bill for each service after paying the Part B deductible.

You also are charged for the medications that you get in the hospital, and you are unlikely to be reimbursed unless your Medicare Part D prescription drug plan covers the medications.

Over the past six years, the use of observation status has doubled in US hospitals. That's because if Medicare auditors decide later that an inpatient should have been called an outpatient, a hospital must return the Medicare payments it receives.

Self-defense: If your status is not immediately clear, have someone check with the hospital's case-management department…ask your regular doctor to get your status changed if you are on observation status…and appeal your charges if you find that your stay at the hospital or subsequent nursing facility is not covered under Medicare Part A. You can download a free appeals kit at MedicareAdvocacy.org.

Medicare Traps Now: Avoid These 4 Costly Mistakes

Robert Carlson, CPA, JD, managing member of Carlson Wealth Advisors, LLC, and chairman of the board of trustees of the Fairfax County (Virginia) Employees' Retirement System. He is editor and publisher of *Retirement Watch*, a monthly newsletter. RetirementWatch.com

If you fail to fully grasp certain Medicare rules, you could end up paying unnecessarily high premiums for the rest of your life. That may be true if you have not enrolled in Medicare yet or even if you already have enrolled. And in some cases, you could even face a gap in coverage and have to pay big medical bills out of pocket.

Four common and costly Medicare misconceptions and mistakes—and how to protect yourself whether you are a current or future enrollee…

•**Thinking that your Social Security retirement age is the same as your Medicare-enrollment age.** Over the years, the age at which people become eligible for "full" retirement benefits has increased. If you were born between 1943 and 1954, for example, your full retirement age is 66, not 65. Trouble is, many people think this full retirement age also applies to Medicare.

Not only is the Medicare-eligibility age still 65 for everyone who qualifies to receive benefits, but failure to sign up during your initial eligibility period can lead to higher Medicare premiums for the rest of your life. (Your initial eligibility to enroll lasts for seven months—the month of your 65th birthday plus the three months immediately before and after.)

How much could a sign-up delay cost you? With Medicare Part B (that's medical insurance), for each full 12-month period that you are late in signing up, a 10% penalty is tacked on to your premiums (basic premiums are $134 per month in 2017) for as long as you keep getting Part B. With Part D drug coverage, the penalty is 1% of the "national base beneficiary premium" ($35.63 per month in 2017) multiplied by the number of full uncovered months you were eligible but failed to sign up. The penalty applies if you are not enrolled for 63 days or more in a row when you don't have creditable prescription drug coverage. (Creditable coverage means that your plan's coverage is comparable to Part D plans.)

All of that could add up to perhaps $3,000 to $5,000 in penalties over the course of your retirement if you are one year late signing up…or climb to more than $10,000 if you are several years late.

Exception: If you are covered by a group plan offered by your employer or your spouse's employer when you reach age 65, you might be able to delay signing up for Medicare without incurring penalties (see next page).

●**Thinking that it doesn't matter which option you choose to pay for Part B.** Medicare enrollees can have their Part B premiums automatically deducted from their Social Security benefits or they can pay for them separately. What most people don't realize is that paying with Social Security deductions could save money.

By law, if you have your Part B premiums deducted from your Social Security benefits, any future increase in those premiums cannot result in a "net reduction" in Social Security benefits. In other words, if the government increases the price of Part B, your premiums cannot increase by more than the amount that Social Security's cost-of-living adjustments increase your benefits. If you pay for Part B separately (not from Social Security), you have no such protection against premium increases.

Exception: If you sign up for Medicare before you begin claiming Social Security benefits, you will have to pay separately for Medicare at that time. Switch to paying via Social Security deductions as soon as you start your Social Security benefits.

●**Thinking that you don't need to sign up for Medicare as long as you're covered by an employer.** People who are covered by group health insurance plans when they turn 65—either through their employers or their spouse's employers—often assume that they do not yet need to sign up for Medicare. But this is correct only if the employer has 20 or more employees. If your health coverage is provided by a small employer—one with fewer than 20 employees—this coverage automatically becomes "secondary" to Medicare when you turn 65. That means it will cover only the portion of your medical bills that would not be covered by Medicare if you had signed up for Medicare. If you haven't signed up for Medicare, you will have to pay most of your medical bills out of pocket.

If you are not 100% certain whether your employer has 20 or more employees, ask the employer's benefits department and its health insurance provider for clarification. Asking both of them decreases the odds that you will receive inaccurate information. If you receive conflicting responses and your initial Medicare-enrollment period is nearing its end, sign up for Part B and the cheapest Part D plan available to you until you can clarify the situation.

Warning: Do not just do a head count to determine whether your employer has 20 or more employees—some people who seem like employees might actually be independent contractors. Sign up for Medicare Part B and Part D immediately if you are 65 or older and the employer providing your group coverage shrinks in size from 20 or more employees to fewer than 20 employees.

Several vital related points…

•Sign up for Medicare Part A (hospital coverage) during your initial enrollment period even if you are covered by a large group health plan. There is no downside to signing up—Part A typically does not charge any premiums.

•If you are covered by an employer's group plan when you first become eligible for Medicare and remain covered with no coverage gaps longer than eight months, you should qualify for an eight-month "special enrollment period." This may be useful if your circumstances change. During this period, you will be able to sign up for Medicare without penalties even if your initial enrollment period has long since passed. Go to *Medicare.gov* for more information.

•Cobra and retiree health plans do not protect you from Medicare late-enrollment penalties because they are based on former employment, not current employment. (With Cobra coverage, a person pays to remain on a former employer's health plans, generally for up to 18 months.) If you are obtaining health coverage through a retiree plan or Cobra, sign up for Medicare during your initial enrollment period (within eight months after leaving your employer) to avoid future penalties and coverage gaps.

•If you are covered by a large group health plan at or after age 65, confirm with both this employer's benefits department and the insurer providing its health plan that the drug coverage component of the group plan qualifies as "creditable coverage" under Medicare rules. If not, sign up for a Part D drug-coverage plan during your initial enrollment period to avoid future penalties. High-deductible health plans are particularly likely to have drug coverage that does not qualify as creditable.

•**Not realizing that a high income you had a few years ago could unnecessarily increase your Medicare premiums this year.** The Medicare system imposes higher Part B and Part D premiums on people who have modified adjusted gross incomes above $85,000 ($170,000 for married couples filing jointly). But the income figure used in this calculation actually is your income from two years earlier—your 2014 income affected your 2016 Medicare

premiums, for example. If this two-year look-back takes you to a time when you and/or your spouse still were working, you could easily be charged higher Medicare premiums even though your retirement income is below the threshold.

If this happens to you, carefully read the paperwork that comes with your Medicare premium notice. It will explain how to file an appeal of your rates based on the change in your financial circumstances.

General Anesthesia Linked to Dementia… Even Years Later

A study, "Exposure to general anaesthesia could increase the risk of dementia in elderly," from researchers at the University of Bordeaux, France, presented at Euroanaesthesia, the annual meeting of the European Society of Anaesthesiology.

Given a choice, many people would prefer to have general anesthesia and sleep through surgery rather than have local anesthesia and be awake for the procedure. But this may change their minds—there's worrisome new evidence that general anesthesia significantly increases a person's risk of developing dementia. Scarier still, this risk may remain elevated even years after the surgery is over, a recent French study suggests.

The participants, all of whom were 65 or older, were interviewed and examined at the beginning of the study…and then again two, four, seven and 10 years later. Each exam included a cognitive evaluation to screen for dementia. From the two-year follow-up onward, 7,008 nondemented participants were asked at each follow-up whether they had had anesthesia since the last follow-up and, if so, what type they'd received.

Analysis: Over the next eight years, 9% of the study participants were diagnosed with some type of dementia, most often Alzheimer's disease. After adjusting for other health problems that might have influenced the results, the researchers calculated that receiving general anesthesia at least once during the study increased the seniors' risk of developing dementia by a startling 35%, compared with participants who did not receive anesthesia.

Caveats: It's way too early to say whether or not general anesthesia actually causes dementia, but this study does show a worrisome association. What could be behind this link? Researchers suspect that certain anesthetizing drugs promote inflammation of parts of the nervous system and/or trigger formation of beta-amyloid plaques and other precursors to Alzheimer's disease. As for whether the same long-term risk applies to younger people who receive general anesthesia, only additional research can answer that question.

Exploring safer options: Are you facing surgery or some other medical procedure for which general anesthesia may be used? If the procedure isn't truly necessary, it's worthwhile to consider all your nonsurgical options before you agree to go under the knife. If you do need the procedure, ask your doctor whether local anesthesia, a sedative or a relatively new technique called ultrasound-guided nerve block might be an appropriate alternative to general anesthesia. If general anesthesia is unavoidable—or if you received general anesthesia in the past, particularly if you had it repeatedly—it would be wise to talk with your doctor about how the two of you can be on the lookout for early warning signs of dementia in the coming years. For dementia patients, early detection offers the best chance for optimal management of the condition.

The Generic-Drug Rip-Off

David Belk, MD, a physician based in Alameda, California, specializing in internal medicine. He is founder of the True Cost of Healthcare blog, which provides information about healthcare cost and billing issues. TrueCostOfHealthCare.net

Using health insurance to fill a prescription for a generic drug could dramatically increase your out-of-pocket costs, particularly if you have not yet reached your policy's annual deductible.

That's because people who use health insurance have to pay the price that the insurance company has set for the drug, and with generic drugs, these prices often are much higher than the prices you might pay when no insurance is used—sometimes hundreds of dollars higher for a 90-day supply.

Here's what happens behind the scenes: Many generic drugs cost pharmacies 10 cents a pill or less. A value-oriented pharmacy, such as those at Costco, Walmart and Kroger, or a reputable online pharmacy, such as GoodRx.com and Health Warehouse.com, might charge as little as $4 for a 30-day supply or $10 for a 90-day supply—if you don't use insurance. What's more, even after you reach your deductible, many insurance policies require a co-pay that is higher than what these types of pharmacies charge for generic drugs.

Among the many widely used drugs that can be purchased without insurance as generics for as little as $10 for a 90-day supply are the blood pressure medications *atenolol, carvedilol, clonidine* and *furosemide*…blood-clot-prevention drug *warfarin*…diabetes drugs *glimepiride, glipizide, glyburide* and *metformin*…cholesterol medication *lovastatin*…antibiotic *amoxicillin*…and pain medication *naproxen.*

What to do: When filling a prescription for a generic drug, check whether it's cheaper to fill the prescription without using your coverage. Also, ask pharmacies whether they have a membership or rewards program that can further reduce the cost.

On the other hand, if you expect to spend a lot more than your deductible for medical costs in a given year, it might make sense to pay the higher prices so that you get past the deductible period more quickly. In some cases, depending on the specifics of your coverage, that might result in greater overall savings.

How to Detox from Anesthesia

Michael T. Murray, ND, one of the country's best-known naturopathic physicians. He serves on the Board of Regents of Bastyr University in Seattle and has written more than 30 books, including *The Encyclopedia of Natural Medicine* with coauthor Joseph Pizzorno, ND. DoctorMurray.com

Most adults are familiar with that woozy state that occurs after undergoing anesthesia for surgery or even a screening procedure such as colonoscopy. In most cases, the aftereffects of the anesthetic wear off within a few hours. But not everyone is so lucky. Some people don't metabolize drugs efficiently. An anesthetic can leave them feeling dizzy, weak, feverish and/or disoriented for days afterward.

This can occur with general anesthesia, which causes a temporary loss of bodily sensation and unconsciousness, or with regional or local anesthesia, which prevents you from feeling pain at the affected site while you remain awake.

Especially for older patients, general anesthesia increases risk for declines in mental function, including difficulty concentrating and memory loss. This condition, known as postoperative cognitive dysfunction (POCD), affects as many as 40% of patients over age 65 for one to three months, while some experience the condition for six months or more.

What you may not know: There are safe, effective ways to prepare for—and recover from—anesthesia. *To minimize aftereffects and get back to normal more quickly, try…* *

A HIGH-POTENCY MULTIVITAMIN

If you don't take one already, start taking a high-potency multivitamin and mineral formula that provides a variety of nutrients, including at least 200 mg of vitamin C…25,000 international units (IU) of beta-carotene…and 22.4 IU of vitamin E each day, for at least two weeks before and after undergoing anesthesia. Many of these nutrients have

*Prior to any surgical procedure, be sure to discuss with your doctor any drugs and/or supplements you take. The recommendations in this article are safe for most people, but many supplements increase bleeding risk and/or may interact with some anesthetics.

antioxidant properties that play an important role in the body's detoxification mechanisms that are facilitated by the liver.

A multivitamin and mineral formula also contains many nutrients that help eliminate heavy metals and other toxic compounds, including anesthetics, from the body. These include all of the B vitamins, but especially thiamine, B-6, folate and B-12…and key minerals such as zinc, magnesium and selenium.

These multivitamin and mineral formulas—usually labeled "high-potency"—are available at health-food stores. Follow instructions on the label.

MILK THISTLE

Milk thistle (*Silybum marianum*) promotes the body's detoxification process by preventing the depletion of glutathione, a natural antioxidant found in the liver. The concentration of this antioxidant is reduced when you are exposed to chemicals, including anesthetics. When glutathione levels decline, liver cells become more susceptible to damage.

Milk thistle not only prevents the depletion of glutathione but also has been shown in laboratory studies to increase the level of this potent antioxidant by up to 35%.

Typical dose for milk thistle: 70 mg three times daily. Start taking it at least one week before surgery, and continue to take it for at least two weeks afterward.

Caution: Avoid milk thistle if you are allergic to plants in the ragweed family or have a history of hormone-related cancer, such as breast, uterine or prostate—milk thistle can affect hormone levels.

LIPOTROPIC FORMULAS

Lipotropic agents promote the flow of fat and bile to and from the liver. Used primarily as treatment for hepatitis, cirrhosis and chemical-induced liver disease, these agents increase levels of two important liver substances—glutathione and S-adenosylmethionine (SAMe).

Most major manufacturers of nutritional supplements offer lipotropic formulas. These formulas are typically rich in choline and methionine, two important nutrients for the liver, along with supportive nutrients and/or herbals.

Look for a supplement with a daily dose of 1,000 mg of choline and 1,000 mg of methionine. Begin taking it one week before and at least two weeks after surgery.

AN ANESTHESIA-RECOVERY DIET

If your body is recovering from anesthesia, steer clear of saturated fats, including meat and dairy (whey protein powder is a good protein alternative)...refined sugar...and alcohol—all of which can increase risk for cholestasis (slowed or blocked flow of bile, which makes it harder for the body to eliminate fat-soluble toxins like anesthetics).

On the other hand, a diet that is rich in dietary fiber—particularly water-soluble fiber—promotes bile secretion.

Good sources of water-soluble fiber: Pears, oat bran, apples and legumes. It's also beneficial to eat vegetables from the cabbage family—especially broccoli, Brussels sprouts and cabbage—as well as artichokes, beets and carrots. All of these foods contain compounds that aid in detoxification.

There are also herbs and spices that will help you detox and recover from anesthesia—especially the antioxidants turmeric and cinnamon. In addition, you should eat foods that are rich in sulfur, which helps the liver clear toxins.

Good sulfur-rich foods: Garlic, onions and egg yolks. Add them to your diet whenever possible.

WATER

Not getting enough fluids—especially water—makes it difficult for your body to eliminate toxins. Bottled and filtered water are the best choices because they usually have fewer impurities, but drink tap water if it's your only alternative.

A good goal for all times—but especially before and after undergoing anesthesia—is six to eight eight-ounce glasses of water each day.

Important: Don't wait until you are thirsty to take a drink—by that time you will already be mildly dehydrated. Take water breaks throughout the day.

Good rule of thumb: Have a glass of water every two waking hours.

Longevity Secrets of the Super Agers

"Super Ager" Secrets for Staying Sharp

Bradford Dickerson, MD, a behavioral neurologist, director of the Frontotemporal Disorders Unit at Massachusetts General Hospital and an associate professor of neurology at Harvard Medical School, all in Boston.

When it comes to research on memory loss, most studies have shown that it is very common in normal aging to have reduced memory, even in the absence of Alzheimer's disease or other late-life diseases.

But much of this research has been done on people who are in their 80s or older. What happens to memory in those who aren't quite that old? After all, by the time we've reached our 60s or 70s, most of us have memory lapses, whether it's misplaced eyeglasses or a forgotten name.

Important recent discovery: By investigating somewhat younger adults, scientists are now uncovering a new breed of "super agers," who do as well on memory tests as those who are 40 or 50 years younger. This research is contributing to a growing body of evidence that could provide significant clues about new ways to prevent and treat memory loss.

To learn more, we spoke with Bradford Dickerson, MD, a neurologist at Massachusetts General Hospital and a leading expert on brain changes and memory disorders…

How much does memory decline in the typical older adult?

In clinical settings, memory can be tested in a variety of ways. One approach involves giving people a short list of words to memorize. When people in their 20s are presented with a list of 16 words—and given time to really study the list—they'll probably remember 13 or 14 of the words. Most people in their early or mid-70s might remember just eight or nine of the words. This would be considered "normal" memory loss.

To test yourself: Study a list of 16 words for a few minutes and then see how many you can remember 20 minutes later.

But some people do better on these tests?

Actually, some do a lot better. Based on research conducted at Northwestern University, it is known that a small percentage of people who are age 80 or older—maybe about 10%—do as well or better on memory tests as people who are in their 50s and 60s.

Our study included adults closer to traditional retirement age. However, we found the same thing: Some people simply don't experience the same degree of memory loss as their peers. This has huge implications.

If we can figure out why some people maintain robust memories, we might find ways to prevent or even reverse age-related memory loss—and possibly some forms of dementia, which can cause other cognitive problems such as impaired reasoning and behavior and personality changes.

Do we know how the brains of super agers differ from those of other people?

Even though the brain is roughly the same size in all adults (about the size of a cantaloupe and weighing approximately three pounds), we found in our studies of super agers that the size of specific brain areas correlated with memory: They were larger in those with exceptional memories and smaller in those with normal memories. This means that we now have a "biomarker" that may be used to study age-related memory changes.

Is it possible to strengthen these brain regions and prevent memory loss?

This is the million-dollar question. Some people, due to genetics, may simply be born with "young" brains. We know that exercise (see below) and following a Mediterranean-style diet with fruits and vegetables, fish, legumes and whole grains can stimulate brain growth. Good sleep and reducing stress can also make a difference. Do the brain changes that are associated with these or other activities lead to better memory? At the moment, we're not sure.

How does exercise help?

Aerobic exercise has been shown to reduce circulating cortisol, a stress hormone that can cause brain shrinkage. It also stimulates the release of growth factors (such as brain-derived neurotrophic factor) that prevent brain cells from shrinking and may even help new ones grow.

A recent study showed that sedentary older adults who take up moderate-intensity exercise—for example, a regular walking program for 30 minutes at least four days a week—for six months to a year show growth in the hippocampus (a part of the brain associated with memory) and also do better on memory tests. This reinforces the idea that exercise is protective.

Important: Don't talk on your cell phone while walking or biking, since you may be more likely

to fall. Head trauma raises risk for Alzheimer's disease.

What about diet?

Studies suggest that heart-healthy diets (such as the Mediterranean diet) can reduce the risk for Alzheimer's disease and other forms of dementia. We're just not sure whether the diet specifically improves brain functions.

However, in a new study from Mayo Clinic, researchers found (based on MRI scans) that the brains of adults who consumed the most foods typical of a Mediterranean diet for a year—legumes, fish, whole grains and vegetables—had greater thickness in some parts of the cortex, which plays a role in memory, language and other cognitive functions. People who ate large amounts of carbohydrates, sugar and/or red meat had less cortical thickness.

And stress reduction?

In studies of older adults, those who participated in an eight-week meditation training program had improved connectivity between the frontal lobes and the hippocampus and other brain structures, which improves memory. It's possible that other relaxing practices, such as yoga, have similar effects. We're hoping to study this more.

How important is sleep?

Very! People who don't sleep well will obviously find it difficult to focus their attention and obtain and retain memories. Also, the brain consolidates memories during sleep (particularly during the deep, slow-wave stages of sleep)—the memories are shifted to brain regions where they become more stable.

It's important to remember, though, that we all require different amounts of sleep. Most adults seem to do best when they get seven to nine hours of sleep a day.

Any other advice?

Socialize. Studies show that adults who regularly connect with friends are less likely to develop dementia. Working past typical retirement age and/or volunteering after retirement also keeps older brains engaged.

Nutritional Medicine for a Long Life

Mark A. Stengler, NMD, naturopathic medical doctor and founder and medical director of the Stengler Center for Integrative Medicine, Encinitas, California.

A 96-year-old reader from Brooklyn recently wrote me a letter. Anita, a retired teacher, has been a health-food enthusiast all her life. She fondly recalls the days when horse-drawn wagons delivered fresh milk unadulterated by today's added hormones, and fruits and vegetables were locally grown without toxic pesticides.

Anita has no major health problems. Incredibly, in this era of prescription-drug mania, she uses no medications whatsoever.

I laughed as I read that when doctors ask what drugs she takes and she replies none, they assume she must be deaf or senile.

When people speculate that her longevity must be due to good genes, Anita counters, "It's good nutrition. When you listen to your body, it tells you what it needs to stay well."

In my practice, I see firsthand how pain, fatigue, poor memory and other common ailments are alleviated with nutritional medicine. A well-nourished body—from newborn to centenarian—has an amazing capacity to heal itself...and age well.

Living to 100—and Beyond

Michael Fossel, MD, PhD, a leading expert on the use of telomerase for age-related diseases. He is the founder and president of Telocyte, a company that is investigating telomerase therapy for Alzheimer's disease. He is author of *The Telomerase Revolution: The Enzyme That Holds the Key to Human Aging and Will Soon Lead to Longer, Healthier Lives.* MichaelFossel.com

W hen we hear about people who live to age 100 or beyond, it may seem like a relatively rare occurrence. But in fact, the number of those "super agers" is dramatically increasing—in 1980, 15,000 Americans had reached the centenarian milestone...by 2014, their numbers had increased to more than 72,000. Overall,

the life span of the average American has increased by more than 60% in the last century. Some experts believe that's just the beginning.

To learn more, we spoke with Michael Fossel, MD, PhD, a leading expert on aging who believes that both aging and chronic diseases can be slowed by "switching on" a gene that controls cellular health.

Are medical and social improvements responsible for longer average life spans in the US?

They've certainly helped. We can now cure many childhood leukemias and treat diabetes and most infections. We are now less likely to experience malnutrition or hygiene-related diseases than we were a century ago—due, for example, to better agriculture and safer water supplies.

But these factors mainly affect the risk of dying young (or younger than you'd like). They don't guarantee that you'll live an extra-long life.

How much does one's lifestyle affect life span?

Less than you'd think. Consider diet. Most people assume that a good diet is the secret to a long and healthy life. But research has failed to find a consistent link. When scientists interview centenarians, they find that their dietary habits are all over the map.

I'm not suggesting that diet doesn't matter. Many well-regarded studies—such as the Framingham Heart Study and the Nurses' Health Study—have shown that diet makes some difference. People who eat a lot of saturated and trans fats tend to get more heart disease and die younger...and those who sip a little red wine tend to be healthier.

But there's a ceiling effect. People who eat a reasonably good diet are more likely to live longer than those who eat poorly. There's just no definitive evidence that going from a reasonably healthful diet to a great diet will help you slow the aging process or stop age-related disease.

Don't people who exercise live longer?

Yes. Studies show that people who exercise tend to live longer. But does the exercise itself get the credit? Or do these people simply have "healthy" genes that make them feel good and want to exercise? Correlation is not necessarily causation. While proving that exercise is good for you isn't as easy as you might think, it is certainly hard to argue against its value. I definitely encourage exercise.

But all our habits are mediated, in part, by how our bodies respond. The cells of young people generally have robust repair mechanisms that can mitigate damage caused by unhealthy behaviors. In older adults, the cells are less capable of self-repair—and that's when diseases get serious. While genes, diet and exercise play a small role, the major factor is still cellular aging.

Does cellular self-repair—or the lack of it—affect aging?

Generally speaking, genetic damage occurs when cells divide. With each division, for example, telomeres (caps on the tips of each strand of DNA on your chromosomes—often compared to plastic tips on the ends of shoelaces) get slightly shorter.

Why it matters: Every shortening of the telomeres changes gene expression, the ability of genes to produce the proteins and other substances that maintain life—and that allow cells to repair themselves.

How does this affect life span?

Every disease is caused in part by cellular breakdowns. Why do young people get fewer chronic diseases? Because their cells can readily recover from infections, inflammation and other "insults." Older cells, with their shortened telomeres and altered gene expression, aren't as resilient, and DNA repair, for example, slows down. This is why the risk for cancer, for instance, goes up exponentially with age.

Is it possible to prevent telomere shortening?

In lab and animal studies, scientists have already found ways to "reset" telomeres to their original length. The evidence suggests that doing so could help people live longer, healthier lives.

The key to this process: Every cell in the body contains a gene for telomerase, an enzyme that lengthens telomeres. However, the gene only "turns on" in germ and stem cells (which can repair/divide indefinitely). Activating this gene in other cells could possibly do the same thing.

In studies, lengthening telomeres has been shown to improve immune function, blood pressure, bone density and other "biomarkers" for aging

and age-related diseases. Now we need a mechanism to reliably use this process in humans.

CAN WE SLOW AGING

Over-the-counter supplements known as telomerase activators are designed to help maintain and rebuild telomeres (caps at the end of each strand of DNA in our chromosomes, which help prevent deterioration of these gene-encoded structures). The supplements, available online, seem to improve some biomarkers of disease (such as cholesterol). Will this type of supplement help people live longer? There's no proof yet. Many experts on aging believe that the supplements may be somewhat helpful—although likely much less effective as they would need to be to prevent/cure age-related diseases. And they're expensive, costing several hundred dollars a month.

In the future: It may be possible to deliver an "active" telomerase gene directly to the body's cells. In theory, this could potentially prevent and even cure many—if not most—age-related diseases. While you could still die of trauma, infections, inherited genetic problems and other causes, we could essentially halt most "age-related" diseases, such as atherosclerosis, Alzheimer's, osteoarthritis, etc. You might have the health of a 30- or 40-year-old and could easily live to twice the current healthy life span.

Website Calculates Your Chance of Living to 100

Thomas Perls, founder, New England Centenarian Study. LivingTo100.com

Estimate your chance of living to 100 by visiting LivingTo100.com and answering 40 questions about family history, health, diet and lifestyle. Have your cholesterol and blood-pressure numbers handy—you need to enter them. The site, created by Thomas Perls, MD, who is the founder of the New England Centenarian Study, lets you see how your answers influence longevity, so you can change life-shortening habits if you want to.

Slow Down the Aging Process!

Mark A. Stengler, NMD, naturopathic medical doctor and founder and medical director of the Stengler Center for Integrative Medicine, Encinitas, California…adjunct associate clinical professor at the National College of Natural Medicine, Portland, Oregon…the author of many books, including *The Natural Physician's Healing Therapies* and coauthor of *Prescription for Natural Cures* and *Prescription for Drug Alternatives* (all Bottom Line Books)

The myth about longevity is that we have no control over how long we live. Reality: We do have some control—even though we all know some people who lived healthfully but died suddenly…and others who didn't take care of themselves and lived on and on.

It is easy to fall back on the idea that we can't escape our heredity, but our parentage isn't as important as you might think. Having long-lived ancestors and siblings does increase your odds of living to old age, but it doesn't guarantee longevity.

Reason: Your genes, the biological programs that govern the activity of your body's 70 trillion cells, may influence only half of the factors involved in aging, according to the Okinawa Centenarian Study. That means we can have a direct effect on our aging process by focusing on the other factors.

Proof: Americans are living longer than ever, although not as long as people in other countries (see chart on page three). The number of centenarians (people who are 100 years old or older) in the US is at an all-time high of about 50,000!

Surprise: Centenarians often are in better health than younger seniors. About 20% of centenarians are "escapers," people who have entirely avoided serious diseases, and 40% were escapers until at least age 85, according to a *Journal of the American Medical Association* (*JAMA*) article.

While there is no one secret to longevity, we can adopt aspects of healthful aging into our lives and improve our chances of reaching the century mark. I have seen many patients improve their health and add years to their lives. You can do the same by following these recommendations. You'll feel better and have greater vitality right away.

ADD YEARS TO YOUR LIFE BY…

●**Protecting your genes.** A strong nutritional foundation safeguards our genes. Crucial to this protection is vitamin B, which can help repair genes and slow gene damage. Advice: I recommend that most adults take a high-potency multivitamin each day that contains at least 50 milligrams (mg) each of vitamins B-1 and B-2, 400 micrograms (mcg) of folic acid and 50 mcg to 100 mcg of vitamin B-12. If your multivitamin is low in B vitamins, take an additional B-complex supplement so that you get the amounts listed above. These amounts are safe for everyone except those taking methotrexate for rheumatoid arthritis and for certain types of chemotherapy patients because high amounts of B supplements can interfere with these treatments.

●**Eating healthfully.** Nutrients serve as the building blocks of our biochemistry. Vitamin and mineral deficiencies can impair our normal biochemistry and increase the formation of age-promoting free radical molecules.

A study in *Journal of the American Geriatrics Society* found that centenarians consume, on average, about two-and-a-half times more antioxidant-packed vegetables than seniors ages 70 to 99. Incredibly, the centenarians ate five times more veggies than typical 40-year-olds. All those antioxidants help protect against the types of cell damage involved in aging. Similarly, studies of Seventh Day Adventists in California—who do not smoke or drink but do eat lots of vegetables—have found that they have higher levels of antioxidants and tend to live longer.

Bottom line: Eat your veggies—lots of them.

●**Taking supplements.** It's difficult to study the specific effects of supplements over 80 to 100 years when so many other variables affect longevity. But both animal and human studies demonstrate the health benefits of supplements.

Recommendation: In addition to taking a multivitamin, there's convincing evidence that a combination of the antioxidant alpha-lipoic acid (300 mg to 400 mg daily) and the amino acid acetyl-L-carnitine (800 mg to 1,200 mg daily) has a rejuvenating effect, making people feel more energetic. These two nutrients are involved in the body's production of energy, which powers every cell in the body. They are safe for everyone, although people with diabetes or seizure disorders should take them under a doctor's supervision. A recent study published in *American Journal of Clinical Nutrition* found that a related supplement, L-carnitine (2 grams daily), which helps transport fatty acids into the mitochondria (cell structures that convert nutrients into energy to power the cells), reduced mental and physical fatigue in centenarians. This supplement is safe for everyone. Magnesium (400 mg daily) helps maintain the length of telomeres, the protective tips of chromosomes. Resveratrol (100 mg twice daily) activates the SIRT1 gene, which is involved in longevity. And vitamin C (1,000 mg daily) enhances immunity and reduces inflammation, both of which can contribute to longevity. It is safe to take all of these supplements.

•**Eating less.** Animal studies dating back to the 1930s have shown that nutritionally complete but calorie-restricted diets (generally with 30% fewer calories than national recommendations) often increase life expectancy by up to 30%. In human terms, that's roughly an extra 22 years, which can bring people very close to the century mark. Studies of people growing up in Okinawa, Japan, during the 1940s and 1950s found that they consumed about 11% fewer calories than their estimated calorie requirements (about 2,000 calories daily for men and 1,600 for women) until middle age, which contributed to greater longevity.

Guaranteed benefit: Eating less will help you maintain a normal weight and lower the odds of developing diabetes and heart disease.

Important: Only 30% of centenarians are overweight.

It takes great willpower to maintain a diet with 30% fewer calories than what feels "normal," but eating less than you do can be an important first step. Assuming that you aren't underweight, I recommend a calorie-reducing compromise—at each meal, eat until you feel 80% full. You may feel hungry initially, but you'll soon adjust to consuming less food.

•**Continuing to learn.** Even more than physical health, mental sharpness (such as memory and the ability to make decisions) is the most likely predictor of independence among people in their 90s and over 100 years of age, according to a *JAMA* article. Researchers say that some deterioration in cognitive function is inevitable as we age but that building a brain "reserve," or extra brainpower, can offset part of this decline.

•**Mental activity builds your brain's reserve.** Be a lifelong learner by taking challenging classes…reading and discussing difficult material…and exposing yourself to new and provocative ideas. All of these activities increase connections among brain cells.

•**Exercising.** The more exercise you do, the better. A study conducted at King's College London in England found that physically active people have healthier cells than those who don't exercise. Researchers found that exercise lengthened telomeres, the tips of chromosomes, which, as I explained earlier, usually shorten with aging.

Recommendation: If you are not physically active, start by walking for 10 minutes daily. Gradually build up speed, time and distance over a few weeks or months.

•**Getting enough—but not too much—sleep.** Seven hours of sleep nightly is the amount most strongly associated with longevity. Getting less sleep—or more—is associated with shorter life spans. People who sleep less than five hours don't give their bodies enough time for physiological recovery, and that may lead to metabolic dysfunction. Metabolic dysfunction also can result from habitually sleeping for more than eight hours.

- **Maintaining a spiritual foundation.** Having a spiritual foundation is associated with longer life. I find that my own spiritual foundation relieves stress. You can develop your inner life through prayer and/or meditation.

- **Being optimistic.** Centenarians tend to be optimists who feel that they have control over major decisions in their lives. Helpful reading: Learned Optimism: How to Change Your Mind and Your Life by Martin Seligman (Vintage).

- **Connecting with others.** Strong ties to family and friends play a big role in longevity. Studies show that married men tend to live longer than bachelors. Research also has shown that having friends is even more important than having family in terms of living longer. My prescription: Take time to thoroughly enjoy the company of family and friends!

WHAT IS AGING?

Over the course of a lifetime, our bodies face inevitable decline. Aging is characterized by an accumulation of cell damage. Some of this damage comes from destructive molecules called free radicals.

Another problem: Wear and tear erodes mitochondria, microscopic cell structures that provide us with energy and stamina. In addition, telomeres, the tips of chromosomes, shorten with age, which may accelerate the aging process.

Surprising Secrets from the World's Happiest People

Dan Buettner, founder of Blue Zones, an organization that studies the regions of the world where people commonly live active lives past the age of 100. Based in Minneapolis, he is a writer for *National Geographic* and author of *Thrive: Finding Happiness the Blue Zones Way.* BlueZones.com

---

We've all heard that "wealth doesn't buy happiness." Neither, it turns out, does social status, youth or beauty.

Social scientists have collected tens of millions of data points that help identify what truly makes people happy. Genetics and life circumstances can influence happiness, but personal choices account for about 55% of it. That means we all have more control over our happiness than we may realize.

National Geographic author and explorer Dan Buettner spent five years talking to people in areas identified by researchers as the world leaders in happiness—Denmark's Jutland Peninsula…Singapore…Nuevo León, Mexico …and the town of San Luis Obispo in California.

In his new book, *Thrive*, he identified the main characteristics of what he calls thrivers, people who consistently report the highest levels of well-being. *Here, secrets from the world's happiest people…*

- **Own one TV, no more.** Americans spend more than four hours a day, on average, in front of the television. This is time that they're not spending with other people, including their families. (Family time in front of the television is not the same as real interaction.)

In the places where happiness is highest, people spend the least time watching television. It's not that they never watch—they just watch less than most people.

I advise people to own no more than one television—and to keep it in an out-of-the-way place, such as the basement. You still can watch your favorite programs, but watching will become a deliberate activity, not something you just do automatically.

- **Create a "flow room."** In Danish society, most families have an area in the house where everyone naturally congregates. I call these rooms "flow rooms" because they're places where time seems to flow away when people are engaged and enjoying one another's company. Flow rooms have no screens (TVs or computers) and no clocks. They are quiet environments where it's easy to engage in meaningful activities with family.

In our house, I chose a room with good lighting and the best views—it's comfortable, and everyone in the family wants to be there. I keep it stocked with good books, musical instruments and the best family games.

There's nothing formal about our gatherings. People wander in and out. Because it's so pleasant, we spend a lot more time there than in front of the TV or separated in different parts of the house.

●**Experience the "sun bonus."** By most standard measures, people in Mexico should be less happy than those in other countries. About 60% of the population is poor. Education and health care are less than optimal. Yet on the happiness scale, Mexico ranks high.

This is partly due to the "sun bonus." People in sunnier climates are consistently happier than those who live in northern countries.

Those of us who live in colder, less sunny climates still can take advantage of the sunny days we do have by getting out and enjoying the sun. The vitamin D that is produced in the body from sun exposure is sometimes called the "happiness vitamin" because it increases brain levels of serotonin, the same neurotransmitter that is increased by some anti-depressant medications.

●**Stop shopping.** The satisfaction that we get from buying things—an expensive watch, a new suit, a fancy car—wears off within 14 months. Yet in the US, we're pressured by the media and social expectations to always want more. In order to get it, we have to work longer hours and take fewer vacations, which generally reduces happiness.

In Denmark, regulations limit the number of hours that shops can be open. In Mexico, most of the inhabitants are not running a status race with their neighbors.

For more happiness, take the money that you could spend on nonessential items and spend it on something that lasts. For example, take a vacation with your family or sign up for a painting class. The experiences and good memories will continue to give satisfaction for the rest of your life.

●**Employ yourself.** Self-employed workers and business owners report some of the highest levels of well-being. It may be because they are more likely to pursue work that they love or simply because they feel more in control.

The happiness zone of San Luis Obispo, California, has far more self-employed people per capita than the average community in the US. These self-employed workers are shop owners, graphic designers, artists, wine-makers and the like. The more

autonomy and control you have over your job, the more likely you will be satisfied with your work.

●**Make new friends.** People around the world report higher levels of satisfaction when they spend time with family and friends. Every additional friend that you make (assuming that these friends are upbeat) increases your chances of being happy by 9%.

People who get together with others for at least seven hours a day have the highest levels of happiness. That sounds like a lot, but the time quickly adds up.

For example, everyone eats lunch. Ask a co-worker to join you, or sit with a group in a cafeteria. Talk with friends during coffee breaks. After work, encourage the family to eat and socialize together, rather than dispersing to separate rooms. Take classes or join a club.

The Danes don't identify themselves as being particularly outgoing, yet 19 out of 20 Danish adults belong to clubs dedicated to arts, exercise and hobbies.

●**Get addicted to this.** The happiest people almost always volunteer in some fashion—at their church, with environmental groups, for social-service organizations and the like. Volunteering means spending time with others, and it also takes your mind off your own problems and increases self-worth and pride in your community.

Studies have shown that altruism has an effect on the brain that is similar to that of sugar and cocaine. It creates feelings of well-being, along with an addictive feedback loop that encourages people to keep doing it.

Also, volunteers are healthier. They tend to weigh less than those who don't volunteer, and they're even less likely to suffer a heart attack.

Commit to volunteering for a set period of time—say, once a week for four weeks. People are more likely to keep doing it when they make this initial commitment—and then get "hooked" on the rewards.

●**Keep the faith.** Religious people tend to be happier than those without faith. It's not clear whether religion makes people happy or if happy people tend to be drawn to religious practices. Either way, those who are religious have less disease, live longer and are less likely to engage in dangerous behavior (such as smoking and heavy drinking).

In Mexico, for example, more than 80% of people who were asked, "How important is God in your life?" responded with a 10 on a scale of one to 10, compared with only 58% in the US. This helps explain why people in some parts of Mexico, despite the hardships of daily life, tend to thrive emotionally.

Even if you're not religious, you can achieve similar benefits by cultivating a sense of spirituality—and a belief in giving back to your community and making the world a better place.

Dating: The Surprising Way to Boost Your Health

Judith Sills, PhD, a Philadelphia-based clinical psychologist. A three-year National Science Foundation fellow, she is a contributing editor at *Psychology Today*. She is also the author of *Getting Naked Again: Dating, Romance, Sex, and Love When You've Been Divorced, Widowed, Dumped, or Distracted.*

I f you're not in a committed relationship, maybe it's time to consider dating again. And if you're age 50 or older—the point at which most of us become much more focused on staying healthy—then it's an especially good time to give dating a chance.

While the prospect of dating as a mature adult can seem overwhelming or downright scary, here's some compelling motivation—the latest research indicates that being in a relationship can improve your health in a variety of ways. And take heart: There are specific tips for daters who are 50+ that can make getting out there again much easier.

HEALTH BENEFITS GALORE

Plenty of singles age 50 or older say they don't need a relationship to be happy. But those who are in committed relationships seem to have significant health advantages over those who fly solo.

Case in point: An analysis of data from more than 300,000 adults found that those without strong relationships were 50% more likely to die from all causes over a seven-year period—a risk that's the equivalent to daily smoking! Additionally, men and women who live alone and have a heart attack are twice as likely to have a second heart attack within a few months.

The list goes on. Married people are less likely to get pneumonia than singles, and those who are married or live together in midlife are less likely to develop dementia.

HOW TO GET BACK OUT THERE

If you have been out of the single world for a long time, you might not be sure that you want to get back in the dating game. But one thing is certain: Humans have a deep need for intimacy and companionship.

And while some people are perfectly satisfied with their close friends and family, a healthy committed relationship generally offers a greater level of stability and support. After all, if your best friend moved to a different state, you wouldn't follow that person, but you likely would if it were your partner.

The advantage of later-life dating is that you've been through it all before. And you probably have some idea of what you're looking for. Also, while you may be a bit insecure in how you look as you age, you may have more confidence in your personality and social skills.

Advice for dating after age 50…

•**Get online.** The Internet is a fantastic way to meet people. The number of potential partners vastly exceeds those you'll meet any other way. If you're willing to put in the time—writing an interesting profile, putting up an attractive photo and wading through the possibilities—you will get dates. (They won't all be fabulous, but many will be fun and you'll start to meet people.)

There are hundreds of dating websites to choose from. The most popular sites, such as Match and eHarmony, have the most members (and potential partners), but they tend to attract younger users.

Helpful: Try sites that target older adults, such as OurTime or SeniorPeopleMeet. Monthly prices are lower if you sign up for a longer time. Plenty of Fish is a free dating site for all age groups, although some features are only free if you "upgrade."

●**Don't waste time.** A survey by the Pew Research Center found that one-third of those who connect online never take the next step and meet face-to-face. Unless your only goal is Internet flirting, pin down a time to meet. You don't want to rush it, of course, but don't wait too long. If you like the person after exchanging three or four e-mails, it's time for a phone call or a meeting (in a low-key public place like a coffee shop). If someone you're interested in doesn't ask you out first, take the plunge and do it yourself.

●**Set aside your preconceptions.** Dating sites have analyzed what their members want—or think they want. Women, for example, tend to respond to men of certain ages, or with particular jobs or education levels. Men tend to reach out to women who are blond. Give other types of people a chance!

●**Give yourself (and your date) some slack.** When dating, you will no doubt have some anxious and awkward moments. What do you do when every attempt at conversation withers and dies? Or when your date doesn't laugh at any of your jokes? Give yourself and your companion a break. First dates are hard, but it does get easier with practice.

Helpful: Forget the traditional dinner date. It's too much for a first meeting, particularly if the chemistry isn't there—or when you discover between the first and second courses that you do not seem to have a whole lot in common. Meeting for coffee, a drink or lunch is easier and less expensive—and you can quickly cut your losses when it just isn't clicking.

●**Keep your insecurities in check.** No, you're not the same person you were 30 years ago. You might have a few extra pounds or a little less hair. Just don't let the nagging negative voice in your head—"I'm not good enough"…"She is way out of my league"…or "What if he doesn't ask me out again"—ruin what could be a perfectly pleasant time.

Your date saw something in you before you met. Relax and enjoy yourself. Besides, everyone is inse-

cure on first dates. The person sitting across from you is probably having his/her own insecure thoughts.

●**It's not a job interview.** An unfortunate first-date strategy is to ask a lot of questions. Granted, asking questions and showing interest will keep the conversation going. But it can also be intimidating—or simply off-putting.

Some women tell me that they "interview" potential partners to save time. They ask things like, "Are you looking for something serious?" "Do you own or rent?" "What kind of relationship do you have with your ex?" Men do their own interviewing but tend to take their cue from the workplace, posing questions such as, "So tell me…where would you like to be in five years?" None of this is friendly give-and-take—it feels more like interrogation.

My advice: Be a little less efficient. A date is a chance to get to know someone…to reveal a little about yourself…and have some fun. Keep it light.

●**Aim for a full stomach.** Think it's time to take a new relationship to the next level? A dinner date with great food could be the best way to do it. There may be some truth to the old cliché—the way to a man's (or woman's) heart is through the stomach. A study in the journal *Appetite* found that women who were shown romantic pictures after they'd eaten had more brain activation than women who looked at the same pictures on an empty stomach!

6 Secrets to Holistic Heart Care

Joel K. Kahn, MD, clinical professor of medicine at Wayne State University School of Medicine in Detroit and director of Kahn Center for Cardiac Longevity, Bloomfield Township, Michigan. He is a founding member of the International Society of Integrative, Metabolic and Functional Cardiovascular Medicine and author of *The Whole Heart Solution.* DrJoelKahn.com

You don't smoke, your cholesterol levels look good and your blood pressure is under control. This means that you're off the hook when it comes to having a heart attack or developing heart disease, right? Maybe not.

Surprising statistic: About 20% of people with heart disease do not have any of the classic risk factors, such as those described above.

The missing link: While most conventional medical doctors prescribe medications and other treatments to help patients control the "big" risk factors for heart disease, holistic cardiologists also suggest small lifestyle changes that over time make a significant difference in heart disease risk.* My secrets for preventing heart disease…

SECRET #1: **Stand up!** You may not think of standing as a form of exercise. However, it's more effective than most people realize.

Think about what you're doing when you're not standing. Unless you're asleep, you're probably sitting. While sitting, your body's metabolism slows… your insulin becomes less effective…and you're likely to experience a gradual drop in HDL "good" cholesterol.

A study that tracked the long-term health of more than 123,000 Americans found that those who sat for six hours or more a day had an overall death rate that was higher—18% higher for men and 37% for women—than those who sat for less than three hours.

What's so great about standing? When you're on your feet, you move more. You pace…fidget…move your arms…and walk from room to room. This type of activity improves metabolism and can easily burn hundreds of extra calories a day. Standing also increases your insulin sensitivity to help prevent diabetes. So stand up and move around when talking on the phone, checking e-mail and watching television.

SECRET #2: **Count your breaths.** Slow, deep breathing is an effective way to help prevent high blood pressure—one of the leading causes of heart disease. For people who already have high blood pressure, doing this technique a few times a day has been shown to lower blood pressure by five to

*To find a holistic cardiologist, go to the website of the American Board of Integrative Holistic Medicine, ABIHM.org, and search the database of certified integrative physicians.

10 points within five minutes. And the pressure may stay lower for up to 24 hours.

During a breathing exercise, you want to slow your breathing down from the usual 12 to 16 breaths a minute that most people take to about three breaths. I use the "4-7-8 sequence" whenever I feel stressed. What to do: Inhale through your nose for four seconds…hold the breath in for seven seconds…then exhale through the mouth for eight seconds.

Also helpful: A HeartMath software package, which you can load on your computer or smartphone, includes breathing exercises to help lower your heart rate and levels of stress hormones. Cost: $129 and up, at HeartMath.com. You can also sign up for some free tools on this website.

SECRET #3: **Practice "loving kindness."** This is an easy form of meditation that reduces stress, thus allowing you to keep your heart rate and blood pressure at healthy levels.

Research has shown that people who meditate regularly are 48% less likely to have a heart attack or stroke than those who don't meditate. "Loving kindness" meditation is particularly effective at promoting relaxation—it lowers levels of the stress hormones adrenaline and cortisol while raising levels of the healing hormone oxytocin.

What to do: Sit quietly, with your eyes closed. For a few minutes, focus on just your breathing. Then imagine one person in your life whom you find exceptionally easy to love. Imagine this person in front of you. Fill your heart with a warm, loving feeling…think about how you both want to be happy and avoid suffering…and imagine that a feeling of peace travels from your heart to that person's heart in the form of white light. Dwell on the image for a few minutes. This meditation will also help you practice small acts of kindness in your daily life—for example, giving a hand to someone who needs help crossing the street.

SECRET #4: **Don't neglect sex.** Men who have sex at least two times a week have a 50% lower risk for a heart attack than those who abstain. Similar research hasn't been done on women, but it's likely that they get a comparable benefit.

Why does sex help keep your heart healthy? It probably has more to do with intimacy than the physical activity itself. Couples who continue to have sex tend to be the ones with more intimacy in their marriages. Happy people who bond with others have fewer heart attacks—and recover more quickly if they've had one—than those without close relationships.

SECRET #5: Be happy! People who are happy and who feel a sense of purpose and connection with others tend to have lower blood pressure and live longer than those who are isolated. Research shows that two keys to happiness are to help others be happy—for example, by being a volunteer—and to reach out to friends and neighbors. Actually, any shared activity, such as going to church or doing group hobbies, can increase survival among heart patients by about 50%.

SECRET #6: Try Waon (pronounced Wa-own) therapy. With this Japanese form of "warmth therapy," you sit in an infrared (dry) sauna for 15 minutes then retreat to a resting area for half an hour, where you wrap yourself in towels and drink plenty of water. Studies show that vascular function improves after such therapy due to the extra release of nitric oxide, the master molecule in blood vessels that helps them relax.

Some health clubs offer Waon treatments, but the dry saunas at many gyms should offer similar benefits. I do not recommend steam rooms—moist heat places extra demands on the heart and can be dangerous for some people.

5 Foods That Fight High Blood Pressure

Janet Bond Brill, PhD, RD, a nationally recognized nutrition, health and fitness expert who specializes in cardiovascular disease prevention. She has authored several books on the topic, including *Blood Pressure DOWN*, *Prevent a Second Heart Attack* and *Cholesterol DOWN*. DrJanet.com

Is your blood pressure on the high side? Your doctor might write a prescription when it creeps above 140/90—but you may be able to forgo medication. Lifestyle changes still are considered the best starting treatment for mild hypertension. These include not smoking, regular exercise and a healthy diet. *In addition to eating less salt, you want to include potent pressure-lowering foods, including…*

RAISINS

Raisins are basically dehydrated grapes, but they provide a much more concentrated dose of nutrients and fiber. They are high in potassium, with 220 milligrams (mg) in a small box (1.5 ounces). Potassium helps counteract the blood pressure–raising effects of salt. The more potassium we consume, the more sodium our bodies excrete. Researchers also speculate that the fiber and antioxidants in raisins change the biochemistry of blood vessels, making them more pliable—important for healthy blood pressure. Opt for dark raisins over light-colored ones because dark raisins have more catechins, a powerful type of antioxidant that can increase blood flow.

Researchers at Louisville Metabolic and Atherosclerosis Research Center compared people who snacked on raisins with those who ate other packaged snacks. Those in the raisin group had drops in systolic pressure (the top number) ranging from 4.8 points (after four weeks) to 10.2 points (after 12 weeks). Blood pressure barely budged in the no-raisin group. Some people worry about the sugar in raisins, but it is natural sugar (not added sugar) and will not adversely affect your health (though people with diabetes need to be cautious with portion sizes).

My advice: Aim to consume a few ounces of raisins every day. Prunes are an alternative.

BEETS

Beets, too, are high in potassium, with about 519 mg per cup. They're delicious, easy to cook (see the tasty recipe below) and very effective for lowering blood pressure.

A study at The London Medical School found that people who drank about eight ounces of beet juice averaged a 10-point drop in blood pressure during the next 24 hours. The blood pressure–lowering effect was most pronounced at three to six hours past drinking but remained lower for the entire 24 hours. Eating whole beets might be even better because you will get extra fiber.

Along with fiber and potassium, beets also are high in nitrate. The nitrate is converted first to nitrite in the blood, then to nitric oxide. Nitric oxide is a gas that relaxes blood vessel walls and lowers blood pressure.

My advice: Eat beets several times a week. Look for beets that are dark red. They contain more protective phytochemicals than the gold or white beets. Cooked spinach and kale are alternatives.

DAIRY

In research involving nearly 45,000 people, researchers found that those who consumed low-fat "fluid" dairy foods, such as yogurt and low-fat milk, were 16% less likely to develop high blood pressure. Higher-fat forms of dairy, such as cheese and ice cream, had no blood pressure benefits. The study was published in *Journal of Human Hypertension*.

In another study, published in *The New England Journal of Medicine*, researchers found that people who included low-fat or fat-free dairy in a diet high in fruits and vegetables had double the blood pressure–lowering benefits of those who just ate the fruits and veggies.

Low-fat dairy is high in calcium, another blood pressure–lowering mineral that should be included in your diet. When you don't have enough calcium in your diet, a "calcium leak" occurs in your kidneys. This means that the kidneys excrete more calcium in the urine, disturbing the balance of mineral metabolism involved in blood pressure regulation.

My advice: Aim for at least one serving of low-fat or nonfat milk or yogurt every day. If you don't care for cow's milk or can't drink it, switch to fortified soy milk. It has just as much calcium and protein and also contains phytoestrogens, compounds that are good for the heart.

FLAXSEED

Flaxseed contains alpha-linolenic acid (ALA), an omega-3 fatty acid that helps prevent heart and vascular disease. Flaxseed also contains magnesium. A shortage of magnesium in our diet throws off the balance of sodium, potassium and calcium, which causes the blood vessels to constrict.

Flaxseed also is high in flavonoids, the same antioxidants that have boosted the popularity of dark chocolate, kale and red wine. Flavonoids are bioactive chemicals that reduce inflammation throughout the body, including in the arteries. Arterial inflammation is thought to be the "trigger" that leads to high blood pressure, blood clots and heart attacks.

In a large-scale observational study linking dietary magnesium intake with better heart health and longevity, nearly 59,000 healthy Japanese people were followed for 15 years. The scientists found that the people with the highest dietary intake of magnesium had a 50% reduced risk for death from heart disease (heart attack and stroke). According to the researchers, magnesium's heart-healthy benefit is linked to its ability to improve blood pressure, suppress irregular heartbeats and inhibit inflammation.

My advice: Add one or two tablespoons of ground flaxseed to breakfast cereals. You also can sprinkle flaxseed on yogurt or whip it into a breakfast smoothie. Or try chia seeds.

WALNUTS

Yale researchers found that people who ate two ounces of walnuts a day had improved blood flow and drops in blood pressure (a 3.5-point drop in systolic blood pressure and a 2.8-point drop in diastolic blood pressure). The mechanisms through which walnuts elicit a blood pressure–lowering response are believed to involve their high content of monounsaturated fatty acids, omega-3 ALA, magnesium and fiber, and their low levels of sodium and saturated fatty acids.

Bonus: Despite the reputation of nuts as a "fat snack," the people who ate them didn't gain weight.

The magnesium in walnuts is particularly important. It limits the amount of calcium that enters muscle cells inside artery walls. Ingesting the right amount of calcium (not too much and not too little) on a daily basis is essential for optimal blood pressure regulation. Magnesium regulates calcium's movement across the membranes of the smooth muscle cells, deep within the artery walls.

If your body doesn't have enough magnesium, too much calcium will enter the smooth muscle cells, which causes the arterial muscles to tighten, putting a squeeze on the arteries and raising blood pressure. Magnesium works like the popular calcium channel blockers, drugs that block entry of calcium into arterial walls, lowering blood pressure.

My advice: Eat two ounces of walnuts every day. Or choose other nuts such as almonds and pecans.

DR. JANET'S ROASTED RED BEETS
WITH LEMON VINAIGRETTE

Beets are a delicious side dish when roasted, peeled and topped with a lemony vinaigrette and fresh parsley. This recipe is from my book Prevent a Second Heart Attack.

6 medium-sized beets, washed and trimmed of greens and roots

2 Tablespoons extra-virgin olive oil

2 teaspoons fresh lemon juice

1 garlic clove, peeled and minced

1 teaspoon Dijon mustard

¼ teaspoon kosher salt

¼ teaspoon freshly ground black pepper

¼ cup chopped fresh flat-leaf Italian parsley

Preheat the oven to 400°F. Spray a baking dish with nonstick cooking spray. Place the beets in the dish, and cover tightly with foil. Bake the beets for about one hour or until they are tender when pierced with a fork or thin knife. Remove from the oven, and allow to cool to the touch.

Meanwhile, in a small bowl, whisk together the olive oil, lemon juice, garlic, mustard, salt and pepper for the dressing. When the beets are cool enough to handle, peel and slice the beets, arranging the slices on a platter. Drizzle with vinaigrette, and garnish with parsley. Serves six.

Shake It Up, Baby: How to Vibrate Your Way to Lower Blood Pressure

Study titled, "Whole-body vibration exercise training reduces arterial stiffness in postmenopausal women with prehypertension and hypertension" by Arturo Figueroa, MD, PhD, associate professor of vascular exercise physiology at Florida State University, Tallahassee, and colleagues, published in *Menopause.*

"Jiggle" machines to lose weight—those belts that vibrate around your middle while you just stand there—go back to the 19th century.

News flash: They don't work too well…for weight loss, that is. The best that can be said is that they may help with weight loss…if you also cut calories. Thanks a lot.

But a new generation of "whole-body vibration" (WBV) machines is showing up in some gyms, in physical therapy clinics and even as home fitness equipment. What gives? It turns out that new research is uncovering other health benefits. They help build muscle, and there is some evidence that they may help build bone, too.

The latest benefit—lowering elevated blood pressure.

KEEPING YOUR ARTERIES FLEXIBLE

Three 30-to-40-minute sessions a week with WBV can bring down blood pressure by an average of 12 mmHg systolic and 6 mmHg diastolic over a three-month period.

That's enough to bring you down an entire blood pressure category. That is, if you are "prehypertensive" (aka "borderline"), with a reading between 120/80 and 139/89, WBV treatment could bring you into the "normal" category—below 120/80. If you are hypertensive, with a reading of 140/90 or higher, you could drop down to prehypertensive—and you might no longer require medication.

How does jiggling work therapeutically? WBV has been shown to make the arteries more flexible—less stiff. Arterial stiffness is a process in which the arteries lose their elasticity. A stiffer artery makes the heart work harder, raising blood pressure and cardiovascular risk. WBV may make arteries—including the peripheral ones that go throughout the body—more flexible by improving the functioning of their lining cells (the endothelium) and by stimulating production of nitric oxide, which helps arteries contract and dilate more efficiently.

READY TO RUMBLE?

To put this research into perspective, remember that regular exercise also reliably lowers high blood pressure, although not as dramatically. Exercise with WBV is no substitute for aerobic exercise and strength training, which have many more benefits for the body and the mind than can be expected from WBV. Indeed, these machines often are used in physical therapy clinics for people who can't do conventional exercise, such as someone recovering from a stroke or with severe arthritis.

Want to add WBV to your exercise routine? First, if you're being treated for hypertension or other ailments, get an OK from your doctor—and don't stop taking any medications without his or her approval. Next, try out one of these machines at a gym or physical therapy clinic that has one—especially before sinking hundreds or thousands of dollars into buying one for home use.

Be aware of possible side effects. As with any exercise, you can experience fatigue and muscle soreness. You may also experience skin redness and itching during the initial sessions due to the increased blood flow to your legs. These are minor. Swelling (edema) in the legs also can happen, but it is rare—if you experience this, tell your doctor.

The most important advice: Whether you use a WBV machine at a gym or get one for home use, you'll get the most benefit if you first get trained by someone who knows how to work with WBV, such as an exercise physiologist. In fact, gyms that have these machines often stick them in an out-of-the-way room because no one knows how to use them properly. There are many personal trainers who are not prepared to provide advice for WBV training. Physical therapists use them with patients who wear shoes during the vibration exercise. That dampens the beneficial effects, negating some of the benefits. There are other subtleties such as how to bend your knees to get the best

benefit, but they're easy to learn from a trained instructor the first time you use one of these machines.

Breakthrough Cancer Treatment: A Radical Approach That's Saving Lives

Louis Weiner, MD, director, Lombardi Comprehensive Cancer Center, Georgetown University, Washington, DC. He is an internationally recognized medical oncologist specializing in the treatment of gastrointestinal cancers. His lab researches novel immunotherapy treatments.

It seems like every week there's a promising new cancer treatment—that never happens. Too often we read about a new theoretical approach that saves lives in one or two studies...only to wait and wait for the treatment to materialize in the practice of cancer medicine. This time is different.

Now the powerful cancer-fighting drugs are not theoretical or another case of overhyping, overpromising and underdelivering. These medications really do work. This new way of fighting cancer uses the body's own immune system to wage war on cancer cells. Many leading cancer experts believe this approach, known as cancer immunotherapy, could revolutionize how we treat many forms of cancer.

When it comes to certain cancers, the revolution has already begun. In fact, former President Jimmy Carter is now said to be "cancer free" (based on MRI scans) after using one of these drugs for the melanoma that spread to his brain.

The new treatments aren't about enhancing immunity in general. Instead, this is an intriguing approach that can prevent cancerous tumors from hijacking our own immune defenses—so that our amazing immune system can do its job.

6 THINGS YOU NEED TO KNOW

Here are the details on this latest form of cancer immunotherapy...

1. It treats the body's immune system so the immune system can fight the cancer. T cells are the immune system's main line of defense, but they're not always effective against cancer cells. In the 1990s, cancer researchers identified a class of molecules in the body that are known as immune checkpoints. These molecules keep T cells from attacking normal cells, but cancer cells can hijack them for their own purposes. Cancer cells employ immune "checkpoints" to turn off killer T cells that would otherwise recognize and destroy a cancer that was growing in a person's body. Drugs that block these checkpoints so T cells can do their job are game changers called immune checkpoint inhibitors.

2. It still has side effects, but early results suggest a less toxic experience. All of us would love to see a day when very toxic chemotherapy agents that cause hair loss, low blood counts, fatigue, etc., are no longer the backbone of therapy for cancer. With checkpoint inhibitors, there will potentially be fewer side effects and certainly different ones. So far, the most common side effects caused by checkpoint inhibitors already in use include fatigue, cough, nausea, skin rash and itching. But more serious side effects including severe diarrhea, colitis and intestinal inflammation (even perforation) have also been reported.

3. It can be very effective and long-lasting. Consider the effects of checkpoint inhibitors against end-stage Hodgkin's disease, where patients had already received every imaginable therapy and were running out of hope. More than 90% of these patients went into remissions, many of them complete. When checkpoint inhibitors are combined against metastatic melanoma—the most deadly form of skin cancer—more than half of those cancers are eliminated or controlled, with benefits that have lasted for many years in some cases.

4. It works against many forms of cancer. In a viewpoint recently published in *JAMA*, James Allison, PhD, who pioneered the use of immune checkpoint inhibitors against cancer, wrote: "The therapy does not target the tumor cell but rather engages a target on the patient's immune system. Thus, there is no inherent reason that it would not be successful against a wide variety of tumors."

At this time, checkpoint inhibitors are FDA approved for treating only certain types of melanoma and lung cancer. But studies show that they also work against no fewer than 20 different cancers, including certain forms of kidney cancer, triple negative breast cancer, stomach cancer, Hodgkin's disease, bladder cancer and head and neck cancer.

5. It is very expensive. It can cost tens of thousands of dollars or more to have a course of therapy with these drugs, especially if you start combining them with other expensive cancer therapies.

6. It is still evolving. One promising innovation in cancer immunotherapy that is currently being researched is chimeric antigen receptor (CAR) T-cell therapy. In this case, a patient's T cells are genetically engineered to produce antibodies against a specific type of cancer. When these T cells proliferate, they pass their cancer-killing modifications along.

So far, this experimental treatment has had outstanding results against a hard-to-treat and deadly form of leukemia called acute lymphocytic leukemia.

WHAT'S AVAILABLE NOW

While many checkpoint inhibitors are in development, currently only three have been approved by the FDA…

● **Opdivo** (*nivolumab*) and **Keytruda** (*pembrolizumab*) are approved for advanced-stage non-small cell lung cancer that has spread and that is not responding to conventional platinum-based chemotherapy…and for advanced melanoma.

● **Yervoy** (*ipilimumab*) is approved for melanoma that has spread within the body (metastasized) or that cannot be removed by surgery.

Until new drugs for different cancers make it through the FDA approval process—or the existing approved ones get future approvals for different cancers—these are the only three of this type of cancer treatment that insurance companies or Medicare are likely to cover. If you have the financial wherewithal, you may be able to have your doctor prescribe the approved drugs off-label and pay for them yourself.

For everyone else, however, there is another potential option. If there is an immunotherapy cancer drug in development for a cancer that you are being treated for, ask your oncologist whether there is a clinical trial that you can join. You can also check the website ClinicalTrials.gov.

4 Secret Cancer Fighters

The late Mitchell Gaynor, MD, founder and president of Gaynor Integrative Oncology in New York City and board-certified oncologist, internist and hematologist. He is also former clinical assistant professor of medicine at Weill Cornell Medical College and author of *The Gene Therapy Plan: Taking Control of Your Genetic Destiny with Diet and Lifestyle.*

My mother died of cancer at age 43, when I was nine years old. But I know I'm not a slave to my genetic destiny, doomed by DNA to die of the same disease. I know that I can do something about my cancer-prone genetic inheritance—and so can you.

The new science of epigenetics shows that it is possible to "upregulate" (trigger) the "expression" (activity) of powerful anticancer genes using a whole-foods diet, regular exercise, restful sleep, stress reduction—and concentrated nutritional and herbal compounds.

These natural compounds can activate genes that tell the body to turbocharge the immune system so that it can locate cancer cells...kill those cells...douse chronic, low-grade inflammation, which generates "growth factors" that fuel cancer...decrease the liver's production of insulin-like growth factor one (IGF), the most deadly "tumor promoter"...reduce a tumor's cancer-spreading blood supply...and even improve the effectiveness of chemotherapy.

In addition to taking vitamin D daily, I recommend these four powerful anticancer supplements for preventing or controlling cancer or stopping its recurrence. Take one, two or all four. At the dosages recommended, they are very safe. Of course, always check with your doctor before taking any new supplement.

MAGNOLIA EXTRACT

This herbal supplement from the bark of a magnolia tree contains honokiol, which has anticancer functions—it is anti-inflammatory and anti-angiogenic (limiting blood supply to tumors), and it targets many biochemical compounds that "signal" cancer to start and to grow, such as nuclear factor-kappaB and epidermal growth factor receptor.

Scientific research: More than 200 studies show that honokiol (and magnolol, another compound in magnolia bark) can fight cancer. In a recent cellular study, published in *International Journal of Oncology*, honokiol activated a gene that "suppressed" the spread of kidney cancer and deactivated two genes that allow kidney cancer cells to invade and colonize the surrounding tissue (metastasize).

Typical dosage: 200 mg, daily.

Suggested product: Magnolia Extract from NutriCology. (I have no financial interest in this or any other product or brand that I recommend.)

ARTICHOKE EXTRACT

This extract from artichoke leaves contains rutin, quercetin, gallic acid and chlorogenic acid—all of which have been shown in laboratory studies to kill a variety of cancer cells, including colon, breast and liver cancers, and leukemia. Artichoke extract also contains cynarin, which decreases inflammation. Plus, the extract has been shown in people to improve insulin sensitivity, the body's ability to utilize the glucose-regulating hormone insulin. When insulin is used efficiently, the body makes less insulin—and less cancer-sparking IGF. Recent study: A cellular study published in *Asian Pacific Journal of Cancer Prevention* showed that artichoke extract triggered tumor suppressor genes.

Typical dosage: 320 milligrams (mg), once daily.

Suggested product: Artichoke Extract from Enzymatic Therapy.

BLACK CUMIN SEED OIL

Many years ago, a patient of mine with prostate cancer started taking black cumin seed oil (Nigella sativa) with honey, three times a day, on the recommendation of a naturopathic physician. His Gleason score (a measure of the severity of prostate cancer) went from nine on a scale of one to 10 (an aggressive, invasive cancer with poor prognosis) to six—essentially, a precancerous lesion. Amazed, I started investigating this compound, which has been used in Turkish cooking for millennia—and started taking it myself, adding the seed to blended shakes and the oil to foods as seasoning. I recommend that patients use the oil—rich in thymoquinone, which is found in few other foods—either in their diets or as a supplement.

Compelling research: Researchers at Barbara Ann Karmanos Cancer Institute at Wayne State University School of Medicine in Detroit reviewed hundreds of cellular and animal studies on thymoquinone and cancer and concluded that the compound is anti-inflammatory…stops cancer cells from dividing and spreading by triggering their death…limits the formation of blood vessels that nourish the tumor (angiogenesis)…and "sensitizes" cells to chemotherapy.

Example: In a recent animal study, published in *Archives of Medical Science*, researchers found that thymoquinone "decreased the expression" of both BRCA1 and BRCA2 genes—genes that increase the risk for breast cancer three- to five-fold and the risk for ovarian cancer as much as 30-fold.

Typical dosage: 500 mg, twice daily.

Suggested product: Black Seed Oil from Amazing Herbs.

BEE PROPOLIS, BEE POLLEN AND ROYAL JELLY

Bee propolis (a waxlike material used by bees to repair holes in hives) is rich in caffeic acid phenethyl ester (CAPE), chrysin and cinnamic acid, compounds that affect cancer genes. Studies show they are immune-strengthening, anti-inflammatory and anti-angiogenic and can reduce the growth of many cancers, including colon, prostate and kidney. Bee propolis also has been used clinically to reduce mouth sores caused by chemotherapy and radiation.

Recent study: In a cellular study on prostate cancer from the University of Texas Medical Branch, researchers found that CAPE boosted the cancer-killing power of chemotherapeutic drugs.

Another cellular study shows that bee pollen can inhibit vascular endothelial growth factor (VEGF), which helps create blood supply to tumors.

Royal jelly (a milky secretion produced by worker bees) contains several epigenetic factors. It has been shown to suppress the blood supply to tumors.

Typical dosage: 500 mg, once daily.

Suggested product: Triple Bee Complex from Y.S. Organic Bee Farms, which contains bee propolis, bee pollen and royal jelly.

Caution: People who are allergic to bee stings should not take bee products.

ANTICANCER SMOOTHIE

This drink is rich in anticancer compounds. Examples: The sulforaphane from broccoli promotes the activation of "tumor suppressor" genes. The quercetin from apples inhibits tyrosine kinase, an enzyme associated with cancer. The lauric acid from coconut milk is linked to a low risk for breast cancer. And the curcumin from turmeric keeps cancer cells from replicating. Drink it daily. *Ingredients…*

½ cup coconut water
¼ cup broccoli
1 peeled cucumber
¼ cup watercress
1 apple, cored with peel
1 Tablespoon coconut milk powder
⅛ teaspoon ground turmeric

Blend one minute on medium. Pour through a strainer.

When to Try "Keyhole" Surgery

David F. Jimenez, MD, FACS, chairman and professor in the department of neurosurgery at The University of Texas Health Science Center at San Antonio. He is the editor and a coauthor of *Intracranial Endoscopic Neurosurgery,* a textbook published by the American Association of Neurological Surgeons.

No one likes the thought of undergoing brain or spine surgery. Traditionally, a neurosurgeon would create a four- to six-inch incision and peel back the scalp before drilling through the skull to expose the brain...or make a similar-sized incision in your back, where muscles are then moved to expose the spine.

Recent development: Endoscopic, or minimally invasive, surgery, which has long been offered for such common procedures as gallbladder removal and knee surgery, is now widely available at major US medical centers for neurosurgical operations that involve the brain, spine and peripheral nerves.

Whether it's the removal of a brain tumor or the repair of herniated disks, spinal stenosis or carpal tunnel syndrome, neurosurgeons can now use sophisticated instruments to operate through an incision that's smaller than a dime or even through a natural opening such as a nostril.

This approach allows for a faster recovery and less pain and swelling than the traditional "open" procedures. Older patients frequently respond better to surgery that has minimal blood loss and requires less time under general anesthesia.

Why this matters: Even though endoscopic (sometimes known as "keyhole") neurosurgery is now available, not all surgeons have the training and experience to perform it. This means that you may not be offered endoscopic neurosurgery when it would be a better option than a traditional procedure—or a surgeon may attempt the endoscopic operation without adequate training and/or experience. *What you need to know…*

A NEW GENERATION OF NEUROSURGERY

What makes most types of surgery so challenging has less to do with repairing a problem—whether it's replacing a joint or removing an appendix—than simply getting access to the specific body part.

With endoscopic neurosurgery of the brain, the surgeon makes one or two incisions ranging from one-third to three-quarters of an inch and drills into the skull. A tube (endoscope) is passed through the narrow opening. Everything that's needed to complete the procedure, such as a lighted camera and cutting and scraping tools, is guided into place through the endoscope. Surgeons enter through the nostrils or above the eyebrow to oper-

ate on pituitary adenomas and tumors in the front of the brain.

The benefits of endoscopic surgery are largely due to the smaller incision, which is obviously less painful than a large one and has less risk for infection. Since there is less blood loss, there is less need for blood transfusion—another benefit.

Because endoscopic procedures can usually be done faster than traditional surgeries, patients also spend less time under general anesthesia, which reduces postoperative complications, such as cognitive dysfunction and nausea, and improves recovery.

In my practice, at least 30% of brain surgeries (including treatment for hydrocephalus—buildup of fluid in the brain that is drained via a shunt… and removal of skull-base tumors) are minimally invasive. Deep areas of the brain cannot be accessed with endoscopic neurosurgery. Most of our spine surgeries and virtually all carpal tunnel procedures are done this way.

Examples of when endoscopic neurosurgery can be used…

•**Herniated disk.** Computerized image guidance creates a three-dimensional image of the spine so surgeons can achieve a superb view of the operating field with an endoscopic incision that's barely more than a half-inch long. They use microinstruments to remove the damaged part of the disk.

•**Spinal stenosis.** This narrowing inside the spinal canal (usually due to arthritis) often causes leg pain or other symptoms. It's relatively easy to "open up" the spinal space with endoscopic surgery. Patients often make a full recovery within a month—and may be symptom-free almost immediately—while traditional surgery usually requires a recovery period of at least three months.

IS IT FOR EVERYONE?

In general, endoscopic surgery is a good option for most patients, especially those who are too old, ill or frail to have traditional surgeries.

One patient's story: My oldest patient was a 96-year-old woman whose spinal stenosis was so bad she could barely walk. She might not have done well with a lengthy open procedure, but I knew that I could complete the operation in about 90 minutes—half the usual time. Her pain was gone almost instantly—and a month later, she was bowling and dancing with her boyfriend.

The complication rate (infections and/or bleeding) for endoscopic surgery is at least as good as—and sometimes better than—that of traditional procedures. The numbers will only get better as surgeons gain experience and new approaches and technologies are developed.

FIND THE RIGHT SURGEON

Before agreeing to any type of neurosurgery, ask the surgeon whether the procedure will be open or minimally invasive. While some operations, such as certain brain tumors, still require a traditional approach, most do not.

Chances are that you'll recover much more quickly—and experience less postoperative pain—if you go with endoscopy. If your surgeon doesn't do endoscopic surgery, get a second opinion. You can find a surgeon at the American Association of Neurological Surgeons, AANS.org.

Experience and training are crucial for surgeons who perform endoscopic surgeries. Compared with traditional operations, endoscopic surgeries require the surgeon to overcome such issues as poor depth perception (from the endoscopic camera) and limited range of motion to manipulate surgical instruments. Make sure your surgeon has several years of experience in performing the procedure you'll be getting and has received endoscopic neurosurgical training.

Turbocharge the Shingles Vaccine—With Tai Chi

Michael R. Irwin, MD, professor of psychiatry and biobehavioral sciences, David Geffen School of Medicine at UCLA. Reprinted from *Speed Healing* by Bill Gottlieb (Bottom Line Books).

Tai chi—a meditative, relaxing, slow-moving martial art from China—may help an older immune system defend itself against shingles.

Recent study: Led by Michael R. Irwin, MD, researchers at the University of California in Los Angeles and UC-San Diego studied 112 people (ages 59 to 86; average age, 70), dividing them into two groups. One group took 40-minute tai chi classes, three times a week. The other group spent those 40 minutes attending educational classes about health. After four months, both groups received an injection of the chickenpox vaccine. (The shingles vaccine was not available when this study was conducted.)

A sign of the effectiveness of the vaccine is "cell-mediated immunity" (CMI)—a measurement of the immune system's specific activation against the virus: in this case against the varicella zoster virus (VZV) that causes both shingles and chickenpox. At the start of the study, the two groups' CMI to VZV were the same. But within 10 weeks of receiving the vaccine, the Tai Chi group had developed twice the CMI to VZV as the education group—and the same level typically seen in 30- to 40-year-olds who receive the vaccine!

Perhaps even more remarkable, the Tai Chi group had a level of CMI to VZV about 40% higher than typically produced by the vaccine alone. (They also had more vitality, more mental clarity, better physical functioning and fewer aches and pains than the education group.)

"Dr. Irwin's research team has demonstrated that a centuries-old behavioral intervention, Tai Chi, resulted in a level of immune response similar to that of a modern biological intervention, the varicella vaccine, and that Tai Chi boosted the positive effects of the vaccine," says Andrew Monjan, PhD, of the government's National Institute of Aging, which funded the study.

Why it works: "There are several ways Tai Chi may affect immunity and health, including relaxation and exercise, both of which have been shown to strengthen the immune system" says Dr. Irwin.

Good news: "These are also exciting findings because the positive results of the study have implications for other infectious diseases," says Dr. Irwin. "Since older adults often show blunted protective responses to vaccines, this study suggests that Tai Chi is an approach that might complement and augment the efficacy of other vaccines, such as influenza vaccines."

Recommendation: Dr. Irwin recommends receiving personal instruction in Tai Chi rather than learning from a DVD. "In our study, the Tai Chi instructor spent a lot of time observing and correcting technique. I think hands-on instruction is critical in gaining the full benefit."

You can find lists of Tai Chi schools and instructors at the website TheTaiChiSite.com. Tai Chi courses are often taught at the local YMCA.

Laugh Your Way to Better Health

Katherine Puckett, PhD, is the national director of mind-body medicine at the Cancer Treatment Centers of America facility at Midwestern Regional Medical Center in Zion, Illinois. She is a licensed clinical social worker and certified laughter leader.

Have you ever laughed and then said, "Thanks, I needed that"? You were so right—because the very act of laughing promotes good health in numerous ways. And in fact, you can maximize these health benefits for yourself by doing fun and simple "laughter exercises."

Want evidence of how laughter helps? Consider a study at Loma Linda University, which involved diabetic patients who had high cholesterol and high blood pressure. One group of participants received standard pharmaceutical treatment for these conditions…a second group received the same medications but also were instructed to "view self-selected humor" (for instance, watch sitcoms or videos that they considered funny) for 30 minutes daily. After one year: In the laughter group, HDL (good) cholesterol increased by 26% and blood levels of C-reactive protein (a marker of inflammation) decreased by 66%, on average…in the other group, HDL increased by just 3% and C-reactive protein declined by just 26%, on average.

Additional research from Loma Linda University suggests that laughter also can boost immunity…relax tense muscles…reduce levels of stress

hormones…and raise levels of mood-elevating hormones called endorphins (the same hormones released during orgasm!).

It is easy to bring more laughter to your life. "The average adult laughs 17 times daily. Keep track for a few days—and if you're not laughing at least that often, make a conscious effort to increase your opportunities to laugh," suggested Katherine Puckett, PhD, national director of mind-body medicine at the Cancer Treatment Centers of America facility in Zion, Illinois, who has extensive experience applying therapeutic laughter. "Since we laugh most frequently during social interactions with others, spend time with people who enjoy laughing and being playful. Also try watching children and pets playing…enjoying funny videos…deliberately smiling more often (it's contagious!)…and observing the world through a 'comic lens' as you look for humor around you even in difficult situations."

Another option is to consciously do laughter exercises with friends, family or coworkers. If you feel self-conscious at first, remind yourselves that you're laughing with each other, not at each other, and that your intention is to have good-natured fun. "At first, the laughter is simulated—but in short order, it becomes real," Dr. Puckett said. *As often as you like, try…*

●**Laughter chant.** As you clap in rhythm, repeatedly say, "Ho-ho ha-ha-ha, ho-ho ha-ha-ha."

●**Roller coaster.** Lift your arms, sway, jiggle and scream as if you were on a coaster. (This is easiest while seated.)

●**Snowball fight.** Lean over and scoop up some imaginary snow, pack it into a snowball and throw it at another person. Everyone naturally laughs while throwing or being "hit." Try putting some pretend snow down someone's back, which may make you both laugh even harder.

●**Sing with laughter.** Even if no one is having a birthday, sing Happy Birthday to You to each other, substituting "hee hee" or "ha ha" or "ho ho" for each word. You can swap this laughter vocabulary for the words in many songs—and before you even finish singing, you'll be feeling happier and more energized.

Sunlight Boosts Immunity

Gerard Ahern, PhD, is associate professor in the department of pharmacology and physiology at Georgetown University, Washington, DC.

Sunlight boosts immunity by energizing infection-fighting T cells. The blue light found in the rays of the sun makes T cells move faster, so they get to the site of an infection and begin their protective activity more quickly. Thus, short sun exposure can be beneficial.

Strong Hands, Long Life?

Elaine LaLanne, wife of the late Jack LaLanne, is the author or coauthor of numerous books on exercise and health, including the classic *Fitness After 50 Workout.* JackLalanne.com

Can our ability to open a jar of pickles or wring out a washcloth give us a greater chance of living longer? That's an implication of recent research published in *British Medical Journal* (*BMJ*).

Scientists in the UK analyzed data on more than 53,000 people from 14 separate studies, ranking them into four groups based on the strength of their grips.

Findings: Compared with the group that had the strongest hands, those with the weakest grips were 67% more likely to die during the study periods (which ranged from less than five years to more than 20 years). The link between grip strength and longevity was seen not only among seniors, but also in studies in which participants were younger than 60 years old, on average.

This research doesn't necessarily prove that strengthening our hands will prolong our lives—but it well might. Besides, strong hands certainly do make countless daily tasks easier.

When I went looking for grip-building exercises to share with readers, I found a hand workout developed by Jack LaLanne, often called the "god-father of fitness," who recently passed away at age 96. I contacted his widow and coauthor, Elaine LaLanne, who told me, "Jack did hand exercises every single morning for strength, coordination, dexterity and flexibility."

Here's the LaLanne daily hand workout, which takes about 10 to 15 minutes. All exercises can be done standing or sitting. Why not try them for yourself? (As with any exercise program, get your doctor's OK before beginning. These particular hand exercises may not be appropriate for people with certain medical conditions—for example, carpal tunnel syndrome.)

●**Big squeeze.** Use a rubber ball that fits easily into your palm. Grasp ball with all five fingers of right hand and squeeze as tightly as possible...hold for a count of three...release. Do 10 repetitions (reps), then switch hands. Work your way up to three sets.

●**Hand flexes.** Extend arms straight out in front of you at mid-chest height, palms up, fingers spread. Quickly clench hands into fists, then open again. Do 10 reps as rapidly as possible...then repeat with palms facing down. Work up to three sets.

●**Shake-a-hand.** Hold hands out in front of you and shake them, moving arms all around in whatever manner you like. Continue for one minute... work up to two minutes.

●**Newspaper roll.** Unfold a section of newspaper (try four full sheets to start—if that proves too easy, use eight to 10 sheets). With both hands, grasp the newspaper at one end so that hands are shoulder-width apart. Elbows straight, extend arms in front of you at chest height, palms facing down. Begin rolling up the newspaper, twisting as if wringing out a towel...when you reach the end, reverse the motion to unroll newspaper. Work up to 10 sets.

●**Five to four.** Hold hands in front of you at shoulder height, elbows comfortably bent, palms facing forward, fingers spread wide (as if each hand were indicating the number five). Then bring thumbs across palms (as if indicating the number four)...then extend thumbs again. Do 10 reps at a moderately fast pace. Work up to three sets.

●**Knuckle sandwich.** Hold hands in front of you at shoulder height, elbows comfortably bent, palms facing forward, fingers together and pointing up. Without making a full fist or bending wrists, curl fingers until fingertips touch tops of palms…hold for a count of five…then uncurl fingers. Do 10 reps. Work up to three sets.

●**Spread 'em.** Place hands flat on a desktop or tabletop in front of you, fingers spread as wide as possible. Press down firmly for 10 seconds, then relax. Do three reps.

Electroacupuncture for Pain Relief and More

Stacy Drinkut Smith, LAc, Dipl OM (diplomate in Oriental medicine), licensed acupuncturist and herbalist specializing in women's health. She is a cofounder of Points of Health, aclinic in Santa Barbara, California. PointsOf Health.org

---

For pain relief, it may seem strange to combine an ancient healing practice with modern technology, but that is basically what electroacupuncture does in sending a small electric current into acupuncture needles. Electroacupuncture is similar to traditional acupuncture in that the same points and meridians (energy channels) are stimulated, but adding electrical current makes theneedle stimulation stronger and steadier.

Does electroacupuncture work better than manual acupuncture? It can, according to a study that directly compared the two techniques in patients with tennis elbow and found superior pain relief and grip strength in the electroacupuncture group. Experts don't agree on whether electroacupuncture helps with all the same conditions as regular acupuncture, but a surprising amount of research does support the effectiveness of the technique. *Electroacupuncturecan help…*

●**Relieve arthritis.** Patients with hip osteoarthritis had electroacupuncture or took a prescription pain reliever/anti-inflammatory (one that is commonly prescribed but has potentially serious side effects). There was significantly more improvement in joint pain, function and range of motion among electroacupuncture recipients than among medication recipients.

●**Improve blood flow.** With Raynaud's disease, fingers and toes feel cold and turn white or blue as blood vessels constrict…then throb, tingle and turn red when blood flow returns. Raynaud's patients reported significantly reduced discomfort and frequency of attacks after receiving a series of electroacupuncture sessions as compared with before their treatment.

●**Reduce postsurgical pain.** The day before heart surgery, patients received either electroacupuncture or a sham treatment…after surgery, the electroacupuncture group reported significantly lower pain intensity and required less pain medication than the other group.

●**Restore damaged nerves.** Patients with peripheral nerve damage and some loss of muscle function had poor prognoses…but after electroacupuncture, function improved or was recovered completely in the majority of participants.

In addition, there are studies supporting the use of electroacupuncture fortreating fertility problems and hormonal imbalances. And electroacupuncture works very well for various types of pain…recovery from joint replacement and other surgeries…menstrual cramps and irregularities…headaches…and stress. Electroacupuncture often is preferable to traditional acupuncture when treating chronic pain and other chronic conditions that involve lots of energy stagnation in the body.

Caution: Electroacupuncture should not be used on anyone who has a pacemaker because the electrical stimulation might disrupt the function of the device. Some practitioners opt not to use electroacupuncture on patients who have a seizure disorder.

WHAT TO EXPECT IN AN ELECTROACUPUNCTURE SESSION

During a treatment session, acupuncture needles first are placed in the target meridians and/or acupuncture points, just as in traditional acupuncture. Then electricity is added by attaching small clips (imagine miniature carbattery jumper cables) that connect a pair of needles to a small battery-operated generator.

With traditional acupuncture (not using electricity), the practitioner can boost stimulation at a particular acupuncture point by twirling or otherwise manipulating needles. With electroacupuncture, electricity provides the stimulation—called e-stim—and the acupuncturist controls its intensity by increasing or reducing the current.

The practitioner may use e-stim on a single pair of needles at a particular acupuncture point or on more than one pair at a time. We can do e-stim on oneside of the body and then switch to the other, but we don't do both sides atthe same time because crossing the midline would interfere with the stimulationeffect, jamming the patient's own signals.

What it feels like: Your acupuncturist should increase the current just to the point where you can feel mild tingling, and then dial it back a bit, so all you feel is an awareness of energy flow. If you perceive any numbness, knocking, thumping or discomfort,the acupuncturist should dial it back more.

Typically an electroacupuncture treatment session lasts about 30 minutes. The number of sessions required depends on the condition being treated, but generally an acupuncturist recommends a course of six and then does another evaluation. Sessions cost about $60 to $120—similar to or slightly more than traditional acupuncture. If your insurance covers regular acupuncture, it probably covers electroacupuncture, too, but check in advance just to be sure.

To find a licensed acupuncturist in your area, consult the American Association of Acupuncture & Oriental Medicine (call 866-455-7999 or visit AAAOMOnline.org and click on Patients and Find a Practitioner). Practitioners' AAAOM profiles may or may not specify the types of acupuncture they provide, but you can phone or check individuals' websites to find out whether they practice electroacupuncture.

It's 3 in the Morning and You're Awake…Again!

Michael Breus, PhD, a sleep specialist with a private practice in Los Angeles. Dr. Breus is also the author of *The Power of When: Discover Your Chronotype—and the Best Time to Eat Lunch, Ask for a Raise, Have Sex, Write a Novel, Take Your Meds, and More.* TheSleepDoctor.com

I n the world of sleep disorders, having difficulty staying asleep is just as troubling as having difficulty falling asleep.

Both sleep problems rob us of the consistent, high-quality rest that helps protect against high blood pressure, obesity, diabetes, stroke and depression.

Plenty of people who have nighttime awakenings turn to a prescription sleep aid, such as zolpidem (Ambien). But these pills are only a temporary fix and can cause prolonged drowsiness the next day or, in rare cases, sleepwalking or sleep-eating within hours of taking them.

A better option: Cognitive behavioral therapy for insomnia, known as CBT-I, is now recommended as a first-line treatment for chronic sleep problems.* With CBT-I, you work with a specially trained therapist (typically for six to eight sessions) to identify, challenge and change the patterns of thinking that keep you awake at night. A 2015 study found CBT-I, which is typically covered by health insurance, to be more helpful than *diazepam* (Valium), commonly used as a sleep aid, in treating insomnia.

But if you are not quite ready to commit to a course of CBT-I—or even if you do try it—there are some simple but effective strategies you can use at home to help you stay asleep and get the deep rest you need.

Best approaches to avoid nighttime awakenings…

•**Get more omega-3 fatty acids.** While the research is still preliminary, a new study published in Sleep Medicine found that the more omega-3–rich fatty fish adults ate, the better their sleep quality.

*To find a CBT-I therapist, consult the Society of Behavioral Sleep Medicine, BehavioralSleep.org. You can also try the free CBT-i Coach app, available at iTunes or Google Play.

My advice: Eat fatty fish…and to ensure adequate levels of omega-3s, consider taking a fish oil supplement (one to two 1,000-mg capsules daily).*

●**Avoid "blue light" at night.** Exposure to blue light—the kind emitted by smartphones, computers, tablets and LED TVs—disrupts sleep patterns by blocking the release of the sleep hormone melatonin. Even if you do fall asleep fairly easily, blue light exposure may come back to haunt you in the form of a middle-of-the-night wake-up.

If you can't force yourself to power down your electronics within two hours of bedtime, try positioning handheld devices farther away from your eyes than usual.

In addition, consider various apps that filter blue light on your smartphone or tablet. Some operating systems are automatically programmed with this feature—Apple's iOS 9.3 offers Night Shift, for example. Using your device's geolocation and clock, the colors of your display are automatically shifted to the warmer end of the spectrum (which is less disruptive to sleep) around sundown. Free apps for Android devices include Night Shift: Blue Light Filter and Twilight.

●**Use special lightbulbs.** If you wake up in the middle of the night and make a trip to the bathroom, the glare of the bathroom light tells your brain "It's morning!" What helps: Use low-blue lightbulbs in your bathroom and bedroom that don't block the release of melatonin. A variety are available from Lighting Science (LSGC.com). Or look online for night-lights designed to emit low levels of blue light.

IF YOU DO WAKE UP

Even if you follow the steps described above, you may still have occasional nighttime awakenings with trouble falling back asleep (meaning you are awake for at least 25 minutes).

Experiment with the following strategies to see what works best for you…

●**Resist the urge to check e-mail or do anything else on your phone.** Even short exposures to blue light are enough to suppress melatonin. Mentally stimulating activities, such as loud TV, are also best avoided. (However, a TV at low volume with the setting adjusted to dim the screen can be a great distractor for an active mind at night.)

My advice: Choose a relaxing activity like reading, listening to soothing music or knitting. If you read, use a book light or a bedside-table lamp that has one of the special bulbs mentioned earlier.

●**Don't look at the clock.** If you do, you'll start doing the mental math of how many hours you have left until you need to wake up. This will cause anxiety that will spike your levels of cortisol and adrenaline, sleep-disrupting hormones that make you feel wide awake!

My advice: Turn your clock around, and try counting backward from 300 by threes to distract yourself and promote drowsiness.

Also helpful: Try the "4-7-8 method"—inhale for four seconds…hold your breath for seven…and exhale slowly for eight. Breathe in this manner for up to 15 to 20 minutes or until you fall asleep. Inhaling and holding in air increases oxygen in the body, which means your body doesn't have to expend as much energy. The slow exhale helps you unwind and mimics the slow breathing that takes place during sleep, which will help you fall asleep.

●**Turn on some pink noise.** The well-known "white noise"—used to mask conversations and potentially startling sounds—is comprised of all frequencies detectable by the human ear. Pink noise, on the other hand, has a lower, softer frequency. Pink noise is generally considered more relaxing and has a steady sound like gentle rain.

Sleep experts believe that our brains respond better to the lower spectrum of pink noise than to the fuller spectrum of white noise. The result is a more peaceful and sleep-conducive feeling.

My advice: Search for a free app that contains pink noise, and listen to it with earphones on your smartphone, laptop or tablet if you wake up in the middle of the night. Just be sure to glance only briefly at the screen when turning on the device, and turn off the screen light while listening. You can set the pink noise to play for a set amount of time, such as 30 minutes. As an alternative, you can purchase a pink-noise generator online.

7 Keys to Happiness Later in Life

How to Stay Together Forever

Terri L. Orbuch, PhD, a psychologist and research professor at the University of Michigan Institute for Social Research, Ann Arbor. She is author of *Finding Love Again: 6 Simple Steps to a New and Happy Relationship*. DrTerriTheLoveDoctor.com

I f you want your marriage to succeed, it pays to know why other marriages fail. I have tracked 373 married couples for the past 26 years as part of a study funded by the National Institutes of Health. The goal was to investigate how marriages really work over the long term—but many marriages don't work, at least not forever. Of those 373 couples, 46% have divorced, roughly in line with national averages.

What went wrong in those failed marriages? And what would those divorced people do differently if they could start over again? When I put those questions to my study participants, key trends emerged.

Surprising: Sex was not a major issue when it came to what divorced people said they would "change" if they could start over again. And it wasn't a key predictor of divorce over time in my study.

EXPAND CONVERSATIONS

Divorced people typically report that a lack of communication wasn't the problem in their relation-ships—they spoke with their spouses often during their marriages. But when these divorced people considered the content of their conversations, many admitted that the vast majority were about the business of the household—what chores needed to get done, what time they would be returning home from work, whether they were running low on peanut butter. Such conversations are necessary in a marriage, but they do little to make couples feel close.

What to do: Discuss your goals and dreams regularly with your partner, and encourage your partner to do the same with you. Do this even if you've been married for years and already know quite well what your spouse wants out of life. Even if very little new information is supplied, having these conversations increases the odds that you and your spouse will continue to see each other as partners in your pursuit of your goals and dreams.

On days when you don't chat about big things such as goals and dreams, at least have conversations about topics you both enjoy talking about. These might include books, movies or current events—anything you both appreciate that's unrelated to your responsibilities and your marriage.

EXPRESS YOUR LOVE DAILY

Many of the divorced people in my study admitted that their partners often got pushed to the back burner when life became busy. Their spouses wound up feeling taken for granted—a feeling that can lead to divorce when it is allowed to persist.

What to do: Make a gesture that shows your love and makes your spouse feel special every day. These gestures can be quite simple. Take your spouse's hand and say, "I love you," or "Thank you for being a great husband/wife." Provide a kiss or hug at an unexpected moment. Or do a little thing that makes your spouse's life easier without being asked, such as bringing in the newspaper or starting the coffee in the morning. It isn't the size of the gestures that prevents spouses from feeling taken for granted. It's the consistency with which these gestures are made—once a day at a minimum.

Warning: Some people believe that wives care more about receiving gestures of love than husbands. In fact, divorce is particularly likely when husbands fail to receive these gestures. This probably is because married women tend to receive gestures of love from their friends and relations in addition to their husbands. Husbands typically receive them only from their wives, so they miss them even more when their wives don't provide them.

TALK MORE ABOUT MONEY

Many married couples don't talk about money any more than necessary. Finances are the number-one source of conflict in marriage, so avoiding this topic can seem like a good way to avoid stirring up trouble. But my research shows that talking less about money actually increases the odds of divorce. True, talks about money can trigger spats—but couples who avoid money talks increase the risk that their money issues will remain unresolved and escalate until they endanger the marriage.

Example: If a relationship's lines of communication about finances are closed, one partner might spend freely, not realizing that the other is becoming angrier and angrier about the couple's inability to save for retirement.

What to do: First, consider what money means to you. Does it represent security? Status? Love? Success as a provider? Think about how your parents handled finances, too, and whether that might be affecting your financial beliefs and be-

havior. Also, reflect upon your financial goals and priorities.

Next, have a few chats with your spouse about noninflammatory money-related topics, such as money you've managed to save or upcoming expenses that you both agree upon. Mixing in some low-stress money talks can prevent anxiety levels from skyrocketing every time money is mentioned.

After you've had a few painless money conversations, share your financial goals and priorities with your spouse, as well as any thoughts you have about what money means to you. Ask your partner to do the same, then try to find common ground with your spouse about family spending rules and limits.

Example: Agree to consult with each other on all purchases over a certain dollar amount.

BLAME "US" FOR PROBLEMS

When one or both spouses chronically blame the other for the marriage's problems, the result tends to be escalating anger. When one or both spouses chronically blame himself or herself for the marriage's problems, the result tends to be feelings of guilt or depression. In either case, the odds of divorce increase.

What to do: When you have a fight, try to blame the relationship or circumstances, not your spouse or yourself. Say things such as, "We were both tired when we said those things"…or "We just weren't communicating well."

Also, people who already have divorced should take care to not blame their former spouses or themselves for the failure of that marriage. Use phrases that absolve you both such as, "We married too young"…or "We just weren't compatible." Divorced people who persist in blaming their exes or themselves are more likely to struggle in future relationships as well.

DON'T LET BOREDOM LINGER

All long-term relationships go through ruts when nothing new happens. If those ruts are allowed to persist for years, the result can be boredom—and boredom increases the odds of divorce.

What to do: Inject passion and excitement into your marriage. *Three potential ways to do that…*

• **Add a new shared activity.** Take a new class together or travel together to an unfamiliar location. Doing new things together mimics the feelings of adventure and passion that you experienced back in the exciting early days of the relationship.

• **Add mystery and surprise.** Leave a love note for your spouse in an unexpected place or plan a weekend getaway for the two of you without telling your partner where you're going.

• **Add adrenaline.** Ride a roller coaster together…see a scary movie together…or exercise together. Anything that gets your heart racing and adrenaline pumping will release chemicals into your brain similar to those experienced by people who are passionately in love. Do such things together with your spouse a few times, and these chemicals could help rekindle your passion, excitement and sexual arousal for each other.

When Couples Don't Agree on Where to Retire

Dorian Mintzer, PhD, a licensed social worker and psychologist and career/life transition and executive coach in Boston, and **Roberta K. Taylor, RNCS, MEd,** a licensed psychotherapist and career, life and relationship coach in Waltham, Massachusetts. They are coauthors of *The Couple's Retirement Puzzle: 10 Must-Have Conversations for Transitioning to the Second Half of Life.* RevolutionizeRetirement.com

For most of our adult lives, we live where our careers take us. When we retire, we finally have the freedom to live wherever we like— perhaps near a beach or near our grandkids—or so we imagine. Trouble is, our spouses might have other ideas.

Many couples don't discuss where they will live in retirement until it is almost upon them. Some assume that their partners share their visions…while others suspect their partners have different destinations in mind and put off these conversations to avoid arguments. Even couples who have discussed and decided where to retire might need to revisit this issue if changing financial circumstances, priorities and/or health status forces a reevaluation.

Example: A couple who enjoyed hiking bought land in the mountains and agreed to build their retirement home there. As retirement neared, however, the husband realized that his worsening arthritis made hiking less fun and his other health problems made proximity to a good hospital a priority.

In generations past, the relatively small number of retirement-destination options made these discussions fairly simple. Most retirees either stayed put or moved someplace warm, such as Florida or Arizona. Today's retirees see many more options. In addition to the Sun Belt and their current communities, retirees are heading to college towns, urban centers and even foreign countries. It's wonderful to have options, but more options mean that it's more likely that partners' retirement visions will differ.

Where to live during retirement should be an ongoing conversation throughout marriage. However, if retirement is near and this issue has not been settled, it's time to sit down for a serious discussion on the subject. Try to schedule the meeting in advance so that both partners have time to think it through.

SEEKING A COMPROMISE

When preferred retirement destinations differ, it can seem as though the only option is for one or the other partner to yield. That can result in heated arguments.

There is more room for compromise in retirement-destination decisions than couples tend to realize. The important thing is to put the "where should we retire" debate on hold for the moment and focus instead on "what factors are most important to each of us in a retirement destination." What is it about the place where you want to retire that makes you want to retire there? Both partners should list and rank their top priorities in a retirement location.

Common priorities include proximity to…

• **Kids and grandkids**
• **Elderly parents**
• **Friends**

Warning: This is more important than many preretirees realize. If you move away from your friends in retirement, you might find that it's not so easy to make new friends and you end up relying totally on your spouse, which can stress even a strong relationship.

●**Specific cultural amenities,** such as theaters, concert halls and interesting restaurants.

●**Natural attractions and recreational facilities,** such as beaches, national parks, golf courses or fishing lakes.

●**Quality health-care facilities.**

●**A major airport.**

Other priorities could include…

●**Certain population density**—which might mean urban excitement, rural tranquillity or something in between.

●**A sense of community or proximity to a specific religious community.**

●**A specific climate**

●**A sense of safety**

●**Affordability**

Some people can and want to "live high" in retirement. Others may want to spend very sparingly.

Couples should compare lists, then brainstorm about locations that combine each partner's top priorities.

Example: Perhaps one partner's top priority is tranquillity, while the other primarily wants culture. This couple might consider Oregon or the Carolinas. Greater Portland and Ashland, Oregon… Charleston, South Carolina, and the Raleigh-Durham area of North Carolina all combine a relaxed feel with lots of culture. Or move to a tranquil town that's near a train station, providing quick access to a vibrant city…or consider a relatively rural town near a large university (large universities offer a multitude of cultural options).

CREATIVE COMPROMISES

If a mutually satisfactory retirement destination does not suggest itself, consider these five potential solutions…

●**Sample possible retirement destinations rather than make a decision now.** Rent a home or condo for three months or longer in each candidate region before choosing. Extended visits will take some of the fear and mystery out of moving somewhere new, and they increase the odds of finding someplace that both of you love.

Warning: "We went there on vacation and I liked it/didn't like it" is not enough on which to base a decision. The experience of living in a place for months is very different from the experience of visiting as a tourist for a week or two.

●**Divide your retirement between two locations.** It's fairly common for retired couples to spend winter months in a warm-weather location and summer months up north, but that's not the only possible way to divide your retirement time. You could have a house in the country and a pied-à-terre in the city, for example.

Not everyone can afford to buy and maintain two homes, of course, but the costs come down considerably if you trade one big home for two smaller ones. Many retirees discover that they are just as happy in a smaller home now that the kids are grown and gone.

Warning: If you maintain two residences, consider making at least one a condo or rental. Otherwise, you'll have to handle every home-maintenance chore twice over. That can be a burden, particularly as you get older.

If proximity to kids or grandkids is a major sticking point, perhaps renting a home near the kids for a month or a season each year would provide sufficient family togetherness. Perhaps you could plan multigenerational trips with your kids and grandkids to keep the relationship close rather than live nearby. Or perhaps if you retired someplace that's interesting and near an airport, your kids would come visit you regularly even if you weren't nearby.

Warning: If your kids are a key factor in your retirement plans, include them in the retirement-destination discussion. You don't want to choose a retirement region close to your children only to discover that they might soon move. Also, note that grandkids often have less time for their grandparents as they grow up.

●**Form an "intentional community."** If proximity to a close circle of friends is important to you, staying in your current home might not be a perfect solution—those friends might retire somewhere else even if you don't. Discuss retirement destinations with these friends. Perhaps some or all of the group can agree to retire to the same region, bringing your own community with you.

•**Live apart part-time.** This might seem extreme, but some time apart actually can strengthen relationships strained by spending 24 hours a day together in retirement.

Example: A New England woman in her 70s rents a condo in Florida each winter. Her husband, who doesn't care for Florida, stays in New England but takes short trips down to visit.

Dating Again? 8 Signs You've Found the Right Person

Sandy Weiner, dating coach, speaker and author who focuses on helping women over 40 date with dignity. Based in Stamford, Connecticut, she is host of the online radio show *Last First Date Radio* (BlogTalk Radio.com/lastfirstdate) and coauthor of *The Secrets to Setting Healthy Boundaries in Dating.* LastFirstDate.com

---

Dating advice often focuses on finding red flags—signs that a potential partner is not really Mr. or Ms. Right. We're advised to avoid anyone who treats waiters poorly…or who leaves his/her phone on the table at dinner, for example. These red flags have merit, but they create an undue focus on the negative.

The secret to finding a great partner is not just about weeding out anyone who has anything wrong with him or her, but rather selecting someone who has lots of great qualities—someone with the traits and temperament to participate in a happy, healthy relationship.

Here are eight of the most important "green flags" to look for in a partner. Some of these may be evident very early in a relationship…some after you've been dating for a while. All are crucial to a satisfying relationship.

1. He/she can express and take responsibility for his own feelings. It's a big green flag if a partner can say, "I'm feeling sad" or "I'm feeling angry," rather than sulk, rage or give you the silent treatment. Such a person is open about his feelings, which is a lot better than bottling them up inside until they explode.

It's even more promising if a partner not only identifies his feelings but also does not hold you responsible for them—even when your actions contributed to them. We are always responsible for our own feelings, regardless of who or what might have triggered them.

Example: You make an ill-considered joke at your partner's expense. It's a good sign if rather than saying, "You made me upset," she says, "I'm feeling upset" or "That joke upset me, but I understand that you probably weren't trying to upset me. I'm a bit touchy about jokes like that because I was teased in school. Would you be willing to not tell jokes like that anymore?"

Similar: It's also a great sign if a partner realizes when he is too emotional to have a productive conversation and says something such as, "I'm too angry to talk right now. I need time to calm down. Can we talk in about a half hour?" then returns to the topic later with less emotion.

2. He/she responds with both empathy and honesty when you mention a behavior that doesn't work for you. What characteristics and behaviors are especially important to you in a partner? If your partner says or does something that's not in alignment with your needs, calmly explain that this matters to you and listen to the response. It's a green flag if that response is not defensive. Your partner calmly discusses your needs while staying true to his. It's a bad sign if your partner makes excuses… denies falling short in this area…belittles your priorities…and/or makes no real effort to improve.

Example: You value punctuality, but your partner often is late. Explain that you need a partner who understands that your time has value and who does not regularly leave you sitting around waiting. It's a great sign if this person acknowledges having a punctuality problem and makes an honest effort to improve, perhaps by starting to get ready for dates 10 minutes earlier—even if he never becomes as punctual as you would like.

3. He/she is responsible with money. This is important even if you never tie your financial lives together by getting married. People who are financially responsible tend to be responsible with other aspects of their lives as well—including their relationships. A partner who lives within his means is much more likely to live up to his promises and make you feel safe and comfortable than one who has revolving credit card debt and likes to gamble.

Similar: It's also a great sign if a partner eats right and exercises. These, too, point to overall responsibility.

4. He/she continues to evolve and learn new things. It's a green flag if a partner continues to seek out new hobbies…enjoys traveling to new places and trying new restaurants…and is interested in a wide range of subjects. A partner who enjoys growing and trying new things is much more likely to continue to be interesting as time passes. When you first meet someone, that person might seem interesting simply because he's new to you. But if this person is set in his ways, there's a good chance that the relationship will eventually stagnate…or that he won't be willing to modify his life to include things that you like.

5. He/she has strong friendships. People who have multiple close friends tend to be people who have the emotional health and interpersonal skills needed to sustain a romantic relationship. They're also less likely to expect their romantic partners to fulfill every interpersonal need, something that is not feasible or healthy.

Similar: Consider it a good sign if your partner wants to introduce you to her friends. It shows that she's proud to be with you and that she is taking your relationship seriously. (Note: It is advisable for single parents who are dating to delay introducing romantic partners to their children until they are in a serious long-term relationship. This is particularly important if those kids are still young.)

6. He/she asks for your input on decisions. Obviously a partner should include you in decisions that involve you. But consider it a green flag if a partner also asks for your opinion on matters that do not directly involve you—a career decision, perhaps, or the selection of a new car. This shows that the partner respects you…and that his general attitude is one of collaboration.

7. He/she accepts a share of the blame for past relationship failures. Most couples eventually get around to talking about what went wrong with their prior relationships. It's a green flag if your partner admits that he was at least partially to blame. This shows a willingness to take responsibility as well as general maturity. It also hints at an ability to improve—people who are willing to admit their mistakes tend to be people who learn from those mistakes and do better in the future.

8. You feel just as good about your relationship when you're apart as when you are together. Some people have sufficient charm or physical appeal to make their partners feel good when they're with them, but that tends to fade fast when they depart. With a good partner, there's usually a deep-down sense of security that the relationship is right—even when the partner isn't around.

Looking for Love Later in Life

Pepper Schwartz, PhD, is a professor of sociology at the University of Washington in Seattle…co-creator of the Duet Total Compatibility System, a profiling service of PerfectMatch.com…and a columnist for AARP (AARP.org/nakedtruth). She also is the author or coauthor of 16 books, including *Prime: Adventures and Advice on Sex, Love, and the Sensual Years and Finding Your Perfect Match.* DrPepperSchwartz.com

---

You haven't been in the dating market for 20 or 30 years or more? Don't despair of finding love in midlife or beyond—it's out there.

In fact, according to relationships expert Pepper Schwartz, PhD, author of *Finding Your Perfect Match*, looking for another Mr. Right at this point offers advantages you didn't have in your teens or 20s. You're probably wiser now about how the world works and where you fit in it…you no longer measure yourself against impossible super-model standards of beauty…and you have developed higher self-esteem as you've grown older. *Here is Dr. Schwartz's advice on how to start your search…*

ON YOUR MARK!
STEP ONE IS TO TAKE STOCK

●**Ask yourself what kind of relationship you're looking for.** For many women, a midlife relationship is about love, sex and companionship—not necessarily marriage. Of course, there's no one-size-fits-all answer…but figuring out what you want—and what you don't want—ups your chances of hitting the mark.

●**Make a must-have list**—but remember, the more attributes a potential partner has to have, the less likely you are to find someone who meets all the criteria. Also, recognize that the qualities you looked for decades ago ("he's ambitious, he wants kids") probably have changed. So make a dream list, then pick just three qualities that are nonnegotiable and let the rest go.

Example: "He must be financially secure… have a sense of humor…and not have school-age children."

●**Do a personal assessment.** Looking your best boosts your confidence. You won't demand perfection of yourself, of course—but maybe you would feel good about updating your hairstyle and wardrobe. Check your attitude, too. Are you hanging onto hurts, resentments or negative behaviors (for instance, being too controlling or too passive) from past partnerships? Talk to friends and/or a therapist about how to move past these problems so they don't sabotage future relationships.

GET SET!
WHERE CAN YOU FIND THE RIGHT KIND OF PERSON?

●**Make a list of places where potential partners might gather.** Art galleries, bridge clubs, dance classes, lecture series or tennis clubs? Research what's available in your area that fits your interests and sign up. Consider online dating sites, too—many now cater to older adults.

●**Devise a safety plan.** Do this before you start accepting dates—it's best to be cautious.

Plan to: Do a basic background check before any first date by talking to mutual friends or looking up the person on the Internet…give out your cell-phone number and/or e-mail address, not your home phone or address…meet in public places and manage your own transportation, so you won't wind up in a car or a secluded area with someone you barely know.

GO!
START ATTENDING EVENTS.

●**Get feedback.** Double-date with a friend and ask her afterward, "Did I talk too little? Was I trying too hard to be funny? Did I seem interested in what was going on?" If you're on a date and the man's demeanor suggests that he's turned off, be straightforward in asking him if you did something to cause that. Use the feedback to improve your dating skills.

●**Be open-minded.** You kill your chances if you say to yourself, "I can tell within 10 seconds whether or not he's for me." Give every date at least 30 minutes (time enough for coffee), and vow to discover one interesting thing about the person. Even if he's not partner material, you might make a new friend…and maybe he'll be the one to eventually introduce you to the right guy for your future.

Living Contentedly with a TV Sports Addict

Judy Kuriansky, PhD, is a clinical psychologist and sex therapist on the adjunct faculty of Teachers College, Columbia University in New York City. She is the author of five books, including *The Complete Idiot's Guide to a Healthy Relationship.* DrJudy.com

---

Your spouse is at it again—staring fixedly or screaming frantically at the TV as the athletes on the screen chase a ball, swing a club or whack a puck. You try to get his attention, but it's like talking to a goalpost. Then you think about all his undone chores and unmet family obligations, and your anger level spikes through the roof.

Being a TV sports "widow" (or widower) is not fun, so it's no wonder you feel neglected, frustrated and infuriated. *But before you throw in the towel on your relationship, try these game-changing strategies…*

●**Resolve to hang onto your temper.** Screaming, nagging or unplugging the TV in the middle of a game will only escalate tensions between you. He may even retaliate by complaining about your favorite pastimes or purposely engaging in other irritating behaviors, such as giving you the silent treatment, which will drive a bigger wedge of resentment between you.

●**Understand his passion.** When you're both feeling happy and calm, ask him sincerely to explain what thrills him about the games—the invigorating sense of competition, the companionable post-game analysis with his buddies, the feeling of being a winner or the chance to forget his own worries for a while. Discuss the qualities he admires in his favorite teams—their toughness, persistence or ability to perform under pressure. Encourage him to talk about the sports he played as a boy and his childhood ambitions for being the next Yogi Berra or Johnny Unitas. The more you know about his inner dreams and desires, the easier it is to help him find ways to fulfill them that don't involve endless TV time. Also, as you identify similarities between his passion for sports and your own love for, say, knitting or 19th-century literature, you'll be more understanding of, and less bothered by, his devotion to sports.

●**Encourage him to turn passive watching into active play.** Guys who love watching sports often miss playing the way they did when they were young. Encourage your partner to join a local tennis club or head for the gym to shoot hoops. Plan an afternoon at the local park where he can play catch with a buddy or grandson—and pack a picnic and go along yourself, so you are a part of the play.

●**Ask him to establish weekly sports-free times for household chores and standing dates.** Knowing that the lawn will get cut every Sunday morning and that you'll have his full attention every Tuesday evening will assuage your feelings of resentment or neglect during those Monday night football games.

●**If you can't beat him, join him.** Sit down next to him on the couch and ask him to teach you about his favorite sport—you may be surprised at how interesting it can be. Or learn about the game on your own and amaze him with insightful questions ("Should they kick a field goal or go for the touchdown with so little time left in the quarter?"). Throw in some quips that make him associate the thrill of the game with you—for instance, when the quarterback gets sacked, you might say, "I like it when you pile on top of me."

●**Be alert to signs that TV sports have taken over his life.** A love for TV sports can become a bona fide addiction—similar to an addiction to gambling, sex, alcohol or anything else. A person crosses the line from fan to sports addict when he cannot choose not to watch…spends endless hours watching sports-related TV or studying stats while his work remains undone and other obligations go unfulfilled…or experiences anxiety or distress when denied access to his games. If you suspect that your partner falls into this category, urge him to seek help from a professional addiction counselor.

Super Sex Every Time: Natural Cures for Impotence, Low Desire, Dryness, More

Brigitte Mars, herbalist, founding member of The American Herbalists Guild. She has been practicing and teaching herbal medicine and nutrition for more than 40 years. She is author of *The Sexual Herbal: Prescriptions for Enhancing Love and Passion.* BrigitteMars.com.

Couples who enjoy sex regularly tend to live longer than those who rarely or never have sex.

Yet millions of Americans struggle to have satisfying sex, or any sex, because of physical limitations. Medications can help with problems such as an inability to get erections or vaginal dryness, but they don't always work—and can carry the risk for side effects.

Better: Natural remedies that improve energy and libido as well as sexual performance. In my 40 years of specializing in herbal medicine, I have found them to be quite effective for many people. (The herbs and supplements noted here are readily available at most health-food stores and online.)

LUBRICATION

Vaginal dryness can be as problematic for a woman as erectile dysfunction is for a man. Women naturally produce less moisture (in the vagina, as well as in the eyes, skin and other parts of the body) as they get older. But it's one of the easiest sexual problems to correct—and without the use of store-bought, chemical-filled lubricants. Try one of the following remedies. If that doesn't work, try another until you find what works best for you.

•**Barley water.** Barley water is an emollient that also nourishes and strengthens vaginal tissues. Cook two cups of light pearled barley in 10 cups of water for two hours. Strain, and reserve the water. Drink a glassful three or four times a day between meals for at least three weeks. If it helps, continue doing it. It can be kept in the refrigerator for up to three days. (You can use the leftover barley in soups and salads.)

•**Acidophilus.** Dryness is sometimes caused by an overgrowth of vaginal yeast. Before going to bed each night, insert a capsule of acidophilus into the vagina. It inhibits yeast and helps the vagina produce more lubrication.

Important: Don't use an enteric-coated capsule—it won't dissolve readily. Use an acidophilus gel capsule.

•**Chemical-free lubricant.** Mix one ounce of softened cocoa butter with one tablespoon each of powdered dong quai (an herb in the parsley family), licorice root and marshmallow root, along with one tablespoon of powdered wild yam and two tablespoons of vitamin E oil.

Optional: Two drops of essential oil of rose for a pleasant aroma.

Roll the mixture into suppository shapes about the size of your little finger. Store them in a glass jar in the refrigerator for up to six months. Insert one in the vagina daily before bedtime.

LOW LIBIDO

If your sex drive is lower than you (or your partner) would like…

•**Eat black foods.** According to Traditional Chinese Medicine, the kidneys govern sexual vitality. Foods with natural black color, such as black olives, black sesame seeds, chia seeds and black beans, strengthen the kidneys and improve sexual energy and performance.

Bonus: Black olives and chia increase the production of mucilage, important for sexual lubrication.

•**Muira puama.** This is a South American herb that traditionally is used as an aphrodisiac and to improve erections as well as orgasms in men and women. It's a warming herb that increases circulation. If you have cold hands and/or feet, you probably have impaired circulation to the genitals as well. Muira puama can help.

Dose: One-half cup of muira puama tea…or 10 to 30 drops of tincture, mixed with an inch of water or taken straight, three times daily. Also available in capsules. Natives of South America sometimes apply the cooled tea directly to the genitals as a sexual stimulant.

•**DHEA,** an over-the-counter hormonal supplement that's converted to testosterone in the body, can increase libido and sexual responsiveness in women and men.

Important: Improper dosing can cause acne, the growth of facial hair in women and other side effects—including an increased risk for some cancers. Take DHEA only under the supervision of a doctor.

ERECTILE DYSFUNCTION

The arteries that carry blood to the penis are just slightly wider than the head of a pin. Even slight buildups of plaque (atherosclerosis) can impede circulation and make it difficult for a man to get and/or maintain an erection.

The same things that improve overall cardiovascular health, such as lowering cholesterol and blood pressure, can improve a man's ability to achieve an erection. *Also helpful…*

- **The Deer.** This is a Taoist exercise that removes energy blockages, stimulates hormone production and improves erections. Sit on the edge of the bed, and rub your hands to warm them. Hold the scrotum with one hand. With the other hand, massage right below the navel in a circular motion. Do it 81 times, then switch hands and rub in the other direction 81 times.

Follow this with 36 Kegel exercises, in which you tighten and then release the pubococcygeus muscles—the same muscles that you would use to stop urine in midstream.

- **Foot massage.** Once or twice a day, massage the entire foot, paying particular attention to the sides of the heels. The meridians (energy pathways) that support sexual potency run through this part of the foot.

- **Yohimbe.** Yohimbe bark extract is among the most effective natural products for improving erections. It increases blood flow to the genitals while at the same time impeding the flow of blood out of the penis—important for keeping an erection.

Dose: One cup of yohimbe tea…or 30 drops of tincture, mixed with an inch of water or taken straight, 30 minutes to an hour before sex. Also available in capsules.

Caution: Yohimbe can elevate blood pressure and cause insomnia. It also interacts with many common drugs, including antihypertensives and heart and diabetes medications. Use it only under the supervision of a doctor and never more than twice a week.

- **Omega-3 fatty acids e**nhance circulation and help the nervous system function better. Eat fish (such as salmon, tuna, sardines) twice per week or supplement with fish oil (follow directions on the label).

BETTER ORGASMS

Women (and men) who eat well, exercise regularly and are comfortable with their bodies experience better and more frequent orgasms. *Also helpful…*

- **L-Arginine.** An amino acid called L-arginine is a vasodilator, which means it helps to widen or open up blood vessels. Arginine cream can be applied to the clitoris (or to the penis) before sex to increase arousal and the intensity of orgasms. You also can take an oral capsule form to increase blood flow to sexual organs. Follow directions on the label.

The Secret to Great Sex At Any Age

Judy Kuriansky, PhD, clinical psychologist and sex therapist on the adjunct faculty of Columbia University Teachers College in New York City. She is author of five books, including *The Complete Idiot's Guide to a Healthy Relationship.* SexualTherapy.com/therapists/jkuriansky.htm.

What you used to look forward to twice a week (or even twice a night!) can drop off, as the years pass, to twice a month…or once in a blue moon. As a woman gets older, sex—which used to provide unparalleled pleasure and promote emotional intimacy—can start to feel like a chore or a bore or a bother.

But it doesn't have to be this way. One effective and enjoyable way to keep your sex drive stimulated—no matter what your age or stage of life—is for you and your partner to explore the mysteries of the highly erotic and deeply sensitive G-spot. Just say to him, "Let's explore something new tonight, as we would on a vacation in Italy or the Islands." Chances are good that he'll happily race you to the bedroom.

SPOT CHECK

Popularized by the book *The G-Spot: and Other Discoveries About Human Sexuality* by Alice Khan Ladas, Beverly Whipple and John D. Perry, first published in 1982, and named after German gynecologist Ernst Grafenberg, who described it in the mid-twentieth century, the Grafenberg spot, or G-spot (more accurately an area or space), can be a locus of strong sexual arousal and powerful orgasms in women. Yet controversy surrounds this erogenous zone, with some people saying it's a must for satisfying sex while experts insist on not increasing expectations. Some experts even contest its existence in every woman despite evidence to the contrary.

As a psychologist and a sex therapist, I assure you that this area does indeed exist—and that every woman has one. The G-spot can be an added source of pleasure, though I warn against considering it the "holy grail" of female sexuality, because preset expectations can raise performance anxiety and put a damper on sex.

Despite its reputation, once you know where it is and what it feels like, the G-spot is not hard to find. It is located on the front wall of the vaginal "barrel," about one-third of the way up. Compared with the smoothness of the rest of the vaginal wall, the G-spot feels slightly rippled, with grooves—and its texture increases as the spot is stimulated. When a woman is aroused, blood and fluid rush to the area and the G-spot swells, sometimes doubling in size.

In some women, G-spot stimulation triggers an emission of fluid (like an ejaculation), helping to lubricate the external area—a special plus for older women, for whom uncomfortable dryness is often a deterrent to sex. Of course, if dryness is a problem, don't hesitate to also use a lubricating product, such as KY-Jelly, Astroglide, Zestra or Eros.

TO TRY TONIGHT

There are a number of simple, straightforward ways to stimulate the G-spot. During foreplay, the man can insert his index or middle finger into the vagina, crook the finger upward and then gently, repeatedly and rhythmically make a "come hither" gesture.

The G-spot also can be stimulated during intercourse, using positions that are angled to allow the best access. *Positions to try…*

• **The woman on her back with a pillow under her bottom to raise the pelvis and hips,** and the man on his knees before her.

• **The doggie position,** with the man angling his thrusts downward.

• **The woman on top,** guiding the man's thrusts to make contact with the G-spot.

What to avoid: It's essential for your partner to take his time and be very delicate in his attentions toward the G-spot, especially at the outset. For successful arousal, he must not push too hard, rub too vigorously or force the stimulation in any way. The unfamiliar pressure and sensations may feel uncomfortable and confusing to you at first—so don't give up too quickly. Also, due to the G-spot's proximity to the urethra, stimulation may at first produce an urge to urinate. To prevent this distracting sensation, it's a good idea to empty your bladder before sexual activity.

Practice makes perfect: As with all aspects of lovemaking, every woman is different, and it may require some patience and experimentation until you find what works best for you. Once you do, awareness of the G-spot can become a very satisfying addition to your lovemaking. You may decide that, when it comes to your sex life today, the "G" stands for great.

Mistakes Parents Make That Push Adult Children Away

Jeffrey Jensen Arnett, PhD, a research professor in the department of psychology at Clark University, Worcester, Massachusetts. He is coauthor, with Elizabeth Fishel, of *When Will My Grown-Up Kid Grow Up?* JeffreyArnett.com

Our children will always be our children, but once they turn 18 or leave home, they also are adults with lives increasingly separate from our own. It's a challenge for parents to step back while also staying connected to their grown-up kids.

Much of the angst between parents and adult children stems from the tug-of-war over whose life it is. There often is a disconnect between parents who still want to shape their grown-up kids' future course and the kids who are determined to live their lives their own way.

For loving parents, their grown children's trials and errors, including failed projects and teary breakups, can be anguishing. It can be wrenching to let go of the old parental omnipotence and not be able to fix everything. But when grown kids cope with these ups and downs, they develop into resilient, self-sufficient people with the confidence that comes from standing on their own feet.

Seven "don'ts" to keep in mind when dealing with grown children...

MONEY AND CAREER

It takes a long time these days for grown kids to achieve financial independence, and my research shows that money issues are the number-one topic of conflict between parents and kids 18 to 29 years old.

●**Don't use your financial support to control your adult kids.** If you're supplying money to your adult child, you certainly can set ground rules about how that money is used—but you should not threaten to withdraw your support if the adult child doesn't make life changes unrelated to finances.

Example: It's reasonable to tell your adult child that money you're providing cannot be spent on a vacation—but don't tell him that it can't be spent on a vacation unless he leaves the girlfriend you don't like.

●**Don't push your kids to take a job in a field that pays well but that they don't like.** Not only might they hold their unhappiness with the hated job against you, their lack of passion for the field could inhibit their career growth.

Also: Don't make snide comments about the job prospects of your college-age child's field of study or the earnings potential of his line of work. It is reasonable to discuss career and earnings outlooks with your kids before they choose a college major, field of graduate study or first job. But trying to control the big decision of what field your adult child will choose is sure to stir up resentment. Keep in mind that although college majors do vary in their future earnings, getting a college degree, in any area, is the most important goal for enhancing lifelong career prospects.

●**Don't insist that your kids find their own way after college rather than return home.** These days, many adult children live at home for a short time. Almost always, their return home is temporary because they prefer to live independently as soon as they can afford to do so.

Helpful: Agree on a division of household responsibilities. The adult child is now an adult member of the household and should do an adult share of the housework, laundry and cooking.

COMMUNICATION

Most adult children like talking to their parents and enjoy having a more adultlike relationship than they did in their teens. *But...*

●**Don't ask probing questions about your children's lives.** If they want to share something personal, they will. Adult children vary a lot in how much they want their parents to know about their lives and how much they want to confide in them.

Take special care not to raise subjects that your adult child has historically been disinclined to discuss. Resist the urge to ask follow-up questions on the rare occasions when your child does raise one of these subjects.

Example: Many adult children prefer not to discuss their love lives with their parents.

●**Don't overdo it.** Today's technology makes it cheap and easy to stay in contact with loved ones, and many adult children and their parents are in contact with one another nearly every day. However, for some grown kids, that's a bit too much togetherness at a time when they are striving to become self-sufficient. In general, it's best to follow your adult children's lead on communications. If they contact you weekly via text message, then contact them weekly via text message, too. Text messaging might not be your preferred communication method, but it's a great way to touch base with today's young adults without seeming pushy. You can always slip in a phone call now and then.

Helpful: Don't feel offended if kids go a few days without answering your text message or voice mail. It doesn't mean that they don't care. It could just mean that they are busy—or that they're not that eager to discuss that particular topic.

ROMANCE

An adult child's romantic relationships can be a minefield for parents...

●**Don't confide that you "never liked" an ex-boyfriend or ex-girlfriend or provide reasons**

why your adult child is better off without this former mate. Keep in mind that ex-boyfriends and ex-girlfriends sometimes reenter the picture. That could create awkwardness if you've previously expressed a dislike.

●**Don't overlook your adult child's romantic partners at family get-togethers.** If your adult child has been seeing someone for a while, be sure to include the partner in family gatherings, then do your best to make him/her feel welcome and comfortable. The more comfortable your grown child's partner is with you, the more you are likely to see of your child.

More from Jeffrey Jensen Arnett, PhD

How to Give Advice to an Adult Child

Many young adults spend their 20s acting in ways that seem irresponsible to their parents. They might change jobs or romantic partners frequently or rely on their parents for financial support or housing.

This is all perfectly normal and does not mean that the young adult is destined to act this way forever.

And while adult children might seem to be in desperate need of advice, there's a good chance that they will react poorly if their parents offer it. Such guidance makes them feel as if their parents still see them as children. This puts parents in a difficult position—they want to help their grown-up kids avoid missteps, but any wisdom they offer is likely to be poorly received.

Usually parents' best option is to bite their tongues and not offer their adult children advice when it hasn't been requested. Such advice might harm the relationship, and there is a good chance it won't be heeded anyway. *But speaking up could be wise if...*

●**You believe your adult child's safety is at risk.** It's worth putting the relationship at risk when safety is at stake.

Examples: Don't offer unsolicited advice if you think your adult child is staying out too late—but do if you suspect he's driving home drunk. Don't tell your daughter you don't like her new boyfriend—but do speak your mind if your daughter has a black eye and you suspect that the boyfriend is responsible.

●**The topic is money-related and you're providing financial support.** If your money is on the line, it's perfectly reasonable to voice concerns about the adult child's questionable financial decisions or even set ground rules for spending. But it will help the relationship if after voicing these concerns or setting these rules, you add something such as, "The final decision is yours, and I will continue to support you emotionally whatever you decide. I just can't continue to support you financially if you make this decision."

Example: You're paying your child's rent while he searches for a job, but you notice that he hasn't been looking for work lately.

●**You obtain permission to provide advice.** The odds of a negative reaction decline greatly if you ask the child if he would like your input before you offer it.

Warning: Respect the child's answer. If he says he prefers to work through the problem on his own, keep your advice to yourself.

When you feel you must provide advice, also ask the adult child for his advice on a different topic about which he is knowledgeable. This can keep the relationship balanced.

How to Stay Close to Your Adult Kids

Scott Haltzman, MD, clinical assistant professor of psychiatry and human behavior at Alpert Medical School of Brown University, Providence. He is a psychiatrist in private practice in Barrington, Rhode Island, and author of *The Secrets of Happy Families: Eight Keys to Building a Lifetime of Connection and Contentment.* DrScott.com

---

In our mobile modern society, many adult children live hundreds or thousands of miles from their parents. Unfortunately, that geographical distance tends to be highly correlated with emotional distance from our kids and grandkids.

Even extended families whose members still live near one another face challenges, with ever-increasing demands on their time.

The good news: Parents can overcome these challenges and build strong relationships with their adult children no matter where they live. *Five ways to make that happen…*

SHOW RESPECT

Make your respect for your grown kids a recurring theme of the relationship. Adult children want one thing from their parents above all else—respect. The more you provide, the greater the odds that your children will want to remain close with you.

One way to show respect is to shower your grown kids with praise just as you did when they were young. Search for any excuse to offer a compliment. Make "I'm proud of you" and "You handled that very well" your mantras.

It also is important not to criticize your grown children when it seems as if they have failed. Criticism will only drive them away from you.

Helpful: If you catch yourself being critical, make at least five positive comments or actions before the end of your call or visit. Research has shown that a positive-to-negative interaction ratio of five-to-one or better can help maintain closeness in our relationships with our children (and our own spouses, too).

BUILD TRADITIONS

A family's traditions help to define it as well as preserve it. These traditions might include a distinctive way of celebrating a holiday or something as simple as gathering each year to watch an annual event on TV. Sure, your kids are busy with their own families and maybe there's been some bickering—but everyone still gathers at your house to watch the Super Bowl because it's a tradition.

It's never too late to create new family traditions. Whenever the extended family gets together and has a good time, single out something distinctive about the occasion—perhaps the place that the family gathered…the board game the family played…or the day of the year on which the gather-

ing occurred. Suggest that the family try this again, perhaps the following year. If everyone has as much fun the second time, it could become a tradition.

Warning: Never make family traditions seem like requirements. If you hold it against your son that he spent Thanksgiving with his in-laws, the holiday could become a source of anxiety, driving your family apart, rather than a tradition that holds you together.

DON'T GIVE ADVICE

Resist the urge to give advice, even when it is requested. Receiving guidance from a parent can make adults feel like helpless children again. They tend to rebel against this unpleasant feeling by pulling away from the parent—even if they asked for advice.

If your adult child requests your advice, say, "I'm happy to help you sort through the pros and cons, but it's your decision to make, and I know you'll make the right choice."

One way to provide guidance to grown children is to ask them to teach you how they do something. Rather than criticize your adult children's decisions or methods, express an interest in these and ask if they could explain them to you. Listen attentively and without criticism, then casually mention that a different method was taught back when you were learning this task. Briefly describe your method and its advantages, then ask whether this strategy is still used. If your child doesn't wish to pursue the discussion any further, let it drop. This should dodge the psychological pitfalls of providing parental advice because the child gets to act as teacher first…and your guidance is presented as something that someone else taught you.

Example: When your son comes to you enthusiastically intending to buy junk bonds, you can ask about the company and its financial health, even look it up online with him. Then you can share how exciting it is to take a risk, as well as how you have learned not to invest any more than you can afford to lose.

Provide direct advice only if the adult child is about to make a massive and potentially irreversible misstep, such as driving an unsafe vehicle or buying an older home without a home inspection.

BEFRIEND YOUR CHILD'S SPOUSE

Search for ways to support and praise your sons- and daughters-in-law—even if you don't really care for them. It's your relationship with your children and grandchildren that will suffer the most if you don't get along with your kids' spouses. Your grown kids might decide it's easier to cut you out of their lives than to deal with the problems created when you and the spouse are together. And your child's spouse is likely to come up with excuses for the child's family not to visit you or invite you over.

Warning: The fact that your child criticizes his/her spouse to you does not mean that you are free to criticize that spouse, too. What you take as serious criticisms might just be your child venting normal marital frustrations. He actually might love and respect this partner very deeply. If so, your criticisms might damage your relationship with your child.

DON'T INTRUDE

Select noninvasive communication methods. Frequent phone calls or drop-in visits from parents can seem overbearing to adult children. *Better options…*

●**E-mail and social-networking websites.** Modern technology lets families keep in touch without interfering with one another's schedules. You can write as much as you like in an e-mail message or on a Facebook page—and your kids can read it whenever they like.

●**Care packages.** Young kids away at summer camp aren't the only ones who appreciate care packages. A batch of cookies that arrives unexpectedly in the mail can be a great way to remind your adult child of your love. My mother sent me clothes that she found on sale for a full decade after I married. My wife and I both appreciated it.

Warning: Do not follow up your packages with calls. These calls could make it seem like you are fishing for a thank-you or an invitation to visit. Gifts are most effective as relationship builders when there are no strings attached.

Also, be sure that gifts won't be misconstrued as subtle hints that your children or their spouses don't measure up. Books about dieting or a free session with a marriage counselor will be seen by your kids as signs of your disapproval, even though in your eyes, you're just trying to help.

How Not to Divorce Your Grandchildren When Their Parents Divorce

Richard S. Victor, Esq., founder and executive director of the Grandparents Rights Organization (GrandParentsRights.org).

After decades of success, grandparents are finding that the pendulum is swinging the other way—against them—in regard to visitation rights. Nevertheless, grandparents should not give up easily when it comes to ensuring opportunities for spending time with their grandchildren.

ADVERSE COURT DECISION

Most grandparents want to spend time with their grandchildren, and most parents are happy to oblige. In some families, though, the parents object and the grandparents find themselves with limited visits or shut out altogether.

In the late 20th century, most state legislatures passed laws that gave grandparents some visitation rights. Generally, grandparents who were denied access to their grandchildren could go to court and ask to be able to maintain the relationship. It was up to the parents or legal custodians to show why a grandparent should be barred.

The situation changed in 2000 because of a Supreme Court decision in a case called Troxel vs. Granville. In this case, after the father of two daughters committed suicide, his widow limited the time that his parents could spend with their grandchildren. The grandparents went to court for greater visitation rights. Ultimately, the Supreme Court ruled that the visitation laws of their state (Washington) were too broad.

In essence, the Supreme Court held that parents, not grandparents, should be the ones to set priorities when it comes to relations with other family members.

The Court noted that the child's mother was not seeking to freeze out the grandparents completely. She was limiting them to one day-time visit per month, plus some holidays. If the mother had tried to bar the grandparents from visiting their grandchildren, the Court might have reached a different decision.

STATES STEP IN

Since the Troxel vs. Granville decision, state legislatures have had to draft new laws governing grandparents' visitation rights. Except for Alabama, Florida and Washington (see next page), all states now have visitation laws on their books that they believe comply with the Supreme Court decision.

These laws usually don't apply when a child lives with his natural parents. It's generally understood that when a couple is still a couple, they have the first and final say on how often grandparents can visit.

The situation is different, though, if only one natural parent is responsible for a child. In most states, then, grandparents can petition a court for greater visitation rights.

Under the laws currently in effect, it's generally up to the grandparent to make the case for visiting grandchildren.

Thus, grandparents who have limited interaction with their grandchildren must prove that their visits would benefit the children—emotionally, intellectually and/or physically. Alternatively, they must show that a lack of visitation harms the child.

For more information on your state's current laws, go to the website of legal publisher Nolo Press (Nolo.com) and search for "grandparent visitation."

AIM FOR RESOLUTION

Considering recent court decisions, legal action should be a last resort for grandparents who want to spend more time with their grandchildren.

Better way: Work with the child's parent or parents rather than against them. If there is a dispute, see if it can be resolved amicably. *Ways to encourage détente…*

•**Reach out to your grandchildren.** Even if your visits are limited, you can send cards and letters—many grandchildren love to correspond via E-mail.

Send gifts, too, on appropriate occasions. Telephone to see how the grandkids are feeling, how they're doing in school and so on.

You can avoid having these contacts backfire if you're supportive of the grandchild without saying anything negative about his/her parents. This will only upset your grandchild and won't help you gain visitation rights.

Key: Keep a record of the efforts you make to communicate with your grandchildren. Such a record may prove helpful if the matter ever winds up in court or in mediation, because it will show that you've maintained a healthy interest in the grandchildren's well-being.

•**Bring in a professional.** Counselors or mediators may be able to help you resolve the issues that are limiting your visitation rights.

When you participate in mediation, you'll hire a neutral third party to hear both sides of the dispute. The object is to create a legally binding agreement that's acceptable to everyone.

Some state courts won't consider a petition for visitation until the parties have attended mediation together.

The costs of mediation may be modest (especially when compared with suing) and the results may be beneficial. *To find mediators in your area, contact either of…*

•**American Arbitration Association** (800-778-7879, ADR.org).

•**Association for Conflict Resolution** (202-464-9700, ACRnet.org).

If the parents are getting a divorce, try to get a visitation schedule included in their divorce agreement. This may give you firmer legal ground if you wind up in an adversarial relationship with the custodial parent.

LAST RESORT

An adversarial relationship with the custodial parent, if not resolved, may ultimately force you to go to court.

Strategy: Consult with an attorney who specializes in family law. Be prepared to incur expenses for legal fees and perhaps to hire psychologists and other experts. You may need to show that your grandchild will be harmed if your access is severely limited.

Ironically, the purpose of paying for lawyers, psychologists, etc., is not to prevail in court. If these cases wind up in court, family relations may be severely damaged.

However, the threat of such a private matter ending up before a judge oftentimes gets parents and grandparents talking with each other, and such talk may eventually reunite families.

That truly would be a happy ending.

A Surprising Way to Handle Difficult People

Judith Orloff, MD, assistant clinical professor of psychiatry at UCLA. She is author of *The Ecstasy of Surrender: 12 Surprising Ways Letting Go Can Empower Your Life* upon which this article is based. DrJudithOrloff.com

When faced with difficult behavior at work or with family and friends, most people tend to revert to automatic reactions. They cave in…get defensive or aggressive… or dig in their heels and refuse to budge.

None of these reactions produces satisfying results, but they are the only alternatives most of us are aware of.

A more effective way to deal with difficult people is to surrender—to let go of the need to control a situation and let go of the illusion that you can compel someone to change. Surrendering means accepting a person or situation as is—if you have done everything possible to create change and nothing is budging. This is very different from caving in, which means giving up your needs simply to make peace without any effort to try to create positive change.

This may sound surprising. Many people equate surrender with defeat or weakness. However, surrender is not the same as failure or defeat. It takes great strength of character.

Surrender is an active choice to accept what life brings you, to be flexible rather than rigid and to see past a momentary block to a greater breakthrough beyond. Surrendering allows you to let go of overthinking and second-guessing.

PRACTICING SURRENDER

Surrender doesn't come naturally to most people. It needs to be learned and practiced.

Surrendering is easier to do when you are only mildly stressed. With practice, you can learn to let go even in more challenging encounters. *Simple ways to practice…*

● **Drink a glass of water or juice—slowly.** Savor the sensation of quenching your thirst. Enjoy the fact that there is nothing you have to do but sip and be refreshed.

● **Take a deep breath.** Inhale deeply, and then release your breath fully. This counteracts the stress-induced impulse to clench muscles and breathe shallowly, both of which increase resistance and tension.

● **Change what you say to yourself.** Any time you notice yourself dwelling on regrets about the past or fears about the future, bring yourself back to the present. Say, I can handle the here and now. I don't have to worry about three weeks ago or 10 years from now.

● **Observe water.** Watch the water in a fountain or creek. Notice how water doesn't keep bumping into the same boulder over and over again—it flows around the obstacle. Water can teach you how to flow.

● **Appreciate your body's natural joyful responses.** Let out a hearty laugh. Put on your favorite music, and dance around the living room. Don't choke off those urges—enjoy them.

● **Let yourself feel awe.** Look up at the night sky, and notice the vastness of the galaxy and universe around you. Like a child, allow yourself to surrender to this mystery and awe.

DIFFICULT SITUATIONS

In most cases, difficult people aren't trying to make your life miserable—they are just preoccupied with their own frustrations and needs. *Guidelines for dealing with difficult behavior...*

•**Pause.** If you feel yourself getting angry or tense, don't say anything. Let go of the urge to express your immediate reaction. Instead, take a few slow breaths to calm your stress. Count to 10 or 20 if it helps you postpone action.

•**Listen without interrupting.** When we are upset about what someone is saying, we typically want to cut the person off in order to stop our discomfort and express our disagreement or anger. However, interruption just escalates hostility. Let go of the need to direct the discussion. Hear the other person out.

Exception: If the person is being verbally abusive, cut off the abuse at once. Verbal abuse includes personal attacks that target your worth—such as You're a terrible mother or You can't do anything right. In cases like these, break in and set boundaries in a calm voice.

Example: "That kind of statement is unacceptable. If you continue like this, I will leave the room."

•**Don't argue.** You may have the strong desire to state all the evidence that shows you are right, but defensiveness in charged situations doesn't change anyone's mind—it just fuels the conflict.

•**Empathize.** Make a genuine effort to see the situation from the other person's point of view. People who behave badly are suffering in some way. This doesn't excuse their behavior, but once you recognize that they are trying to avoid pain or anxiety, letting go becomes easier.

•**Be willing to concede a point.** Even if you agree with only 1% of what the person is saying, acknowledge that point of agreement. You can say, "That's a good point, and I'm going to think about it."

Also be willing to apologize for your own difficult behavior.

Example: "I'm sorry I snapped at you. I didn't act with love." Too many relationships disintegrate because no one will give ground. Let go of the need to protect your turf. Look at the larger picture—which is more important, this battle or the relationship?

•**Use a pleasant, neutral tone.** No matter how carefully you choose your words, they will get you nowhere if your voice has an edge of irritation, condescension or sarcasm. Practice a neutral tone by role-playing with a friend until you are able to keep the edge out of your voice.

THREE DIFFICULT TYPES

Here's how to deal with three common types of difficult people...

•**The Guilt Tripper.** Blamers and martyrs activate your insecurity to get what they want. Their sentences often start with, "If it weren't for you..."or "I'm the only one..." *What to do...*

•Be compassionate with yourself. When you feel bad about any area of your life, work on being compassionate with yourself. By understanding your own guilt triggers, you will be better able to keep your balance when someone tries to activate them.

•Make a matter-of-fact statement. Tell guilt trippers that those comments hurt your feelings and that you would be grateful if they would stop making them. If you don't get emotional, most guilt trippers will lose interest in baiting you.

•**The Control Freak.** Control freaks micromanage, give unsolicited advice, voice strong opinions relentlessly and are rarely satisfied. *What to do...*

•Let go of needing the controller to see things your way. Don't try to control a controller or win over the person to your way of thinking—it's a waste of time. Say, "Thank you for your input. I'll take it into consideration" or "I value your advice, but I want to work through this myself."

•Be patient. Control freaks don't give up easily, so repetition is key. Continue to be calm and pleasant even when you have to repeat the aforementioned statements many times.

•**The Anger Addict.** Rage-aholics intimidate by accusing, yelling or cursing. *What to do...*

• Let go of the impulse to cower or to lash out in return. The more impulsively you react to someone else's rage, the more you reinforce the anger addict's aggressive behavior. Even if you are upset, stay as neutral as you can. Get centered before you respond.

• Use imagery. Picture a martial artist who finds a balanced, grounded stance and then transforms the opponent's energy by flowing with the person's movements instead of resisting them. Imagine that the person's anger can flow right through you and that you are breathing the anger out with every breath.

• If the anger addict is your boss, acknowledge the person's point of view. Say, "I can see why you would feel that way." Then bring the discussion back to a solution focus. Say in a calm tone, "I have a different take that I'd like to share" or "That's fine—tell me what you need, and I'll do it."

Look for another job if you can, because being the recipient of chronic anger takes a physical and mental toll. In the meantime—or if changing jobs is not possible—remind yourself that the rage is about the other person, not you.

• If the anger addict is a spouse or family member, set limits. Say, "Your anger is hurting me. We have to find a better way to communicate" or "I care about you, but I shut down when you raise your voice. Let's talk about this when we can hear each other better." Later, when you are both calm, request a small, doable change.

Example of a small, doable change: "When we are in the midst of a disagreement, I propose that we each wait five seconds before saying anything. Would you be willing to try that?"

If the person doesn't try to change, observe how your health is affected. You may need to let go of the relationship to protect your well-being.

When Siblings Get Stuck in a Cold War

Judy Kuriansky, PhD, clinical psychologist and sex therapist on the adjunct faculty of Columbia University Teachers College in New York City. She is the author of several books, including *The Complete Idiot's Guide to a Healthy Relationship.* DrJudy.com

Betsy had barely spoken to her sister for several years. For a while, she was too angry about their last argument to mind the estrangement. Over time, though, as her ire mellowed, she started to miss her only sister. But she wasn't sure how to end the cold war, so she let month after month slip by without trying. Then she got the devastating news—her sister was dead. Betsy had lost her chance to make peace…and now she's living with the heartache and regret.

Are you, too, experiencing a rift with a sibling? You don't have to make the same mistake Betsy made. If your sibling is truly toxic—for instance, if there is a history of abuse, criminal behavior or ongoing pathological selfishness that poisons every encounter—you may be better off keeping your distance. But otherwise, making the effort to rebuild sibling ties is likely to boost your own psychological health and improve the emotional well-being of the whole family. *Here's how to get started…*

• **First, figure out what's really behind the conflict.** On the surface, it may seem that the estrangement sprang from the most recent big fight. But chances are that its roots extend back to childhood, when you two saw yourselves as rivals for parental attention and affection.

Example: When your grown brother asked your parents for yet another "loan," you wrote him off as a leech and a loser—because you still resent the preferential treatment he always received as the "baby" of the family. Alternatively, you and your sibling may unconsciously repeat negative family patterns, mimicking the dysfunctional ways your parents treated each other. Whatever the true source of your sibling conflict, identifying it is the first step toward working through your feelings and finding healthier ways to interact.

- **Resolve to be the one who reaches out.** No matter who initiated the schism between you two, you can extend the olive branch. Yes, you may fear rejection—but don't let pride take precedence over peace. Remind yourself that life is too short to hold a grudge.

- **In reestablishing contact, appeal to your sibling's sense of nostalgia.** You might break the ice by sending your sibling a favorite old photo of the two of you together. Or mail a birthday card that expresses how much you miss the family connection. Or write a letter inviting your sibling to reconnect in light of an important life event that deserves to be shared, such as a parent's illness or the birth of a new grandchild. Don't give up too easily—if your first overture goes unacknowledged, wait a bit and then try again.

- **Acknowledge your own role.** Many people have trouble seeing the truth in this, but in the majority of cases, both parties contribute something to the conflict. Even if the bulk of the blame lies with your sibling, you probably played at least a small part. Admitting this to yourself lessens your resentment…acknowledging it to your sibling may make it easier for him or her to accept responsibility, too. Apologize sincerely—"I'm sorry that I teased you about your weight." Resist the urge to end with a "but" phrase (as in "but there was no reason for you to call me a nasty name, throw my favorite vase across the room and then refuse to speak to me for months"). Instead, end with a request for forgiveness—"Please pardon me for not giving you the respect you deserve."

- **Forge a new friendship.** Once contact has been renewed, strengthen ties by planning fun times together. Start small—for instance, with a siblings-only bike ride or an afternoon at a spa. While you're together, ask about your sibling's joys and concerns…truly listen to the responses and offer to help with a problem if possible. Remember, it's never too late to change the competitive, rivalrous relationship of childhood into one based on sharing and caring.

Expanding Your Circle of Friends

Judy Kuriansky, PhD, is a clinical psychologist and sex therapist on the adjunct faculty of Teachers College, Columbia University in New York City. She is the author of five books, including *The Complete Idiot's Guide to a Healthy Relationship.* DrJudy.com

Two tickets to your favorite opera just fell into your lap, but no one you know shares your passion for arias. Or you need to get something upsetting off your chest but fear that none of your usual confidantes would really understand. Or maybe you're just a bit bored being at home by yourself and wish you had more pals to hang out with.

Whatever your reason for feeling alone, the solution is to find some more new friends. *Here's how to get started…*

- **Go to places where you'll see the same people repeatedly.** Familiarity fosters friendship. Clubs and classes provide the opportunity for repeat encounters that promote increasing comfort with and connection to fellow members. As a bonus, they also guarantee a shared interest upon which to build a bond.

So: Register for that fascinating history course at the local community college…sign up for that spin class you've been meaning to try…or join your town's gardening club.

- **Pursue activities that invite interaction.** You may love going to the movies or the theater, but a dark auditorium is not a great venue for getting a conversation going.

Better: Go to lectures about movies, where people will be exchanging ideas…or join a community theater or improv group, where participants naturally get to know each other on personal levels. Or if sports are your passion, don't just stay home alone to watch games on TV. Instead, go to a local restaurant where the games are broadcast or, better yet, become a booster for a local team. The high-energy environment at the restaurant or playing field helps dissipate shyness and encourages strangers to interact enthusiastically with fellow fans. You don't even have to spend big bucks to see professional athletes—your local school teams would welcome your support.

●**Take a fresh look at current acquaintances.** Sure, it's great to meet new people, but don't be too quick to dismiss those you already know in passing. Your initial indifference (for instance, to the foreign-born coworker who never laughs at your jokes) or even aversion (to the neighbor who looks like the vixen who stole your high school boyfriend) might be unwarranted. Challenge yourself to see beyond superficial characteristics to recognize that a person with a different outlook or background can provide a refreshing change of pace as a new pal.

●**Make the first move.** Once you've found another woman with whom you'd like to be closer, show that you're interested and can be counted on. Pass along a book she had mentioned wanting to read or a CD you think she'd enjoy…invite her to go for a bike ride or to come by your house to sample a new recipe you discovered…offer to walk her dog or run an errand for her when she's feeling overwhelmed or under the weather. Remember, the easiest way to make a good friend is to be a good friend.

The Secrets to Strong Friendships at Any Age

Jeffrey Zaslow, coauthor of the best-selling book The Last Lecture and author of *The Girls from Ames* (GirlsFromAmes. com), also a best seller.

Friendship is good for mental and physical health—research shows that having close friends raises self-esteem, boosts immunity and improves sleep. A study from Flinders University in Australia even found that people with many close friends live longer than those with few friends.

Best-selling writer Jeffrey Zaslow spent two years getting to know a close-knit group of women, now in their 40s, who met as girls in Ames, Iowa. As the 11 women moved to different states, pursued careers,

married and became mothers, they maintained a powerful bond that has endured to this day.

We spoke to Zaslow to find out what the girls from Ames can teach us all about developing strong friendships at any age…

What is different about the Ames girls that has allowed their friendship to last so long?

They are not as unusual as you might think. I first learned about this group of women after writing a *Wall Street Journal* column about turning points in women's friendships. Hundreds of readers wrote to me in response, describing their own lifelong friendships. Jenny—one of the girls from Ames—was among them. I was surprised at how many people I heard from who had been able to keep their friendships strong over the years.

What do long-term friendships give us that short-term ones don't?

Newer friends may know us in a limited context—as colleagues, as volunteers, or as someone's spouse or parent. Friends from childhood or college have a fuller picture of us. They see beyond the roles that we have assumed in life. They see the ways that we have changed and the qualities in us that have not changed.

Longtime friends can provide a greater depth of emotional support during difficult times. For example, when Marilyn's father developed Alzheimer's disease, her newer friends in Minnesota knew her father only as someone with dementia. Her friends from Ames remembered him as the beloved pediatrician who often gave them wise, practical advice and served the community with dedication for many years. These memories were a great comfort to her.

How are men's friendships different from women's?

According to research, men continue building friendships until around age 30, after which the number of friends steadily declines. Men then tend to get their emotional needs met by their wives. In contrast, women tend to neglect their friendships most in their 20s and 30s, while they are raising young children, but return to them when they reach their 40s and beyond.

One dramatic difference between men's and women's friendships is that women build trust by talking about highly personal topics. Men's conversations with one another tend to be less personal—they bond by doing things together.

How can people go about reconnecting with old friends?

Technology can help. Look up your old friends on Facebook.com or through your alumni association's database. There even are Web sites, such as Classmates.com, designed to help you find old friends. Then send an e-mail or a note—a few paragraphs catching the person up on your work and family or news from your old town or school.

You may have fewer interests in common with older friends than with newer friends. Focus on the commonalities—the history and memories that you share.

Keep expectations modest, and read the social signals. If your five-paragraph missive about your life gets a one-sentence reply, don't take it personally. Accept that the timing or the match may not be right, and reach out to other old friends.

Can friendships formed in adulthood ever be as strong as friendships begun earlier in life?

While there is no substitute for the people who knew you when, we live long lives, and a friend you make later in life is one you can potentially value for years.

THE 6 KEYS TO FRIENDSHIP

The Ames friends share a number of unspoken ground rules that are crucial to maintaining trust and connection in any friendship…

1. Work at staying connected. The friends are in e-mail contact with one another nearly every day, hitting "reply all" to keep the whole group in the loop. They get together as a full group at least once a year and in smaller groups several times a year.

2. Root for one another. They celebrate one another's successes, sending cards, flowers and congratulatory e-mails. Sometimes they feel envious, but they don't undercut one another. They recognize that friendship is not a competition and take pleasure in one another's good fortune.

3. Don't gloat. They don't boast about their incomes or their spouses' incomes. When they talk about their children's achievements, they don't do it in a competitive or domineering way.

4. Show up for important events. In 1986, Sheila, one of the 11 friends, died in a fall. The women were in their 20s, spread across the country, and only half of them could afford to travel back to Ames for the funeral. Those who didn't attend still regret that they weren't able to show support for Sheila's family or get closure.

Years later, when Karla's teenage daughter died after a long illness, every Ames girl came to the memorial service.

The friends make a point of being present for the landmark events in one another's lives—from weddings to serious illnesses and funerals.

5. Be flexible and understanding. The friends recognize that people's needs and capacities ebb and flow. While they expect loyalty and goodwill from one another, they don't demand constant attention. If an e-mail or a phone call isn't returned right away, they don't get resentful or worry that they're being snubbed. They give one another room to live full lives and be busy and tired.

They also are generous when one member of the circle needs more attention than usual. When Kelly was going through a divorce, the others listened for as long as she needed to talk.

6. Protect confidences. Secrets shared among group members stay within the group. Disagreements with one another also get hashed out within the group—they don't complain to spouses or to other friends.

Example: The biggest disagreement the girls hashed out with one another was how much to share of themselves in the book. Some girls shared more private details about themselves (and the relationship and their friends) than others were comfortable with. There were times when feelings were bruised, and they had to reach a consensus on how much from their diaries and letters they were willing to share for inclusion in the book.

How to End Any Grudge…and Keep New Ones from Starting

Barbara LeBey, Esq., an attorney and a former Georgia state court judge who saw firsthand how grudges escalate into serious conflict. LeBey lives in Atlanta and is author of *Family Estrangements: How They Begin, How to Mend Them, How to Cope With Them and Remarried With Children: Ten Secrets for Successfully Blending and Extending Your Family.*

Although grudges can cause great harm, they occur so often that many of us think of grudges as hardships that we're obliged to endure. In fact, says Judge Barbara LeBey, ending grudges is often easier than people realize. *Here LeBey shares her strategies to end a grudge and keep new ones from beginning…*

WHAT EXACTLY IS A GRUDGE?

It's a feeling of resentment or ill will that one person harbors against another. In families, grudges often result from divorce, disputes over inheritances, sibling rivalry or quarrels over lifestyle, such as the choice of a spouse or accepting a gay person into the family. Inside and outside of the family, grudges can occur after arguments over politics, religion, sports or any other issue that arouses passion.

WHAT'S THE HARM IN HOLDING A GRUDGE?

Grudges create stress that can be physically and psychologically harmful. They also lead to estrangements. For instance, when a grudge keeps you from getting together with a cousin, it can have a ripple effect with other family members.

Holidays, birthdays and other family occasions can be ruined by the absence of the estranged loved one.

Work environments can also be affected by grudges. At the office, feelings of ill will can prevent two people from working effectively with each other. When that happens, they can both get a reputation for being difficult to work with—a trait that's a handicap in the business world. Grudges are not worth the consequences.

WHAT ARE THE BEST WAYS TO END A GRUDGE?

If you've caused a slight—intentionally or otherwise—apologize, but don't rehash. Instead, talk about subjects on which both of you agree or share an interest. If a topic arises on which you disagree, try to avoid expanding on that topic. Or, in a friendly way, agree to disagree. With politics, for example, say something like, "I disagree with the Republican (or Democratic) philosophy, but I respect your views." Most people are eager to bury the hatchet.

If a friend, loved one or coworker won't speak with you, you might ask for help from a third party. While a third party may not solve your dispute, he/she may open the door so that the two of you can get back together and resolve it. The third party, for instance, might know that the other grudge holder believes that you insulted him. As a result, he'll likely suggest that you apologize.

For example, a pastor, rabbi or other religious leader can often help prevent lingering ill will in the case of divorces. Your house of worship can usually help you contact appropriate professionals to deal with disputes involving substance abuse, inheritances or a family business. Marriage counselors frequently have helpful advice on grudges involving in-laws.

As previously mentioned, rehashing is not a good idea.

Example: One divorced lawyer I knew had not seen his two sons for almost eight years because they sided with the mother. The father kept trying to meet with his sons to have lunch or dinner and talk.

His new wife cautioned him about meeting with his sons to talk about the problem. Instead, he invited his older son to be his partner in an amateur golf tournament. "We don't even have to talk," he said. The son, an avid golfer, couldn't refuse.

During the tournament, they rarely spoke, but they came in first. Afterward, when they were putting their clubs in their cars, they looked at each other and then embraced. Later, they went to ball games with the other son, and all three eventually became good friends.

Similar strategies to break the ice are often just as successful—going to a movie, a block party or any other event that both parties enjoy.

WHAT STEPS CAN YOU TAKE TO END A GRUDGE BEFORE IT CAUSES SERIOUS HARM?

Take action as soon as you sense that a relationship has soured. A good friend, for example, might stop keeping in touch or decline your repeated invitations. Call the person and suggest getting together. If he or she declines, point out that you haven't seen each other in a long time. Come right out and ask, "Have I done anything to offend you?" You may discover that you unintentionally did slight your friend.

On the other hand, people's interests often change. Maybe you and your friend used to go fishing together but now he's taken up tennis. Or maybe the friend might not be eager to socialize because he has gained weight.

Again, that trusted third party can be of help. He might point out what the friend won't tell you—that you forgot to invite him to your holiday party last year...or that he's fallen on hard times and is embarrassed about a loan that he can't repay.

But if the friend actually interpreted something you said as an insult, quickly explain that you meant no insult, and apologize for saying what you did. Don't be concerned about who was right or wrong in interpreting your remark. The harm caused by a grudge nearly always outweighs the discomfort of swallowing your pride.

Sometimes it's best not to continue a toxic relationship because the harm was too great and likely to last. To avoid holding a grudge and all the negativity that this implies, be polite. Tell the person that you need a lot more time to work through your feelings, and that maybe someday you and he can resume contact. But for now, it's best to leave things as they are.

Result: You have addressed the problem with maturity and an element of hope. You've closed the door but you haven't locked it.

How to Gracefully End a Bad Relationship

Henry Cloud, PhD, a leadership coach and clinical psychologist based in Los Angeles. He is author of *Necessary Endings: The Employees, Businesses, and Relationships That All of Us Have to Give Up in Order to Move Forward.* DrCloud.com

Endings can be as important as beginnings in personal and professional relationships. But people often are reluctant to face the awkwardness and pain—on both sides—of ending a bad relationship.

Why it's crucial: Although it may sound harsh, the time and energy that we waste on bad relationships could be more enjoyably or profitably devoted to people and pursuits that we prefer. Worse, when we spend time with people who have bad attitudes, bad habits or chronic bad moods, we dramatically increase the odds that we will suffer from these, too—a phenomenon called "social contagion."

Example: A study published in *The New England Journal of Medicine* found that our odds of becoming obese increase by 57% if one of our friends becomes obese. The same research team also found that having a single unhappy friend increases the odds that we will be unhappy by about 7%.

Yet most people rarely, if ever, end bad relationships, aside from failed romantic relationships. They continue putting up with unpleasant, unproductive or even toxic associations because they don't want to hurt anyone's feelings...they don't want to endure the difficult conversation required to end a relationship...they don't realize the price they're paying for having this person in their life...they view ending relationships as a form of failure...and/or they think only mean people intentionally cut other people out of their lives.

Ending bad relationships is not selfish. If we don't end them, we have less time and energy for the friends, loved ones and business associates who need and deserve our attention. And we risk dragging those people down with the bad habits and moods that we pick up from our troubled relationships. It is perfectly natural for relationships to end.

What's not natural is maintaining relationships that bring more bad than good to our lives.

PICKING PEOPLE TO DROP

Consider what you want your life and career to be like. Now consider each of your personal and professional relationships. Which are not helping you move toward this vision? Which are pulling you away from it? These are the relationships that may have to end.

Exception: It might be worth continuing a difficult relationship if there are overriding reasons, such as a marriage worth salvaging, and especially if there is a reason to believe that this person and relationship could improve in the near future. Perhaps the relationship used to be better and turned sour only because this person is going through a difficult phase...or perhaps this person recently has begun taking action to address his/her problems.

SECOND CHANCES

If someone you're considering eliminating from your life is wise enough to respond positively to feedback, that is reason to have hope that the relationship could improve. *Before ending any relationship...*

●**Discuss with the other person the trouble that you are having with the relationship.**

Example: "Lately, when we are together, you complain about something the entire time. I need friends who will help me grow in life, solve problems and feel good about life. I would like you to be one of those friends. If you can do that, I would love to continue to spend time with you. If not, I'm not going to be able to socialize with you anymore."

Be open about your own faults, too, during this discussion. Try to frame your concerns as issues that you bring to the relationship as well, not just complaints about the other person's behavior.

Use a soft and caring tone of voice, and say how much the positive aspects of the relationship have meant to you.

If this person listens to your concerns and strives to correct the problems you raise, the relationship could be worth continuing. If he/she becomes defensive, angry or combative when faced with these problems, there's much less hope for the relationship. *What to do...*

●**Lay out the specific, painful consequences** this person will incur because of his misbehavior.

Example: "Because you keep getting drunk and belligerent when the family gets together, you're no longer invited when there might be alcohol present."

Leave it to this person to decide whether he can do what is necessary to continue the relationship.

●**Presented with an ultimatum,** this person might try to improve or he might quietly disappear from your life. If neither of these things occurs, proceed to the section below, and do so without guilt—you are not the one ending this relationship. Your former acquaintance is ending it by declining to do what is necessary to save it.

HOW TO PREPARE

To make a break in a way that lets you feel it is a positive step, you have to prepare yourself in various ways...

●**Keep your vision for your life in front of you.** Position photos of the people you love spending time with where you'll see them frequently. This should continually remind you what you're sacrificing when you waste time on toxic relationships. Budget time for the relationships you value and make them a priority.

●**Increase your interactions with the problem person.** We normally attempt to limit our interactions with those we don't like so that we can avoid facing the problem. But by distancing ourselves from bad relationships, we make it possible to pretend that they're not really so bad. Stop screening calls from people you don't want to talk to, and stop coming up with excuses to cut conversations with them short. The more you face the pain that the relationship causes you, the greater the odds that you'll reach the point where you're willing to end it.

Helpful: When you speak with these people, picture yourself dealing with them not just today but next month, next year and for the rest of your life.

●**Seek out new, fulfilling relationships.** Your desire to end bad relationships is likely to climb dramatically if you have numerous enjoyable, productive relationships and activities vying for your time.

Helpful: Volunteer with a variety of nonprofit causes that you care about. This should increase your awareness that your time is valuable and help you meet new people who have a positive outlook on life.

HOW TO END IT

To minimize hurt feelings and raised tempers, place the blame for the failed relationship on the way you and this person interact with each other, not solely on the other person's shoulders.

If the other person becomes angry, express empathy, then return the conversation to the issue.

Example: "I know this is hard to hear. It's hard for me to say. But this really is an issue, and it isn't getting any better."

This is not fun, but it's the only way you can spend your time with people you have decided to invest in—and the only way that those people will get as much of you as they deserve.

Purpose and Passion

Science Discovers the Secret to Happiness

Robert A. Emmons, PhD, professor of psychology, University of California, Davis. A leading scholar of positive psychology, he is author of *Thanks! How the New Science of Gratitude Can Make You Happier.*

Surprise! Research suggests that becoming more grateful could make each of us 25% happier—and that being happy is the key to a longer, more successful life. Our lives do not just seem better when we are happy—they actually become better, according to a recent analysis of hundreds of psychological studies. Happy people tend to have longer, more loving marriages…are healthier…live an average of seven to nine years longer than chronically unhappy people… and have more successful careers. According to one study, happy college graduates had annual salaries $25,000 higher than unhappy graduates 16 years after graduation.

While an endless procession of self-help gurus have claimed to know the path to happiness, psychological studies generally have failed to confirm that proposed happiness strategies actually work.

One notable exception: Research conducted in the past decade appears to indicate that we can become happier by feeling more gratitude.

Psychology professor Robert A. Emmons, PhD, of the University of California, Davis, provides more information…

What is "gratitude" to a psychologist?

In simple terms, gratitude is our affirmation of a benefit that we have received and our recognition that this benefit has come to us from outside of ourselves.

You say that becoming more grateful will make us happier, but how do we know that it isn't the other way around, and happiness creates gratitude?

Our research suggests that increases in happiness do not lead to increases in gratitude, but increases in gratitude do in fact increase happiness. We designed a study to test this. Participants were divided into two groups, each of which were initially equally happy. Members of one of these groups were asked to write in a journal the things that they were grateful for, which made them more conscious of and grateful for the good fortune that came their way. At the end of the study, the journal-keeping group was 25% happier than members of the group that did not keep gratitude journals.

Why does feeling gratitude make us happier?

Primarily, I believe, it is because gratitude increases our sense of connection to other people. Having strong relationships is the single best predictor of happiness, and our relationships become stronger when we acknowledge the support we receive from those around us. Acknowledging the support we receive from others provides us with confirmation that we have value in other people's eyes. Gratitude also buffers us from envy, resentment and regret, emotions that inhibit happiness.

Why do people often have trouble being grateful for what they have?

Lots of reasons. Most of us are fortunate to have pretty good lives, so our default reaction might be to take the benefits that come our way for granted. Consumerism and other cultural pressures can foster a sense that we deserve even more than we have. Our desire to see ourselves as self-sufficient makes it difficult to admit that someone else has helped us. And admitting gratitude can create uncomfortable feelings of indebtedness.

Can we consciously choose to become more grateful and thus happier?

Yes, I do believe it is a choice. Chronically unhappy people do not greatly differ from happy people in terms of their life circumstances—they just approach life with a different set of attitudes. Unhappy people tend to see themselves as victims of their past, and feel entitled or exaggeratedly deserving when good fortune comes their way. Happy people are thankful that good things happen to them—even though their lives might be no better than those of the unhappy people next door. We cannot always alter the events of our lives, but we can alter our attitudes.

What, specifically, can we do to become more grateful?

Make an effort to speak about your life using words of gratitude even if you do not feel very grateful. Though it seems counterintuitive, we can become more grateful by forcing ourselves to feign gratefulness that we do not initially feel. Speak in terms of gifts and givers, not regrets and setbacks. Refer to yourself as blessed or fortunate, not deserving or lacking. Say that you live in abundance, not in need. For example, say "I feel so grateful when I can sleep through the night," rather than "Most nights I wake up every few hours."

Keeping a gratitude journal also seems to encourage gratefulness. Every day or every week, write down five or more things for which you are grateful. Be specific—"I'm grateful for my spouse" is little more than a cliché, but "I'm grateful that my spouse picked up my dry cleaning this afternoon" reminds us that we are grateful to our partner today for a particular reason. Try not to repeat entries—gratitude journals are most effective when we think of new items each day.

Incidentally, if you are struggling to get to sleep at night, don't count sheep, count your blessings. Grateful people sleep better and longer than ungrateful people, and wake feeling more refreshed.

What is the secret to being grateful in the face of struggle or tragedy?

The secret is not to wait until tragedy strikes. Become more grateful while your life is running smoothly, so that gratitude becomes an ingrained part of your "psychological immune system." That will make it easier to view difficulties as temporary and surmountable setbacks, or even as opportunities in disguise.

A grateful person mourns the passing of a close friend, but he/she also feels lucky to have known the friend as long as he did, and is glad that he has so many other friends remaining.

Many prayers are expressions of gratitude. So, do religious people have an advantage when it comes to actually feeling gratitude and being happy?

Yes, to some degree. One of the foundations of virtually every religion is that people should give thanks to God and to each other. Religious texts and religious teachings typically provide models of how to be grateful, such as prayers of gratitude and rituals of giving thanks. Spirituality appears to be particularly helpful for maintaining a grateful outlook in the face of suffering and adversity.

The Kissing Prescription

Kory Floyd, PhD, professor of communication, The University of Arizona, Tucson.

Committed couples who increased their daily frequency of kissing reported less stress and greater relationship satisfaction after six weeks than couples who did not pucker up as often.

Bonus: The kissing couples also experienced significant drops in cholesterol levels.

Possible reason: Expressing affection as well as physical contact decreases the physical and psychological effects of stress.

Having a Purpose in Life Prevents Dementia

Patricia A. Boyle, PhD, neuropsychologist, Rush Alzheimer's Disease Center, and associate professor, department of behavioral sciences, Rush University Medical Center, both in Chicago. Her study was published in *Archives of General Psychiatry.*

You already know that staying physically and mentally active may help stave off dementia, but researchers have found yet another protective trick—having a purpose in life.

This doesn't mean having a goal that has a definite end point, such as telling yourself that you'll run a marathon or write a novel.

For brain protection, having a purpose in life is a little bit different.

What are some examples of "purposes," and how can you figure out what yours is if you don't already have one?

WARDING OFF BRAIN FOG

Researchers analyzed 246 senior citizens who received annual cognitive testing for about 10 years. Each was asked questions to determine whether he or she had a strong purpose in life. When participants died, they underwent brain autopsies.

What the researchers found was that in participants who had a lot of plaques and tangles in their brains—abnormal structures in and around the brain's nerve cells that are hallmarks of Alzheimer's disease—the rate of cognitive decline had been about 30% slower for people who had a strong purpose in life compared with those who had had a weaker purpose or no purpose at all.

Here's what (hopefully) these findings mean: The stronger your purpose in life, the less likely you'll suffer cognitive decline as you age, even if your brain is affected by Alzheimer's signs. If that's true it means that you can preserve your cognitive ability by making sure that you have a purpose.

Of course, it could be the other way around—it could be that some people have a biological problem that makes them less able to cope with brain plaques and tangles and, also, less able to feel that their lives have purpose.

GO FOR IT ANYWAY

According to lead study author Patricia A. Boyle, PhD, a neuropsychologist in the Alzheimer's Disease Center at Rush University Medical Center in Chicago, her research doesn't prove whether purposefulness helps our brains work better or is simply a side effect of a brain that is already working better. Maybe research will determine that one day. But on the other hand, since having a sense of purpose seems to make people happier, she said, why not cultivate one?

Based on her work with the study subjects, Dr. Boyle defines a life purpose as "the sense that one's life has meaning and direction—that one is intentional and motivated to engage in activities that one finds important and fulfilling." In other words, it's what gets you out of bed each day and makes you feel that life is worth living.

A purpose doesn't have to be ambitious or complicated. In fact, many purposes are simple, said Dr. Boyle. It just can't have a definite end point—it has to last throughout your life. For example, some purposes include spending time every day with loved ones…helping other people (for example through long-term volunteer work)…learning something new every day…or passing down a certain set of knowledge or skills to a younger generation. If you love running marathons or writing novels, make sure that your goal is to continue pursuing those goals through life—and not just run one marathon or write one novel.

It's not so much what your purpose is, Dr. Boyle said—what's critical is how it makes you feel. If it stirs you up inside and makes you feel passionate, energetic and excited, then you've found it!

Turn Your Retirement Dreams into Reality

Joanne Waldman, director of training for Retirement Options, which certifies retirement coaches, and founder of New Perspective Coaching, a nationwide retirement-planning practice based in Chesterfield, Missouri. She is a professional certified coach (PCC), a board-certified coach (BCC), a licensed professional counselor and a certified gerontological counselor. RetirementOptions.com

Some people dream of playing golf every day in retirement, while others plan to travel the world, work part-time, take up a hobby, see grandchildren or just relax. The trouble is, no matter what they envisioned, many retirees discover that it's very difficult to turn their dreams of retirement into a satisfying reality.

There are lots of reasons why the reality of your retirement might not match your dream. But there also are many ways to improve things—if you know some important truths about retirement…

●**Leisure activities must provide much more than just relaxation in retirement.** If you ask people who are not yet retired what they expect to do with their free time in retirement, many will say that they'll do the same types of things they currently do on weekends—but do them on weekdays, too. Many discover, however, that their weekend pastimes are much less satisfying as full-time pursuits.

Example: Golf or tennis might be very enjoyable and relaxing when you play once or twice a week during the years when you still are working, but it could begin to feel boring—or even stressful—if you play most days in retirement.

What to do: Engage in a variety of leisure activities that collectively supply the following six needs—relaxation…physical exercise…social interaction…intellectual stimulation…cultural enrichment…and creative expression. Yes, you actually should make a list of your leisure activities, and then write down which needs are met by each. If retired life ever starts to feel empty and unenjoyable, review this list…determine which of these six needs are missing from your retirement…then explore activities that fill this niche until you find one you enjoy.

Example: A retired entrepreneur who had no creative outlet in retirement discovered that he loved glassblowing.

●**The single best way to make your retirement better is to make someone else's life better.** If you're like most people, a career isn't just a way to earn a paycheck. It also provides purpose—your clients, coworkers, employees and/or employers depend on you. Life in retirement can feel empty without this sense that you are doing things that are useful to other people.

What to do: Consult…or take a part-time job in a field that interests you…or volunteer with a nonprofit organization. If you don't already have a favorite nonprofit, check whether your local library has a "community service directory" or some other list of local nonprofits. Leaf through this until you find a few that seem appealing, then arrange meetings with these groups or volunteer with different ones until you find one that makes you feel truly useful.

Examples: A retired teacher who had survived cancer found meaning by volunteering at a cancer education center. A former high-level executive who discovered that making children laugh made his life feel meaningful went to clown school and then volunteered to entertain at children's hospitals.

Alternatives: Feeling useful generally is the most effective way for retirees to find meaning in life, but it is not the only way. Some people find meaning in tracing their heritage—research your family tree and/or travel to places that have a connection to your family history or ethnicity. Other people find meaning in going back to school to study something of deep interest.

●**The retirement you're planning may not be the retirement your partner is planning.** Most people approaching retirement think that they are on the same page as their spouses when it comes to retirement plans. Many will discover how far from the truth that is. Spouses often have different ideas about when to retire…where to live during retirement…and/or how to spend time and money during retirement. That's true even when couples believe they have hashed these things out—because one or both partners might not have fully communicated priorities…or simply might have had a change of heart.

What to do: Do not just chat informally with your spouse about retirement—hold a retirement-planning meeting to put a plan down on paper. Don't be surprised if your spouse's ideas are different from your own, and try not to get angry. If certain differences cannot be immediately resolved, schedule additional meetings.

Example: A husband did not realize that his younger wife would not be ready to retire when he was, and he feared that he might be too old to travel by the time she concluded her career. The couple agreed that the wife would cut back on her work hours, providing sufficient time for travel, while the husband continued working part-time as a consultant. Then they set a full retirement date roughly halfway between the dates each originally had in mind.

●**Your dream retirement destination might not be so dreamy in reality.** Some people dream of retiring where it's warm…others of living near the kids and grandkids…or in an exciting city. But if your retirement destination is not somewhere you have spent lots of time in recent years, living there might be quite different from what you imagine.

Example: A retired couple dreamed of returning to their long-ago hometown in retirement—but they hadn't lived there in 30 years. When they moved back, they discovered the people they knew were gone and the town no longer felt like the home they remembered.

What to do: Rent homes in possible retirement destinations before finalizing a move there. If your goal is to live near your children or other family members, chat with them about their long-term plans—are they planning to stay where they currently live? If moving close to young grandchildren, consider whether you will enjoy being an always-on-call baby-sitter…and whether your grandkids are likely to have time for you as they get older.

●**You're not going to hear from your old work friends as much as you expect.** Loss of socialization is not just a problem for older retirees who can-not easily get out of the house. It's also a problem for recent retirees whose friends still are working. Office friends are particularly likely to lose touch with you.

What to do: Join new groups and form new friendships when you retire.

One more thing you are likely to lose in retirement—status. You may have worked for decades to reach a respected position in your profession. When you leave that profession, it's natural to feel diminished. In fact, people who retire from management positions sometimes try to fill this void by treating their spouses like employees. They might not even realize they are doing it—and it really can strain a marriage.

What to do: If you owned a small business, worked for a Fortune 500 company or simply would enjoy helping small-business owners succeed, volunteer with the nonprofit association SCORE, which helps owners of small businesses, and serve as a mentor. Or volunteer to take a leadership role on projects for nonprofit organizations.

●**Your travel plans might be cut short.** People who plan to travel extensively in retirement almost always travel much less than they expect—around half as much, on average. They discover that frequent travel is tiring…that health issues can make travel a challenge…and/or that travel is more expensive than they thought. For couples, retirement travel tends to decrease as soon as either partner grows disenchanted with it.

What to do: If you plan to spend much of your retirement traveling, develop some contingency plans, too.

Example: A wife became frustrated when her husband did not want to travel in retirement as much as the couple had anticipated. She solved this by taking trips with a group of female friends while her husband stayed home.

Don't Waste Your Time Volunteering...When You Do It, Do It Right

Mark A. Stengler, NMD, naturopathic medical doctor in private practice, Encinitas, California...adjunct associate clinical professor at the National College of Natural Medicine, Portland, Oregon...author of *The Natural Physician's Healing Therapies.*

I recently asked one of my patients—Joe, a retiree in his 80s—what he had been up to and joked with him that whatever it was, it was keeping him healthy. He told me that his favorite activity is volunteering as a docent at the local art museum. He got to learn about each new exhibition and got to know it so well that he could lead tours. Volunteering is a kind of "medicine" for many of my patients. It keeps people like Joe active, mentally alert and engaged with other people, all of which contribute to his overall health. But volunteer experiences are not all alike. Based on current research, there seems to be a "right" way to volunteer—and when that happens, it can help you, too, no matter how old you are.

BEING NEEDED AND VALUED

As study after study has found, we get a lot when we give. In 2007, the federal government's Corporation for National and Community Service evaluated the health benefits of volunteering. Volunteering offers a variety of benefits to people of different age groups. For younger adults, it expands their skill set and introduces them to new situations and people that they might not otherwise encounter. While volunteering, people of all ages can experience what's known as a "helper's high," a feeling of euphoria, often followed by an ongoing feeling of well-being created through the act of giving.

Older adults who volunteer also reap distinct health benefits, even more so than their younger counterparts. The 2007 government report, which looked at 730 studies, found that adults over age 60 experienced improved mental and physical health, greater satisfaction with life and less depression. Older adults who volunteer live longer than adults who don't volunteer—they also have a greater sense of purpose and accomplishment, improved functional ability and tend to be less lonely and isolated than nonvolunteering adults.

Recent research bears this out. A 2011 study by Penn State College of Medicine researchers found that volunteering in a kindergarten class helped older adults with mild-to-moderate dementia by lowering their stress and enhancing their quality of life, relationships and self-esteem.

HOW TO BENEFIT FROM VOLUNTEERING

Research shows that for older adults to reap the psychological and physical health benefits of volunteering, certain criteria must be met...

•**Amount of time.** Health benefits from volunteering become evident for both younger and older adults after a certain "volunteering threshold," as researchers call it, has been met. Volunteers who help on a sporadic, irregular basis do not receive any benefit. Instead, people benefit most when they volunteer for two or more organizations...and perform between 40 and 100 hours or more of service annually, says the 2007 government report. (The study did not find that giving more hours provided more benefit.)

•**Level of engagement.** People who reap the benefits of volunteering are engaged with what they are doing—they aren't bored or just whiling away the time.

Lesson: Do something you enjoy.

•**Motivation.** Attitude makes a difference. In a study published in *Health Psychology*, University of Michigan researchers found that people who volunteered regularly without concern for their own interests had a lower risk for death four years later. People who volunteered for self-centered reasons (as an escape from their own troubles or because of other people's opinions) had the same mortality risk as nonvolunteers. If you are not sincere about your motivation to help others, you won't reap the benefits.

Interested in volunteering? Several websites provide lists of opportunities by region and interest, including Volunteer Match (VolunteerMatch.com) and the US government's United We Serve program (Serve.gov). To find out about opportunities if you don't have access to a computer, inquire at schools, churches and hospitals in your area.

Don't Retire! "Semi-Retire" to the Encore Career of Your Dreams

Nancy Collamer, a career counselor, speaker, and author of *Second-Act Careers: 50+ Ways to Profit from Your Passions During Semi-Retirement.* She also writes a semi-monthly career column for NextAvenue.com (PBS) and Forbes.com. MyLife styleCareer.com

---

After 30 or 40 years of working long, hard days, you may be getting ready to dial it down a little, but you're not ready for retirement. What can you do to ease up on your workday…or possibly adopt the career of your dreams?

We spoke with Nancy Collamer, a leading career coach, speaker, and author of *Second-Act Careers: 50+ Ways to Profit from Your Passions During Semi-Retirement*, to discover the numerous options…

Bottom Line: For many Baby Boomers and older Xers, the word "semi-retirement" is a dismal, scary word. How do we wrap our heads around it? What we want is a gradual way to lay off the 10-hour days and the long commutes and all the pressure and burden of what we've been doing for several years.

Collamer: I don't want semi-retirement to be a scary term. It really just indicates the time period between when you leave that full-time, high pressure lifestyle and when you'll be embracing full retirement. We used to think of retirement in terms of years; now we need to think of it in terms of decades. You want to fill that time with meaning and purpose and to have a reason to get up every day—hence the term "semi-retirement."

Bottom Line: When someone's thinking about semi-retirement, do they think about jobs that might be less of what they were doing before, or maybe the same thing they were doing closer to home, or whole new areas?

Collamer: Both.

Bottom Line: All of the above, right?

Collamer: All of the above…and then some. Let's start off by talking about people who may really enjoy what they've been doing, but they're just tired of doing it full-time, and they're trying to figure out, "How do I take all this expertise and experience that I have and just downshift a little bit?"

There are lots of different ways that you can do that. The first and most obvious is just to speak with your employer about going to a part-time or a flexible position. Some people actually leave their employers and they become consultants to their own companies. People often joke that they are semi-retired; what are they doing? They became a consultant.

Bottom Line: And doubled their rate, usually.

Collamer: Possibly. But there are lots of other things that you can do too. I put all of these things in the broad category of multiple streams of expert income. In addition to doing things like consulting, people become adjunct professors. These days, there are people who have created their own online courses. They write books, they write articles, they speak. All different ways that you can leverage that expertise during semi-retirement. So that's the first big bucket of jobs.

Certainly, another area that we see huge interest in is what we call encore careers. Encore careers mean jobs that combine purpose, passion and a paycheck. They're really second careers for the greater good. Somebody who had been an executive, let's say at a law firm, now goes to work as an advisor to a nonprofit, for example. It also includes people who go and do things like starting their own business, but a business that has an element of social good to it.

As another example, in my book I interviewed a woman who started a company called Cool Jams, which is an online company that sells pajamas for people dealing with night sweats. As part of her business model, she gives back 20% of her proceeds to charities that are meaningful to her. So there are lots of different ways that you can do those encore careers.

Bottom Line: What kind of decisions do semi-retirees need to make...and/or what kind of review of their finances is necessary before they take the leap into a risky career change?

Collamer: With any career change, it's obviously very important to take a look at your finances. For most people, this is a time in life when a couple of things are going on. First is that hopefully they've paid off their mortgage. Not true for everyone, but for most people. Also, nests are empty and household expenses (hopefully) have gone down.

People also might be able to claim Medicare and/or Social Security. In general, it's best to hold off on collecting Social Security for as long as you can so that you'll eventually get a larger monthly payout. But maybe claiming it earlier will help you get going on the career of your dreams. Be aware that working while collecting Social Security can affect your payout. These are all important issues that need to be addressed. Just be sure that you don't delay your dream job to accommodate Social Security regulations!

That being said, most people are at a point where they can afford to take a cut in salary compared to what they were earning before. That opens up a lot of different options for them.

Bottom Line: So they can continue the same but less of what they've been doing, or they can do what you call these encore careers. They get to bring their passion and their goodwill into it. What else? Anything else that they could be doing?

Collamer: One of the areas that I think has tremendous growth for the Boomers is the whole area of entrepreneurial support services. By that, I mean more and more people are starting their own businesses. You have a plumber or a jeweler or a photographer, all of whom are great at their core business, but they either don't have the time or the interest in doing all those other tasks that they need to keep their business running smoothly.

That can cover anything from doing the bookkeeping, social media, marketing, strategic planning—all of those things that you need these days to keep a business healthy. And people semiretiring from the corporate world have those skills. It can be a great way to work on a part-time basis, often from your home. You can help another small business owner get his or her feet off the ground.

Bottom Line: That's an interesting area. Is there a website or a network or some place where people can find entrepreneurial startups? Because it's not so easy to find.

Collamer: I'd say the best way to do that is to go to local meetings through Meetup.com. Check in at your Chamber of Commerce. There are all sorts of different entrepreneurial and networking groups that filter through the C of C and it's a great place to meet other people who have small businesses. Or quite frankly, just go out on Main Street and take a look into office buildings and see who's doing what.

You're somebody who can bring 30 years of experience to a brand new venture. If they're hiring you on a freelance basis, they're not paying benefits. It can be a great arrangement for both parties.

Bottom Line: The bottom line is if you're ready to downshift your career, go ahead, you can do it. Number one, stay within your field. Use your well-honed skills, but reduce your time; see if you could actually stay within your own company with less hours. Or leave your company, but perhaps sell your skills back as a consultant. Or go to your competitors. Go to others that are in the industry.

Similarly, you could do entrepreneurial support. Seek out startup companies that need part-time or short-term executive or other kind of skills to help grow their businesses, but they're not ready to hire your specific position full-time.

On the third hand, go after your passion. Semiretirement might be the time to start working for a nonprofit or working in an area that you didn't think tenable before (such as the arts). Now that your living expenses have gone down and you don't have to accommodate the long commutes for the high salary, you can venture into areas that you had previously considered impossible. It's all a great opening for you.

Make Your Donation More Meaningful

Tracy Gary, a philanthropic adviser for thousands of non-profit groups, grant-making associations and private and community foundations. Based in Ross, California, she is author of *Inspired Philanthropy: Your Step-by-Step Guide to Creating a Giving Plan and Leaving a Legacy*. InspiredPhilanthropy.org

D o you want more control and/or credit for what happens to your charitable contributions, even if you have just a few hundred or a few thousand dollars to give?

Here's how…

FOR SMALLER AMOUNTS

Join a "giving circle." In a giving circle, friends or colleagues organize around a common interest, such as environmental conservation or education reform. They pool their resources and meet several times a year to select local charities or community projects for grants. Individual donations typically range from just $25 to $500 per year. Members are expected to take an active role in researching and visiting potential grantees.

Example: Bread For The Journey (BreadForThe Journey.org) is a giving circle started by a minister and community advocate in Sante Fe, New Mexico, in 1988. It now has local chapters in 20 cities that make what they call "micro-grants," typically ranging from $300 to $3,000, to recipients that include a Seattle clinic that offers free acupuncture to traumatized US war veterans…and a grassroots organization in Austin, Texas, that provides free transportation for the elderly and cancer patients. Chapter members feel a great sense of control over their charitable giving because they interact closely with the recipients in planning how the money will be used and they witness the benefits and results firsthand.

•**Create a scholarship.** School funding has taken a big hit since the 2008–2009 recession, and your former college or high school—or the college or high school of a loved one—may be eager to accept a donor-specified gift.

How it works: Call the individual in charge of charitable donations at the school and describe the type of scholarship that you would like to es-

tablish. He/she will work with you to create an annual scholarship in your name or in memory of someone, typically for $100 to $1,000 a year or more. For example, if you weren't a good student in high school, you could start a scholarship for an underperforming high school student that offers money for a tutor.

Note: Larger educational institutions may have much higher minimums ($5,000 and up) to create a named scholarship or a donor-specified gift. But even at those schools, you still can donate smaller amounts to already existing scholarships with criteria that align with your philanthropic wishes.

FOR MODERATE AMOUNTS

Set up an account at a donor-advised fund. These independent public charities, run by well-known investment companies such as Fidelity, let you grow your money in an investment portfolio and make grants from the portfolio.

How it works: You open a brokerage account at a donor-advised fund, then make a tax-deductible, irrevocable contribution (typically at least $5,000), which means that you can no longer use the money for any purpose other than charitable giving. Your account can be funded with cash… publicly traded securities…mutual fund shares… and/or the cash value of a life insurance policy. You choose from investment portfolios with aggressive, moderate or conservative allocations. You are allowed to decide what grants are made, when and to whom as long as the grants are to IRS-qualified public charities.

Costs: The donor-advised fund handles all the administrative, legal and tax-related tasks for an annual fee that typically is 0.6% of total assets. Additional investment fees range from 0.1% and up annually.

Tax advantages: When you make a contribution to a donor-advised fund, the IRS allows you to take a deduction on your adjusted gross income (AGI) for that amount. Depending on how much cash you donate, you are allowed up to 50% of your AGI. For donations of securities such as stocks, you can take up to 30% of your AGI. Deductions for any contributions exceeding these annual limits may be carried forward for up to five years.

Recommended: Fidelity Charitable Gift Fund (800-262-6039, FidelityCharitable.org), the largest donor-advised fund in the US, has made more than $13 billion in grants. For the Calvert Giving Fund (800-248-0337, ImpactAssets.org/giving-fund), your contributions are invested in Calvert's "socially responsible" mutual funds.

Establish a charitable fund through a community foundation. These are supported by local donors and typically focus on benefiting a specific community.

How it works: There are similar rules, costs and tax advantages as with a donor-advised fund. Typical donations are in the thousands of dollars, but you can contribute as little as $100 to many community foundations. You give directly to the foundation, but the staff typically is willing to consult and work closely with you to determine and address the areas of greatest need in your community and what grants your money should fund. This also gives you the opportunity to network with other donors on charitable issues.

Example: The Cleveland Foundation in Ohio was the first community foundation in the US. Recent grants of nearly $80 million were made to local programs such as the Cleveland Shakespeare in the Park festival and scholarships to Montessori schools for children in financial need. There are about 1,000 community foundations across the US today. Find one near you at COF.org.

Give a donor-designated contribution to your local hospital.

How it works: Contact the hospital's development office. The staff will work with you to fund existing programs or designate specific tax-deductible gifts ranging from a donation to a certain department to purchasing a piece of medical equipment. For example, I had a client who recovered from breast cancer at a teaching hospital. She donated several thousand dollars to fund breast cancer research there.

Give to your local municipality. Visit your municipality's website. You typically can find donation programs under the mayor's office or a specific department to focus your philanthropy. Your name and donations may be listed online or in printed materials. And in many areas, there are opportunities for even more direct acknowledgment, such as a plaque with your name and an inscription.

Examples: The Central Park Adopt-A-Bench program allows you to adopt a bench for a onetime gift of $7,500. And in Stamford, Connecticut, Mill River Park will put your name on a stepping stone for $500…a bike rack for $2,000…or a carousel horse for $10,000.

New Breakthroughs in Retirement Living

9 Worst Retirement Regrets: Many You Still Can Fix

Jeff Yeager, AARP's official "Savings Expert" and host of a weekly AARP web show on YouTube (YouTube.com/CheapLifeChannel). Based in Accokeek, Maryland, he is author of several popular books about frugal living, including *How to Retire the Cheapskate Way.* UltimateCheapskate.com

Enjoying retirement is near the top of most people's wish lists. But when I was researching my book on retirement, I heard again and again from retirees what they wished they had done differently before retiring—and many of these retirees had the same regrets.

By heeding the advice of the already-retired, you can avoid the common regrets and enjoy your retirement that much more…

●**Not retiring sooner (because maybe you can afford to do so).** Most of the retirees I spoke with were enjoying their retirement immensely, and when I asked about any regrets, they often said, "My only regret is that I should have retired sooner!" Many went on to explain that once they settled into retirement, they found that their spending and general cost of living dropped to a level where they realistically could have afforded to retire earlier. While undersaving for retirement is a scary and real possibility for many people, oversaving for retirement happens quite a bit, in part because, according to data from the Bureau of Labor Statistics, we naturally spend less and less as we age throughout our retirement years on nearly all types of consumer goods and services…with the notable exception of health care.

●**Not doing your homework.** Many retirees admitted that they took the time to learn how some of the most basic features of retirement worked only when they were on the cusp of retirement or even after they were fully retired. Many retirees confessed that they waited too long to learn the ins and outs of Social Security and Medicare…what benefits they were entitled to receive under their pensions and retirement accounts…and the fine points of things such as long-term-care insurance and reverse mortgages. Not doing this type of homework earlier cost one person I interviewed $6,000 a year in lost pension benefits that she could have started collecting years earlier, while she still was working. She told me, "I looked into it only when I was actually ready to stop working—a big mistake."

●**Not burying the hatchet sooner.** It's never too early to patch things up with family members or others with whom you have a strained relationship, but carrying that emotional baggage with you into retirement really can tarnish your later years. Not only will you have more time in retirement to sit around and brood about such unpleasant affairs (if that's how you choose to spend your time), but having close, supportive relationships with family and friends—a care network that you can depend on—can be a tremendous asset, particularly in retirement.

•**Not planning for all that leisure time.** If you are used to working full time and have few leisure-time interests, filling all that newfound time during retirement can be a real challenge. Retirees say that you should cultivate hobbies and other activities before you retire so that you're not overwhelmed by all of that additional free time. Also, if one spouse is used to being alone around the house and has been primarily responsible for managing the household, injecting a second person into that situation can create stress in a relationship, to the point where one woman told me, "I wanted to get a job when my husband retired because having him around all the time drove me crazy." Respecting each other's boundaries and need for alone time, and agreeing upon and sharing responsibilities for household management, before you retire make the transition easier.

•**Not downsizing earlier.** Downsizing your household and lifestyle—by doing such things as moving to a smaller home, getting rid of unwanted items and maybe selling off a second car—is a pretty common practice among retired folks. And once they've done it, many retirees say they wished they had done it years earlier, long before they retired. "It's so liberating being free of all that extraneous stuff," one retired man told me. "I just wish I'd done it when I was 50 instead of 70…well, actually, I wish I never would have bought most of that stuff in the first place." Of course, downsizing earlier also can allow you to build your retirement nest egg that much faster and allow you to retire with less debt—or better yet, with no debt.

•**Not kicking a bad habit earlier.** Having more time on your hands can prompt you to further indulge in any bad habits. Maybe the cocktail hour you have always enjoyed starts earlier in the day and lasts longer…or an occasional trip to the racetrack becomes a daily gambling obsession. Being relatively isolated at home and having more free time to indulge are among the chief reasons why substance abuse among elderly people is a growing problem, according to a 2011 study by the Substance Abuse and Mental Health Services Administration.

•**Not drawing Social Security at the best time.** Many financial experts suggest holding off as long as possible, ideally until age 70, when you're entitled to the largest monthly benefit, nearly 75% more than if you start drawing at age 62 (the current minimum age).

While that may be a good strategy for many, when my wife recently turned 62, we did the math and found that since she wants to continue to work part time and we are in a position to invest rather than spend her Social Security checks, she should start drawing benefits immediately. In all likelihood, she will come out ahead in the long run, compared with waiting until she's 66 (currently the full retirement age for many people).

Here's a calculator to help you figure out the optimum age at which you should start drawing Social Security—SSA.gov/retire2/otherthings.htm.

•**Not traveling earlier in retirement.** Many older retirees expressed regrets about not traveling or pursuing other activities that require more physical stamina at the front end of their retirement years. There is a tendency to postpone those activities when you're newly retired, both because you believe that your health will remain largely the same and you fear burning through too much of your retirement savings too soon. "Do what you can when you still can," one globe-trotting retiree told me, "because you never know how much longer you'll be able to do it."

•**Not taking better care of your health.** Mickey Mantle once said, "If I knew I was going to live this long, I'd have taken better care of myself." Entering retirement in ill health can have dire consequences in terms of both quality of life and finances. Maintaining optimum health throughout life and specifically "going into training" leading up to retirement, as one retiree put it, truly can make your retirement the best years of your life. But don't despair if your health is less than perfect when you hit retirement. A number of retirees said they were able to markedly improve their health once retired, when they had more time to devote to fitness.

4 Steps to an Amazingly Happy Retirement

Dave Corbett, founder, New Directions, Inc., which offers planing in career and postcareer fulfillment to accomplished individuals, NewDirections.com. He is author of *Portfolio Life: The New Path to Work, Purpose, and Passion After 50.*

The traditional definition of retirement is no longer appropriate for today's world. Now that life expectancy for an American woman is age 85 and for a man, 82, the arc of life has changed. It's no longer education, career, a few years of retirement and death. Now, it's education, career and, for many of us, another 20 or even 30 years in reasonably good health—a long, extended middle age, not old age.

Many active, intelligent individuals don't want to go from full-time career to full-time golf or knitting. Even people who are already years into their retirement choose to start a new, fulfilling phase of life. So, what do you do?

YOUR NEXT PHASE

To help individuals who want to remain active and engaged in this new chapter of their lives, I developed the idea of a "portfolio life."

Goal: To help you come up with a balanced combination of five elements that define who you are and help you decide what your next steps will be. Even though you may remain gainfully employed part time or full time, your portfolio life is an expression of you, not of your company or job title. *A typical portfolio life has these parts…*

●**Continue to work and make money in ways that you choose.**

●**Spend more time with loved ones.**

●**Enhance your hobbies**—make time for personal pursuits and recreation.

●**Continue your education with lifelong learning and self-development.**

●**Give back to society.**

To these five elements, many older adults also add a sixth—reground yourself and find your spirituality.

Why do I call this a portfolio? Just as you continually adjust, rebalance and diversify a financial portfolio as you get older, you can do the same with your life. Your portfolio life doesn't have to be evenly divided among all its parts. At some point, the need or desire to keep earning may occupy a larger part of your life…at another, giving back to society may take precedence. Developing a portfolio of different life activities and continually rebalancing and diversifying it as you go along brings flexibility and engagement to your later years. There's no chance that you will feel bored, useless or adrift during retirement.

DEATH BY RETIREMENT

A lot of people think retiring to someplace new and different is automatically going to be fabulous—near the beach, in the mountains, on a golf course…just fill in the blank. When they get there, though, some big issues set in—social isolation, being largely without goals for the first time, missing family members and friends who are now far away. They settle into a retirement rut, a routine of golf, worrying about their investments and making sure the pool is just the right temperature. Frankly, they accept lack of accomplishment as being the normal retirement lifestyle.

Example: One of my clients is a retired executive who ran a $600 million company. Now he times his daily trip to the newsstand to buy the *Wall Street Journal* so that a drawbridge on his route will be open—that way, he kills 40 minutes instead of 20. His day is full of little events like that. He came to me for advice because while he's busy, he's not engaged. He wanted to fill his empty time with meaningful activity.

HOW TO CREATE A PORTFOLIO LIFE

The skills you need to retire successfully you don't learn in business or at business school. You can't learn these skills solo—you need outside advice. The people who do best are the ones who say, "I ran things successfully in my career, but I can't run this process alone. I need help." Why do they need help? Retirement is not a job switch or career change, it's a behavior change. And, as we all know, while a job title is easy to change, old habits die hard.

While we're working, we tend to look at life from a narrow career perspective and to define ourselves by our jobs. But now is the time to let go of the old labels and to start exploring aspects of your life that you couldn't when your job took precedence.

In the working world, we're under pressure to move quickly, to multitask, to make fast decisions. Now that the job pressure is off, don't create new pressure for yourself. Instead, slow down. Give your creative juices a chance to flow.

Ideally, you should start thinking about what you want your portfolio life to be in your 50s. But it's never too late to plan, even if you're already retired.

How to get a portfolio life: These steps will help you get your plan together…

STEP 1: **Shift into neutral.** Take some time to just stop and think…to bring the previous chapter of your life to a conclusion by shifting your energy into slower, more contemplative activities—spending more time reading and in the garden, for example…seeing what new beginnings are available to you by exploring what interests you.

STEP 2: **Consider what you want to do.** What matters now isn't your job title or what you or others call you…what matters is how you spend your time.

STEP 3: **Write a personal mission statement.** Consider the things that fire your enthusiasm, where your passions lie, what you want to devote your energy to when composing your statement. Think broadly here—don't be concerned about details. Ask yourself about professional pursuits, ongoing learning and spiritual development, recreation, family and friends, giving back to your community.

STEP 4: **Create a personal board of advisers.** These should be loved ones and other people you trust. Meet once every four to six weeks, one-on-one or in groups, and talk as frankly as you can about your goals and how to reach them. Include colleagues and friends from your work life…other friends…neighbors…your pastor, rabbi or other spiritual adviser…adult children.

IT'S NOT ABOUT THE MONEY ANYMORE

You don't have to have a lot of money to enjoy your retirement years. Some people may still need

or want to continue to earn at a high level, but one thing I've seen in a lot of my clients is that as people move from careers to callings, their values and needs change. You never want to stop being open to new ways to generate revenue, but a truly happy retirement is not about how hard you work or how much you earn—it's about how satisfying the mission is. That's what makes it a different, new phase of your life.

Surprise! Retirement Is Good for Your Health

Paper titled "Does Retirement Improve Health and Life Satisfaction?" Working Paper No. 21326 by Aspen Gorry, PhD, Utah State University, Devon Gorry, PhD, Utah State University, and Sita Slavov, PhD, George Mason University, published in *National Bureau of Economic Research*.

Study titled "Retirement—A Transition to a Healthier Lifestyle? Evidence From a Large Australian Study" by researchers at University of Sidney, Australia, published in *American Journal of Preventive Medicine*.

For years, we've heard dismal statistics about retirement and health. Keep working as long as you can, we're told, because people who retire tend to see their health status plummet in the years to follow. The purported increased risks included poor heart health and increased risk for depression.

Fortunately, we now know that for most people, the opposite is true. People who retire tend to be healthier—and happier—after they take the plunge.

Why did earlier studies get it so wrong? One reason is that many lumped data from all retirees together. But some people have to retire because of failing health, so not accounting for this fact made it seem that retirees overall were less healthy than their peers who continued to work. Once the less-healthy must-retire folks were not driving the results, a rosier picture emerged.

When researchers from the National Bureau of Economic Research, for example, analyzed data on around 6,000 Americans over age 50, they found that health status got better after retirement for those who retired simply because they became eligible for Social Security or pension benefits. Since many people, even those in good health, retire when they become eligible for benefits, they were able to measure the impact of retiring for reasons unrelated to health. Even more promising—health status continued to improve, so it was better four years later compared to the first year of retirement.

Life satisfaction improved, too.

A TIME TO GET HEALTHIER

A recent Australian study sheds light on how retirement may improve health. Researchers followed 27,000 Australians over age 45, tracking their lifestyle habits over about three years, during which time about 11% retired. *Compared to those who kept working, the retirees…*

• **Got about 52 minutes more physical activity a week.**

• **Spent about 40 minutes less in sedentary pursuits.**

• **Slept about 15 minutes more a night.**

These stats include everyone who retired. But when the researchers looked closer, they found that those who retired for health reasons still improved their health habits a bit—but not nearly as robustly as those whose health was not the prime reason for quitting work.

IF YOU CAN AFFORD TO RETIRE, WHY WAIT?

Some people love working and never want to quit. Others think they'll love retirement but end up finding themselves bored stiff—or lonely and depressed. Some take to drink. In short, just quitting work won't make you healthier and happier, and it's not the best choice for everyone—even if you can afford it.

But the new research does suggest that retiring when you can best enjoy the time will likely lead to a healthier and happier time of your life.

To paraphrase the old song, it's nice not-work if you can get it.

10 Affordable Cities That Are Easy to Walk

Matt Lerner, cofounder of Walk Score, a website that calculates walk times to nearby amenities, then uses this data to evaluate how convenient areas are for people on foot. Walk Score also evaluates how suitable locations are for bikers and the quality of public transit systems. WalkScore.com

Walkable cities tend to be vibrant, interesting places to live. When people are able to run their errands or enjoy a day out without getting in a car, they feel more connected to their communities.

Walkable cities can be money savers, too. If you can do without a car entirely—or even trim the number of cars owned by your household from two to one—you're likely to save around $9,000 a year, according to AAA. And property values in walkable areas with good public transit systems tend to be particularly resilient. Houses in these locations hold their value very well.

Trouble is, America's most famous walkable cities—New York, San Francisco and Boston—are also among its most expensive places to live. However, there are places in the US that are walkable…affordable…safe…and well served by public transit. Locating these requires a bit more digging because rather than choosing a city well-known for its walkability, you must seek out specific neighborhoods in cities that are not highly acclaimed for their walkability. These can be great places to live. *Ten of the best…*

• **Baltimore.** Baltimore's Mount Vernon neighborhood is very walkable—most everyday errands, such as grocery shopping and picking up dry cleaning, can be handled on foot. This neighborhood also is the home of the Walters Art Museum, the Maryland Historical Society, several theaters and many excellent restaurants. Other walkable Baltimore neighborhoods include Charles Village, home to Johns Hopkins University, the Baltimore Museum of Art and lots of attractive 19th-century architecture…and Seton Hill, a historic neighborhood that is home to the beautiful St. Mary's Park. All three neighborhoods have affordable homes and apartments and good public transit. And unlike some sections of Baltimore, their crime rates are not especially high by urban standards.

•**Buffalo.** The Buffalo neighborhoods of Allen, Bryant and Front Park are very nice places to live without a car. Not only are they walkable, they are well served by Buffalo's very good public transit system—which comes in handy in the winter when this famously frigid city is too cold or snowy for long strolls. Rents and home prices are extremely affordable in Buffalo even in desirable neighborhoods such as these.

•**Chicago.** Chicago is your best option if you want to live in a very large US city where you do not need a car but you cannot afford New York. Chicago has one of America's best public transit systems and some very appealing walkable neighborhoods. And while it is not inexpensive, there are some nice, walkable neighborhoods where it is possible to find decent apartments for less than $1,000 a month. These include Lake View, home of Wrigley Field…Uptown, home of the Uptown Entertainment District…and Hyde Park, home to the University of Chicago. If you can stretch your budget, pricier Chicago neighborhoods including Near North, Printers Row and Gold Coast are among the best places to live without a car—and they're a lot less expensive than desirable parts of New York and San Francisco.

•**Cleveland.** Cleveland can be a great place to live affordably without a car, but only if you live downtown. The city is not especially easy to get around on foot or well served by public transit overall, but its downtown neighborhood is virtually on par with San Francisco in terms of walkability and public transit quality—and Cleveland is much, much less expensive. There's plenty worth walking to in downtown Cleveland these days, including a wide range of museums, sporting venues, theaters and shopping districts—plus more than 300 bars, restaurants and coffee shops.

•**Dallas.** Sections of Dallas near the city center are surprisingly appealing places to live without a car. That hasn't always been the case—Dallas's downtown used to have little to offer beyond office buildings, and the rest of the city is so spread out that a car is a virtual necessity. But Dallas's Main Street District has become a wonderfully walkable area with abundant shopping, dining and nightlife, plus Main Street Garden Park. The nearby Farmer's Market District and Government District are walkable, too. Public transit is very good in these downtown areas, and affordable condos and apartments are available.

•**Milwaukee.** Milwaukee's Juneau Town neighborhood (also known as East Town) is walkable, relatively affordable and well served by public transit. The neighborhood features more than 200 dining and drinking establishments…the indoor Milwaukee Public Market…and Juneau Park. The Milwaukee Art Museum and the Bradley Center, home of the NBA's Bucks, are both within walking distance. Other walkable Milwaukee neighborhoods with good public transit include the Lower East Side…Yankee Hill…and Murray Hill.

•**Minneapolis.** Minneapolis's downtown is extremely walkable…its public transit system is very good…and the city has many miles of bike lanes and an extensive bike-sharing program. Minneapolis's relatively hill-free terrain is a big plus for walkers and bikers, too. The city's Lowry Hill East neighborhood (also known as "The Wedge") is arguably the best choice for people who don't own cars. It's home to many shopping, dining, entertainment and cultural options, including the Art Fair of Uptown and the Minneapolis Sculpture Garden. The Whittier and Loring Park neighborhoods are worth considering as well.

•**Pittsburgh.** Pittsburgh has been transformed in recent decades into a vibrant place, with river views, interesting restaurants and abundant cultural and entertainment options. It's a world away from the smoggy, declining Pittsburgh of the past—yet it remains affordable. Many parts are not great options for people who lack cars—steep hills make walking and biking a challenge, and the city's public transit system is only average. But certain neighborhoods including the Central Business District, Shadyside and Southside Flats are relatively level, walkable and bikeable and well served by public transit.

•**Rochester, New York.** Rochester's Central Business District remains fairly walkable even in the depths of the upstate New York winter because of the Rochester Skyway, a network of enclosed walkways. The neighborhood is well served by bus lines as well. The Pearl-Meigs-Monroe neighborhood (also known as the Garden District) is another nice part of town for people without cars. It has beautifully landscaped gardens, an active commercial district, a strong sense of community and adequate bus lines. Homes and apartments are very affordable in Rochester.

●**St. Louis**. Sections of this engaging city are very walkable and relatively affordable. The Downtown neighborhood, for example, features Busch Stadium, home of baseball's Cardinals…the Peabody Opera House…about 150 restaurants, bars and coffee shops…and plenty of park space, including the famous Gateway Arch. Central West End is another walkable, affordable St. Louis neighborhood. It borders on Forest Park, a large park that's home to the city's art museum and zoo.

Less-Known Costs of Moving in Retirement

MarketWatch.com

If you're planning to move to a southern state with little or no state income tax for retirement, there are several things to consider…

State residency laws require you to be there physically to say that you are a resident…or not be there to say that you are not a resident…for a specific number of days per year—and this must be documented. You may also have to change your address…mailing, voting and driving status…and establish local bank accounts. Additionally, states that are popular for not having income tax may have high property or sales taxes, which may increase your living expenses in the new home. Finally, there are emotional costs of a move, such as being far from family as well as creating a new network of health professionals for your medical needs.

How to Get Grown Kids to Move Out

Kevin Leman, PhD, a psychologist based in Tucson, Arizona, who specializes in parenting, family and marriage issues. He is author of numerous books including *Making Children Mind Without Losing Yours* and *Planet Middle School: Helping Your Child Through the Peer Pressure, Awkward Moments & Emotional Drama*. DrLeman.com

For an increasing number of young adults, growing up no longer means moving out. About 25% of Americans between the ages of 25 and 34 are living with their parents or grandparents, compared with just 11% in 1980. Some have pressing reasons to live at home—perhaps they recently experienced a divorce or layoff and are in a period of turmoil. But many are simply choosing to live "at home."

This arrangement doesn't just complicate parents' lives…it prevents these young adults from truly launching their own lives. The kindest thing parents can do is not coddle these "kids" but nudge them out of the nest.

Here's how to respond if an adult child wants to move back in…and how to get an adult child currently living in your home out the door…

WHEN AN ADULT CHILD WANTS TO COME BACK

There's nothing wrong with letting an adult child live at home temporarily during times of turmoil. A child who has lost his/her job or his partner might need a safe place to lick his wounds. But it is in no one's interest for a parent's home to become a place where this adult child can hide from life. So when a child asks if he can return, say yes—but that you're concerned that he might not be happy if he does, because of the rules he would have to live by. *These rules might include…*

●**You must get a job.** If the child protests that he can't find anything better than flipping burgers, tell him he'll have to flip burgers. It's not enough for the child to promise to "look for work." This could mean nothing more than sending out a résumé every now and then. He must understand that living in your house will not help him escape or delay joining the work force. Besides, working in an unpleasant or low-paying job could be the motivation he needs to go out and find something better.

•You must contribute 25% of your take-home pay as rent. This reinforces the message that living at home is not a free ride. The adult child also should be responsible for paying his personal expenses.

Helpful: If you do not need this rent money, set it aside in an interest-bearing account. If the adult child works hard to get his life on track, present the money to him when he moves out. This return of rent must come as a surprise, however—if the child expects it, that could undermine the message that he must pay his own way.

•You will have to do housework. List specific chores that he will have to do such as his laundry, clean his room, take out the garbage, etc.

Also: If this adult child has young children who will be moving in, too, and you have offered to help with child care, set limits. Perhaps you will provide child care one or two days a week or you will help when the adult child is working, but he should not expect you to babysit every evening while he goes out with friends.

You will have to abide by the house schedule. This might mean guests must be out by 10 pm… the TV volume must be turned way down (or off) by 11 pm…or that there's a midnight curfew.

•You must deal with your own debts. Do not get sucked into your adult child's financial problems. Not only could this cripple your retirement, it could cripple the adult child's sense of financial responsibility. It's fine to offer guidance, but don't bail him out.

•You must move out by a specific departure date. This could be one month, three months or six months down the road—the timetable is up to you. The important part is that there is a deadline so the adult child doesn't start to see living at home as a permanent solution.

If these rules sound severe, they're meant to be. If living in your house is unrestrictive, the adult child will have less reason to move out and get on with his own life.

When you pitch all of this to your child, explain that you understand that it probably doesn't sound very appealing and that you won't be offended if he opts to get together with some friends and split a cheap apartment—no harm in floating this idea.

If the child still wants to move in, get a handshake agreement that he will abide by the terms you laid out. If he does, treat him with respect—don't joke about the bad job he has been forced to take or tell him he's made a mess of his life. Instead, commiserate by sharing stories about your struggles as a young adult—the child might not realize that you faced challenges early on, too. Offer advice when it is requested, but do not try to run his life—that will not foster the sense of responsibility you are trying to help him develop.

IF AN ADULT CHILD ALREADY IS LIVING IN YOUR HOME

If you failed to establish strict rules and a departure date before your adult child moved in, this child might now be showing little interest in moving out. If so, tell the child these five words—"I owe you an apology." This is more likely to get the child's attention than yet another admonition to get a job or an apartment.

When the child asks the reason for the apology, reply, "When we let you return home, we had the best of intentions, but in retrospect, it wasn't what was best for you. We should have had an agreement in place for how this would work, because without that, it clearly isn't working for anyone. We realize that you're not going to like this, but if you're going to continue staying here, this is what will be required…" then list rules and deadlines such as those described earlier.

HOW TO RAISE KIDS WHO RETURN ONLY FOR VISITS

Four ways to increase the odds that young children and teens will move out when they grow up…

•Encourage without overpraising. By all means tell your child "good job" when he works hard and accomplishes something—but do not consistently tell your child that he is the greatest thing in the world. Overpraised children can turn into adults with an inflated sense of self-worth. They might consider entry-level jobs beneath them and end up living at home when no one offers them a six-figure salary and corner office right out of school.

•**Assign children chores.** Kids raised in households where everyone pulls his weight tend to become adults who understand that they must work hard and take responsibility to achieve anything.

•**Remind laggard teens that your home has a check-out time.** If a teen lacks drive and responsibility and doesn't want to adhere to your rules, remove a strip of 18 squares of toilet paper from a roll, then sit the child down for a talk. Count off one sheet of the toilet paper for each year this teen already has lived—16 for a 16-year-old, for example—then hold up the small number of remaining squares and say, "You have just two more years living under my roof." This is likely to earn you some teenage eye rolling, but it truly can be an effective wake-up call.

•**Let the child take the lead on college money matters.** College is supposed to prepare kids for adult life. Taking charge of college finances is a crucial part of that. Help your kids pay their tuition (or even pay for college outright) if you are in a financial position to do so—but insist that college kids take part-time or summer jobs to cover some costs. If college loans are needed, the child—not the parent—should take these out. Your role is to help the child understand loan terms and the dangers of going deeply into debt.

Sell Your Home and See the World—How Lynne & Tim Martin Did It

The Martins—Lynne, 72, and **Tim,** 67—a retired couple who, for the past two years, have traveled the world without a fixed home. They run the website HomeFreeAdventures. com. Lynne is the author of *Home Sweet Anywhere: How We Sold Our House, Created a New Life, and Saw the World.*

How would you like to make the world your retirement home? Lynne and Tim Martin did just that. Two years ago, they sold their home in California, and they have been traveling the world ever since.

The Martins' advice for anyone interested in a full-time travel retirement…

MAKING THE MONEY WORK

Our financial manager sends us $6,000 per month generated by our investments, but we also have Social Security and a small pension. People certainly could live on less than we do. Accommodations are a good place to cut back—the cost of rentals overseas varies considerably with size, season, location and amenities.

•**Housing.** Most tourists stay in pricey hotels and visit areas for only a week or two. We rent furnished apartments and stay a minimum of one month in each location, usually longer. That greatly lowers our housing and travel costs and lets us get a far better feel for the area before we move on.

In California, our total housing expenses added up to around $3,600 a month, including the mortgage, home-maintenance bills, utility bills, homeowner's insurance, taxes and so forth. On the road, our rentals typically cost $1,500 to $2,500 per month and include utilities and Internet service. Those rental prices are modest in part because we usually rent one- or two-bedroom apartments, not large homes. With just the two of us and few personal possessions, that's sufficient space.

Renting tips: We've had success using the rental-listing websites VRBO.com and HomeAway.com. These sites seem to do a good job vetting their property owners. *Also…*

•**We arrange rentals at least several months in advance**—even longer for popular travel destinations such as Paris. The best deals are long gone by the time the rental date approaches.

•**We favor properties whose owners live nearby.** That makes it much easier to solve any problems that arise.

We avoid properties that receive negative feedback on the rental website from prior renters.

•**We use the Internet**—and conversations with other travelers we meet—to vet neighborhoods before renting there. Google Maps can supply a look at the neighborhood, and Googling the name of the neighborhood can provide a sense of what others think about it.

●**Destinations.** We try not to spend too much time in pricey cities such as London and Paris. When we do visit an expensive location, we balance our budget by staying some place much more affordable next, such as Portugal, Mexico or Turkey. We often can keep our spending to $5,000 a month in such places. Turkey was extremely affordable and is among our favorite places.

●**Dining.** We try not to eat more than three or four meals per week in restaurants. Furnished rental apartments include kitchens, cookware, dishes and utensils, so we easily can cook for ourselves. One of the first things we do when we arrive in a new rental is find a nearby grocery store—the sooner we get groceries into the apartment, the lower our temptation to eat out.

●**We also look for local farmers' markets.** They're a great source of fresh and affordable local ingredients and fun to visit, too. We avoid stocking up on ingredients that we won't finish before moving on in a month or two.

●**Transportation within a country.** We usually choose properties near a public transit system. Monthly public transit passes are quite affordable in most cities, and there often is a senior discount. In many months, our transportation expenses are comparable to, or even below, the $700 we previously paid each month to own and insure two cars in California.

●**Transportation to and from countries.** We take planes and trains and, when it's practical, rent cars. We buy almost everything with a credit card so that we can rack up mileage points.

●**We also use repositioning cruises.** These are voyages that cruise lines schedule primarily to move a ship from one part of the world to another. They can be an economical and enjoyable way to travel between continents. You can find repositioning cruises listed on RepositioningCruise.com or on the cruise lines' own websites.

Example: We recently paid $2,500 for a nice cabin on an 18-day cruise from Miami, Florida, to Venice, Italy. That's a great deal considering that in addition to passage for two to Europe, we got all of our food, housing and entertainment for more than half a month.

LIVING WITH LESS STUFF

When we decided to travel full-time, we put some of our possessions in storage, gave some to our kids and got rid of the rest. One of our daughters receives the mail, which has dwindled to almost nothing.

We each have a 30-inch rolling duffel bag and a carry-on bag. We initially worried that living with limited possessions would be a challenge. In fact, it's been liberating and wonderful. Our lives have become less about our stuff and more about the things we do, the places we visit and—above all—the people we meet.

Traveling light does mean that we have to wash and rewear relatively few garments over and over again, but that's not a great inconvenience.

One thing we do travel with in abundance is electronics. *We each have…*

●**A laptop computer.** These allow us to pay our bills online, though we have few bills since we eliminated home ownership.

We also use our computers to stay in touch with friends and family via e-mail and Skype. And we can watch movies and TV shows over the Internet when we wish to spend an evening in.

Helpful: We travel with an HDMI cable so that we can connect our laptops to TVs to watch movies and shows on full-sized screens. We also travel with a portable speaker so that we have decent sound quality when our only option is to watch shows or movies on our laptop screens.

●**A smartphone.** These serve as our phones only when we're in the US. Overseas we use them to run apps, but it can be difficult and expensive to make a US cell phone work abroad. We've found that it's usually cheaper and easier to purchase inexpensive local cell phones when we arrive in a region and load minutes onto them.

●**An E-reader.** We use Kindles from Amazon, but you may prefer a different brand. E-readers allow us to travel with an entire library of books without carrying much weight.

FRIENDS AND FAMILY

Skype and e-mail aren't our only options for keeping in contact with friends and family. When we want to reconnect with our old life, we simply rent a furnished apartment back in our former hometown. We recently spent two months there.

And once your friends and family realize how much fun you're having traveling the world, don't be surprised if they want to join you on occasion. One of our daughters visited us in Italy recently, and another met up with us in Paris. She even brought along one of our grandkids.

FLEXIBILITY NEEDED

Full-time travel isn't worth the trouble unless you and your partner are both onboard with the idea and can be flexible.

Consider how well each of you copes with inconveniences such as language barriers and unfamiliar public transit systems, grocery stores, plumbing and appliances. Some retirees consider overcoming changes and challenges such as these a fun way to keep their minds agile…while others find such things extremely frustrating.

HEALTH MATTERS

Health care can be a concern for fulltime travelers. Living on the road means that you can't see your regular doctor when you're sick…and Medicare doesn't cover medical care obtained outside the US.

We pay around $400 a month for a high-deductible international insurance policy that provides coverage for foreign medical emergencies and will evacuate us back to the US for medical care if necessary. Companies offering policies such as these include Seven Corners (SevenCorners.com) and Allianz (AllianzWorldwideCare.com), among others.

We're fortunate to be very healthy. We take few medications, and the prescriptions we do use, we take along with us. We schedule checkups with our regular doctors and dentists when we return to California. If we become ill in another part of the world, we ask the owner of the property we're renting for a doctor recommendation or we ask other ex-pats or locals we've met in the area.

In our experience, very good medical care is available around much of the world, and it often costs substantially less than in the US.

Retire on the Road? Pros and Cons of Traveling the Country In a Deluxe RV

Bob Livingston, senior vice president and group publisher of Good Sam Media and Events, the company that publishes *Trailer Life* and *MotorHome* magazines. He has been traveling in and writing about RVs for 40 years, including a year as a full-timer. He intends to return to full-timing when he retires. TrailerLife.com

Can't decide where to retire? There's no need to choose if you retire to a recreational vehicle (RV). Today's RVs can be spacious and plush. And full-time RVers can drive their homes from town to town, living near their grandkids one month, just outside a vibrant city the next, then in a warm beachfront community over the winter.

The flexibility and adventure of life on the road hold tremendous allure for many retirees and even for some people still in the workforce if they have portable jobs. And most full-time RVers love it. But people who haven't previously lived full-time in an RV may find that the lifestyle is different from what they expected—the fact that someone has enjoyed RV vacations in the past is no guarantee that he/she will enjoy living in an RV long term.

Here's what you need to know…

THE FULL-TIMER MIND-SET

Five questions to ask yourself before you embark upon an RV retirement…

●**Will my partner and I get along well in close quarters?** Even the largest RV doesn't provide nearly as much room as the typical house. Some couples have trouble adjusting to this loss of personal space.

●**How badly will I miss being part of my current community?** Full-time RVers get to meet many new people and enjoy the camaraderie of the RV community, but they sometimes lament that they no longer feel close to the place they used to call home.

Helpful: This feeling can be reduced or eliminated by returning to your home region in your RV for a few months or more each year.

●**How do I respond to minor annoyances?** Frustrations are inevitable when you drive an RV. You'll make wrong turns down roads where there isn't room to turn the RV around…you'll endure mechanical glitches…you'll occasionally have a loud neighbor. People who can't laugh off small problems struggle as full-time RVers.

●**Will it bother me to see doctors I don't know?** RV park and campground directors usually can provide excellent doctor, dentist and veterinarian recommendations upon request. But these won't be the professionals you know, and the RV life may not be suitable for people with chronic conditions.

●**Do I understand how fuel prices have altered the full-time RV lifestyle?** In decades past, full-time RVers often woke up each morning thinking, Which way should we drive today? Because of high fuel prices, most full-time RVers now carefully select their next destination before they hit the road…and spend several months exploring each region before they move on. It's still a life of freedom and exploration, but no longer one of day-to-day spontaneity.

Example: When gas hit $3.85 per gallon, making the 1,500-mile journey from Florida to Maine in an RV that gets 10 miles per gallon (mpg) cost close to $1,200 round-trip.

LIFE ON THE ROAD

Most RV parks and campgrounds are comfortable, clean and social. They provide electrical, water and sewer hookups, a measure of security and perhaps access to a swimming pool and a clubhouse.

But parking an RV in campgrounds every night can get expensive. Renting campground space by the month, when possible, is one potential money saver. Monthly rates often are around 50% lower than daily ones. Expect to pay perhaps $400 to $750 per month on average, though rates at high-end facilities and near major cities and resort towns can climb to more than $1,000 per month.

Skip the campgrounds when you're just passing through an area. Many Walmarts and other retailers allow RVers to camp overnight in their parking lots—though usually not for more than one night. Free or low-cost RV camping also is allowed on some public lands, particularly in the western US. (Some free and low-cost RV parking options are listed on websites such as FreeCampgrounds.com and FreeCampsites.net.)

Your water and power will be limited on nights when you don't stay in a campground—you won't have the power to run your air conditioner without an auxiliary generator, for example—but your onboard batteries and water tank should meet most of your needs.

Satellite dishes now can be installed on RVs to provide both television and Internet access. RV parks usually provide Wi-Fi, but it's often slow and unreliable. Cell phones with nationwide service plans are a must for full-time RVers.

Tax advantage: Full-time RVers who don't own a house or apartment can select any state as their official state of residence. States such as South Dakota and Texas that have low taxes, auto insurance rates and auto registration fees are popular with full-time RVers.

The Ultimate Bucket List... Amazing Places to Visit and Things to Do

You'll Love These Places! Often-Overlooked Travel Destinations You Shouldn't Miss

Patricia Schultz, a New York City–based travel journalist. She is author of *The New York Times* number-one best seller *1,000 Places to See Before You Die* as well as the recently updated *1,000 Places to See in the United States & Canada Before You Die*. 1000Places.com

Tired of overcrowded, overhyped vacation destinations? Writer Patricia Schultz, author of the newly updated *1,000 Places to See in the United States & Canada Before You Die*, here names some of her favorite destinations and activities in the US (or within a short drive of the US border) that most people overlook…

• **Explore a slice of Spanish history without leaving the US—St. Augustine, Florida.** The oldest continuously inhabited European settlement in the continental US isn't Jamestown, Virginia, or Plymouth, Massachusetts—it's St. Augustine, a coastal city 105 miles northeast of Orlando that was settled by the Spanish in 1565. While much of Florida's coast is overrun by cookie-cutter motels and strip malls these days, St. Augustine's historic district still has a distinctly Old World Spanish charm, with many buildings dating back to the 16th through 19th centuries. The Castillo de San Marcos is the only 17th-century fort still standing in the US, for example…and the romantic Casa Monica Hotel is completely unlike any other hotel in Florida—it's a 19th-century Moorish Revival–style castle.

The best time to visit St. Augustine is between late November and early January when the weather is not sticky hot and the historic district is lit by three million holiday lights. Rooms in the Casa Monica Hotel start at $179 to $259 per night, depending on the season. CasaMonica.com

• **Take a cruise the old-fashioned way—The Maine Windjammers, Rockland and Camden, Maine.** A cruise on a historic 19th- or early 20th-century sailing ship is a wonderful way to see the craggy coast and islands of Maine. These three-to-six-day cruises typically include stops in fishing towns that are anything but touristy…and in quiet coves for lobster bakes. They are trips that transport passengers not just down the coast but also back in time to when ships were made of wood and propelled by wind.

These ships are not luxurious by modern cruising standards. Their cabins tend to be small and simple, and bathrooms often are shared. But the lack of luxury is easily made up for by the memorable and unusual experience. Details about specific ships' accommodations, amenities, rates and schedules are available online. Find links through the website of the Maine Windjammer Association (SailMaineCoast.com). Prices for three-night cruises start at $610 per person, all inclusive. Ships operate late May through mid-October.

•**Visit one of the prettiest little towns almost in America—Niagara-on-the-Lake, Ontario.** Niagara Falls is among the best-known tourist destinations in the US, but few visitors seek out this little waterfront town just to the north, across the Canadian border. They're missing out on one of the most picturesque communities in North America...and on an opportunity to take advantage of a favorable exchange rate in a location just 10 miles from a US border crossing—one US dollar recently was worth $1.31 Canadian.

Stroll or bike along the Niagara Parks Garden Trail, which follows the edge of the Niagara River... catch a play during the highly regarded Shaw Festival, which celebrates the work of George Bernard Shaw and his contemporaries from April through November each year...shop in the town's eclectic boutiques...or go wine tasting at the region's numerous surprisingly fine wineries—Canada might not be the first nation that comes to mind when you think of wine, but this part of Ontario produces an excellent award-winning dessert wine known as Icewine. Top wineries include Peller Estates... Inniskillin Wines...Château des Charmes...and Vineland Estates Winery. Tickets for the Shaw Festival can be purchased at ShawFest.com with prices starting at $21.60 US at recent exchange rates. Keep in mind that US travelers must have valid passports to visit Canada. NiagaraOnTheLake.com

•**Escape to a simpler time and place—The Shaker Village of Pleasant Hill, Kentucky.** The Shakers, a religious sect that believed in gender equality, communal living and pacifism, flourished in the US in the mid-19th century (only a handful exist today). The Shaker Village of Pleasant Hill, located in a pastoral part of central Kentucky, closed in 1910, but 34 of its original buildings have been painstakingly restored. Guided tours are available, and costumed historical reenactors demonstrate traditional Shaker skills such as weaving and woodworking. The Village's property includes 40 miles of nature trails through 3,000 acres of beautiful rolling hills. The Trustees' Table is an excellent restaurant that serves traditional Kentucky and Shaker dishes—try the country ham and tart lemon pie. You can stay in the village overnight at the Inn at Pleasant Hill (rooms recently were available for $100). If you're looking for an action-packed getaway, look elsewhere—but if you're looking for a peaceful place in Kentucky's rolling bluegrass country to take a break from the modern world, it's hard to do better. The village is located 25 miles southwest of Lexington. ShakerVillageKY.org

•**Explore a world where canoes outnumber cars—Boundary Waters Canoe Area, Ely, Minnesota.** This wilderness preserve located along the northern border of Minnesota is the largest in the US east of the Rockies, with more than one million protected acres. Together with the even larger Quetico Provincial Park just across the border in Canada, there are more than 1,000 lakes scattered across this vast pine forest.

There are few cars and motorboats allowed, creating a world that feels untouched by time. Most visitors bring or rent canoes—there are more than 1,200 miles of canoe routes—and then paddle and portage (carry the canoe short distances overland) for days or weeks, camping onshore and dining on the fish they catch. A permit system ensures that the woods are never very crowded.

Ely is 100 miles northwest of Duluth. Overnight visitors must pay a "user fee" of $16 per person per trip ($8 for those under 18 and people who have an "Interagency Senior Pass" or "Interagency Access Pass"). For more information about permits, visit the US Forest Services' website (FS.Fed.us, select "Destinations" from the "Visit Us" pull-down menu, enter "Minnesota," then select the "Boundary Waters Canoe Area Wilderness"). If you wish to hire a guide or rent canoes and equipment, contact Williams & Hall Outfitters (Williams AndHall. com). If you're looking for a good hotel nearby, the log cabins of the Burntside Lodge are an excellent choice (from $171 off-season, from $219 peak summer season, Burntside.com).

• **Watch the world take flight—Albuquerque International Balloon Fiesta, New Mexico.** It isn't accurate to call this well-attended fiesta an "overlooked" event, but it is underappreciated and not well-known outside the region. It's an astounding, unforgettable experience to stand on the fiesta field early in the morning as the sun rises and more than 500 colorful hot-air balloons inflate to the size of houses around you and take flight. Arrive early—gates open at 4:30 am for the morning session (3:30 pm for the evening session), and cars are lining up by 4 am. (There are nine morning and five evening sessions in all.) In 2017, the fiesta will be held from October 7 to 15. General admission tickets cost $10 per "session." Admission is free for children age 12 and under. Parking costs $15 per car. BalloonFiesta.com

• **Go wine tasting without being overrun by tourists—Walla Walla Wine Region, Washington.** More than 100 wineries have sprung up in and around Walla Walla, a small city in southeastern Washington State approximately 150 miles south of Spokane by car. There are wineries in almost every state these days, but the Walla Walla region vineyards produce highly regarded wines. Walla Walla's wineries and inns are much less overrun with tourists and are more affordable than California wine regions such as Napa and Sonoma, making this an excellent place for a relaxing, enjoyable wine-tasting trip.

Wineries to visit include Abeja, which is on a restored early 20th-century farmstead, and Seven Hills Winery, which is next door to Whitehouse-Crawford Restaurant, one of Walla Walla's best eateries. WallaWallaWine.com

Don't want to fight the crowds on your next vacation? *Try these wonderful but undervisited travel destinations instead…*

DURANGO, COLORADO

This small town, nestled in a river valley at the foot of the forested San Juan Mountains in Southwest Colorado, offers an irresistible mix of history and activity.

There's a caught-in-time feel to Durango—the Durango & Silverton Narrow Gauge Railroad, in operation since 1882, uses Victorian coaches to carry tourists along a 45-mile route that gains 3,000 feet in elevation as it crosses narrow bridges and roaring white-water canyons. The railroad was featured in the train robbery scene of the movie Butch Cassidy and the Sundance Kid (round-trip tickets start at $59).

Durango also offers white-water rapids, a ski resort and close proximity to Mesa Verde National Park, 35 miles to the west. Durango makes a great starting point for a drive on the San Juan Skyway, a 233-mile scenic route through stunning mountain passes.

Information: Durango.org

Where to stay: The Strater Hotel (rooms start at $109).

MOAB, UTAH

This small town in Utah's "Red Rock Country," about 240 miles southeast of Salt Lake City, offers movie-quality scenery and outdoor adventure. It's 10 minutes from Arches National Park (pictured above), with its thousands of natural salmon-colored sandstone arches, and 40 minutes from Canyon-lands National Park, Utah's largest park, offering hiking and scenic drives.

Moab sits in a green valley split by the Colorado River, making it a prime location for river rafting. Summer can be very hot, so the best time to visit is either between April and early May or between September and mid-November. September also is notable for the renowned Moab Music Festival, featuring chamber music, jazz and bluegrass.

Information: DiscoverMoab.com

Where to stay: Gonzo Inn offers retro 1970s' charm (from $160).

BOUNDARY WATERS CANOE AREA, MINNESOTA

The Boundary Waters Canoe Area along the northeastern edge of Minnesota is a magnificent wilderness preserve, with one million protected acres. Another 1.2 million protected acres lie across the border in Canada's Quetico Provincial Park. Together these parks have more than 1,000 lakes. This massive wilderness is free of cars and largely free of motorboats. The transportation of choice is the canoe. Some visitors paddle and portage (carry their canoe over land) from lake to lake for days or weeks, camping on the shore and dining on walleye and northern pike that they catch themselves.

Winter is magic here, too. Nearby Ely, Minnesota, is the Sled Dog Capital of the continental US. Polar explorer Paul Schurke offers dogsled trips at his Wintergreen Dogsled Lodge.

Information: 218-626-4300, FS.fed.us (select "Superior" from the "By Name" pull-down menu, click the link for "Boundary Waters Canoe Area Wilderness").

Where to stay: When not camping, try the handsome log cabins of the Burntside Lodge (from $156).

BLUEGRASS COUNTRY, KENTUCKY

This is among America's most genteel and elegant landscapes. Tara-style manor houses and oak-plank fences abound. It's also the world's leading center of thoroughbred horse breeding.

Bluegrass country is dissected by two of America's most scenic byways, the Old Frankfort Pike and the Paris Pike. These roads meander past bucolic horse farms and through charming towns. The International Museum of the Horse in the Kentucky Horse Park north of Lexington is worth a stop, as is The Keeneland racecourse in Lexington. Keeneland is the South's most beautiful track, with elegant limestone grandstands in a tree-shaded setting. Watch workout sessions at Keeneland from dawn to 10 am, then enjoy breakfast at the Track Kitchen, a local favorite.

Nearby Berea, Kentucky, is an idyllic town known for its hundreds of potters, painters and other artisans.

Information: VisitLex.com

Where to stay: The Beaumont Inn in Harrodsburg (from $100) or Boone Tavern Hotel in Berea (from $130).

BRANDYWINE VALLEY DELAWARE/PENNSYLVANIA

Brandywine Valley, straddling the Delaware/Pennsylvania border, is an unparalleled region of manicured gardens, grand historic estates and interesting small museums. It's best experienced by following the 25-mile Brandywine Valley Scenic Byway from Wilmington, Delaware, to the Brandywine Battlefield, where one of the largest battles of the Revolutionary War took place on September 11, 1777.

Several former du Pont family residences in and around Wilmington are worth a visit, including Nemours, which is filled with exquisite furniture, rugs, tapestries and museum-quality art and has the largest formal French garden in the US, and Winterthur, arguably the leading museum of 17th-, 18th- and 19th-century American antiques and decorative arts.

Also worth a stop is the Brandywine River Museum in Chadds Ford, Pennsylvania, which displays art by the Wyeth family.

Information: VisitWilmingtonDE.com or The Brandywine.com.

Where to stay: The Inn at Montchanin Village in Montchanin, Delaware (from $192), or Hotel du Pont in Wilmington (from $161).

BLOCK ISLAND, RHODE ISLAND

Block Island manages to be both sophisticated and unpretentious. It's a barefoot-and-bicycle kind of place, with rolling green hills, hundreds of freshwater ponds, 17 miles of beach and dramatic 250-foot bluffs that remind many of Ireland. The Nature Conservancy considers Block Island "one of the last great places in the Western Hemisphere."

Roughly one-third of Block Island's land is set aside as wildlife refuge, with more than 30 miles of hiking trails and gorgeous cliffside biking paths.

Block Island isn't exactly undiscovered—thousands of tourists squeeze onto this 11-square-mile gem on summer weekends—but it's little-known outside its region. Visit in September or October for much sparser crowds and the best bird-watching.

The island is 12 miles from the mainland and can be reached by ferry from Narragansett, Rhode Island...New London, Connecticut...or Montauk, New York.

Information: BlockIslandChamber.com

Where to stay: Great options include Hotel Manisses (from $75) and The 1661 Inn (from $90) or the Sea Breeze Inn (from $150).

GRAFTON, VERMONT

This is a lost-in-time, picture-perfect New England village of 600 people less than 60 miles northeast of Bennington. It's a wonderful destination for those who like the lazy pace of yesteryear. Historical buildings include The Grafton Inn, built in 1801, where Rudyard Kipling once honeymooned.

There's a cluster of interesting shops along the tree-lined main street, and the town is credited with restarting Vermont's handcrafted cheese industry—watch one of the world's finest cheddars being made at the Grafton Village Cheese Company.

Drive to nearby Bellows Falls to catch the Green Mountain Flyer, a vintage sightseeing train that makes a 90-minute round-trip run past covered bridges, bucolic small towns and an explosion of color each autumn when the leaves change.

Information: GraftonVermont.org

Where to stay: The Grafton Inn (from $155).

Cities to See Before Prices Rise

Analysis by Booking.com, reported at GoBankingRates.com.

Demand for travel to some cities is increasing, which means that the cost to visit them is likely to go up in the near future. Ho Chi Minh City, Vietnam, had the highest percentage growth in bookings. Other cities with big increases in year-over-year bookings: Shanghai, China...Dublin, Ireland...Edinburgh,Scotland...Kyoto,Japan...Lisbon, Portugal...Seville, Spain...Singapore...Stockholm, Sweden...Kuala Lumpur, Malaysia...Copenhagen, Denmark...Bangkok, Thailand...Milan, Italy...Athens, Greece...Taipei, Taiwan. For a less expensive trip: Consider visiting during each location's off-season—winter in Stockholm and Copenhagen, for example, and summer in Kyoto.

When Different Generations Travel Together

Pauline Frommer is a nationally syndicated radio talk-show host and newspaper columnist based in New York City. She is a member of the Frommer guidebook family. *Pauline Frommer's New York City* was twice named "Best Guidebook of the Year" by the North American Travel Journalists Association.

I don't know if I've ever dreaded a vacation as much as I did the trip that was planned to celebrate my father's 75th birthday. It's not that I was against a Mediterranean cruise (who would be?) or spending time with my father. But having 14 family members in one place for 10 unbroken days seemed like an exercise in masochism. Our histories were too tangled...our tastes too different.

I needn't have worried. With nearly 3,000 other passengers, I could melt into the crowd when needed. I could put the kids in the kids' club and go to a lecture or the gym. On days in port, we split up into small family groups and followed our own interests. And at night, and sometimes at lunch, we all would meet to share stories of the day's adventures. Instead of pushing us apart, the trip brought us closer together.

That balance of togetherness and independence is the key to enjoying a multigenerational vacation. It's also important to find a vacation that fits everyone's needs and budget. *Here are some great vacation venues for family fun...*

ALL-INCLUSIVE BEACH RESORTS

For many families, vacation means time at the beach, and you'll get that—but also much more—at the best-run all-inclusive beach resorts. All-inclusives typically offer specialized programs for youngsters (arts and crafts, pool games, teen clubs), spas, gyms, tennis courts, water sports and evening entertainment. Some even throw in golf...trapeze lessons (a specialty of some Club Meds)...rock-climbing walls...and classes in cooking, yoga, dance or foreign languages. With this level of activity, there usually is something to interest everyone, no matter what age.

Another advantage of the all-inclusive is that once the room is paid for, guests typically don't have to open their wallets for food, alcoholic drinks and activities. So there are few, if any, ugly surprises in terms of budget.

Which all-inclusive to pick? If everyone in the group is over age 18, you can choose adults-only resorts such as Sandals and SuperClubs. If you have younger kids, Club Med is a good choice because it offers baby care at many of its resorts, as well as kids' clubs. It periodically offers "kids stay free" deals. A "kids stay free" promotion also is available this summer from Palace Resorts, a small chain on the Mexican Riviera that's great for families.

If you're going to be a big group, free rooms are important. Rooms at all-inclusive resorts can range from $300 to $500 a night. Most hotels give one freebie for every 10 booked, but AMResorts (which encompasses Dreams, Zoëtry, Secrets, Sunscape and Now Resorts) offers one free room for every five rooms purchased, a bonanza for those planning large family reunions.

A final suggestion, for families seeking luxury—Azul Resorts of Mexico. Though pricey, this is one of the few all-inclusive chains that has multibedroom villas appropriate for large groups (up to 14 people in some). At Azul, there often are discounts for children, and kids under age three are free.

To get the best rates at any of the above places, either bargain directly with the group manager at the resort...or use a site that bundles hotel and airfare together such as VacMart.com, VacationKids.com and BookIt.com.

DUDE RANCHES

Another all-inclusive option is the dude ranch, which typically focuses on horseback riding but offers a variety of other outdoor activities such as hiking and fishing. Dude ranches can range from very simple places to glamorous resorts with full spas and gourmet meals. They generally require participants to be fit and so may not be the best choice for families with elderly or very young members. For the rest, though, they represent an iconic American adventure.

The best source for information on dude ranches is RanchWeb.com. Along with reviews, the site regularly posts discounts, often up to 25% off the usual cost. Sometimes these savings are offered to large family groups willing to rent out the entire ranch, so do ask the manager about the benefits of bringing lots of "cowhands," and don't be shy about bargaining.

TOURS

For the family that enjoys traveling from place to place, tours specially geared for a wide range of ages can be the right choice. Just this past January, Adventures By Disney announced it would be offering its first "multigenerational" tours (in Europe). Like Disney's regular family tours, they will be led by two leaders, but in this case, the leaders are specially trained to create additional activities should one-half of the group move more quickly than the other. The other difference? A photographer goes along on each tour to make sure that the memories are picture-perfect.

Though Disney grabbed the headlines for adding multigenerational tours, Road Scholar (formerly know as Elderhostel) is the company that pioneered this type of vacation. It offers a good mix of activities each day that grandparents and grandchildren can do together, along with programs just for kids. Educational and interactive in nature, Road Scholar's programs tend to concentrate on nature destinations (taking place in locales ranging from Kenya to Yellowstone National Park), though one-quarter are cultural programs (you might learn to paint at the Chicago Art Institute or make Carnevale masks in Venice). Because Road Scholar often bases its groups at universities, with stays in their dorms, costs can be lower than usual for these tours (though they're not always). The other two big names in intergenerational touring are Collette Tours and Tauck Bridges.

CRUISES

All major cruise lines offer kids' clubs, though many experts think that Royal Caribbean, Carnival and Disney are the best for young children. That being said, many seniors prefer a less frenetic atmosphere than what's usually found aboard Royal Caribbean or Carnival (think loud pop music playing in the common areas). Ships that give a good balance of amenities for both young and old? Try

Celebrity, Princess or Disney (yes, Disney, which has a number of areas on its ships just for adults).

Travel agents compete fiercely for group business (they get a higher commission for group bookings) and usually can get discounts and special amenities for your group. Try such cruise specialists as CruiseBrothers.com, CruisesOnly.com and VacationsToGo.com—go with whichever gets you the best rates. On most cruise lines, travelers who book eight to 10 cabins are offered one cabin free (the number will vary by length of itinerary). Groups often are treated to cocktail parties, free photos, free uses of meeting rooms and other niceties, so be sure that your agent is pushing for your family's freebies—and choose a new agent if he/she isn't.

The Best Train Trips in North America

Jim Loomis, author of *All Aboard: The Complete North American Train Travel Guide*, now in its fourth edition. He is vice chair of the board of directors of the nonprofit National Association of Railroad Passengers and has traveled approximately 200,000 miles on trains in the US. TrainsAndTravel.com

Vacation travel need not involve endless airport security lines or stop-and-go highway traffic. Trains cannot match planes' speed or cars' flexibility, but they can make getting where you are going a relaxing and enjoyable part of the trip.

Here are eight of the best train rides in North America...*

MULTIDAY TRIPS

●**The California Zephyr,** a two-night Amtrak route between Chicago and the San Francisco Bay, is perhaps the most scenic train trip in America. It's at its best west of Denver as the train follows the Colorado River through the stunning Byers, Gore and Glenwood canyons. Later it crosses the Sierra Nevada and California's majestic redwood forests.

*All routes mentioned in this article are one-way trips that can be taken in either direction, except as noted. Amtrak fares fluctuate based on demand, so prices might differ from the prices cited here. Travelers age 62 and over qualify for a 15% discount on many, though not all, Amtrak coach seat fares. You do not have to travel the entire distance on routes via Amtrak and Canada's VIA Rail.

The western terminus is across the Bay from San Francisco, but there is a connecting bus to the city.

Fares: A coach seat recently cost $166 in the winter...$211 in fall...and $255 in the summer. A two-person "roomette" (see box on page 12) cost $640 in the winter...$970 in fall...and $1,082 in summer. Amtrak.com/California-Zephyr-Train

Note: You can ride between Denver and San Francisco and see most of the trip's highlights for about two-thirds of the full journey's price.

●**The Coast Starlight,** a one-night. 35-hour Amtrak route between Los Angeles and Seattle, is the only Amtrak train that still features a parlour car—a comfortable space providing overstuffed recliners and wine tastings. The atmosphere in a parlour car tends to be extremely social, and you even can take your meals there if you like. But the parlour car is exclusively for the use of passengers who have booked roomettes or bedrooms.

The scenery is beautiful, too, with views of Puget Sound, the Cascade Range and the Pacific Ocean.

Fares: Coach seats recently cost $118 in fall or winter...and $149 in the summer. A two-person roomette, which includes parlour car access, cost $480 in fall or winter...and $703 in summer. Amtrak.com/Coast-Starlight-Train

●**The Cardinal,** a one-night Amtrak route between New York City and Chicago, does not travel a direct route. Instead it dips south through the mid-Atlantic states and southeastern heartland... across the beautiful Blue Ridge and Allegheny mountains...and through the Shenandoah Valley. The big scenic feature of this route is the New River Gorge in West Virginia—the train follows the New River through the gorge for several hours, crossing back and forth across the river several times.

Fares: A coach seat cost $106 in fall or winter...and $170 during summer. A roomette cost $517 in winter...$437 in fall...and $747 in summer. Amtrak.com/Cardinal-Train

●**The Canadian,** a four-night trip between Vancouver and Toronto on Canada's VIA Rail, is the most luxurious long-distance train trip you can take in North America. The food is outstanding... the level of staffing and service feels first class...and the train cars themselves are sleek, restored stainless steel cars from the 1950s.

The route provides memorable views of Canada's varied landscape. The spectacular Rocky Mountain crossing is the highlight, but the country's vast farms, prairies and forests are impressive, too.

Fares: Economy tickets recently started at $310 year-round, while two-person sleepers started at $2,438 off-season (October 22 through May 31) and $2,708 in-season (June 1 to October 21). Two-person Prestige Class cabins that include showers and toilets started at $5,318 off-season and $6,017 in-season. (Rates are based on double occupancy of sleepers and cabins and on an exchange rate of 78 US cents to the Canadian dollar.) On ViaRail.ca, select "Rockies and Pacific" from the "Explore Our Destinations" menu and then choose "Toronto-Vancouver."

SINGLE-DAY TRIPS

●**The Adirondack,** a 10-hour Amtrak trip between New York City and Montreal, treats you to the lush wine country of the Hudson River Valley during the southern part of the journey, then to the dramatic and historical scenery of Fort Ticonderoga, the Adirondack Trail and Lake Champlain. The views are pretty year-round and become truly spectacular in the fall when the leaves change color.

Fares: Reserved coach seats (the only class available) recently cost $69 to $77 regardless of season. Amtrak.com/Adirondack-Train

●**The Pacific Surfliner,** a six-hour, single-day Amtrak route between San Luis Obispo, California, and San Diego, stands out for its stunning Pacific Ocean views. For the best views, get a seat on the west side of the train—that's the right side if headed south, the left if headed north. If you're visiting Los Angeles, the Surfliner offers a relaxing, car-free way to pop down to San Diego or up to San Luis Obispo. (These half-route trips each take around three hours.) The train has special racks for surfboards and bikes, reservations required.

Fares: Coach seats cost $61 for the entire route. Trips between LA and San Diego cost $37, while those between LA and San Luis Obispo cost $41. Amtrak.com/Pacific-Surfliner-Train

●**The Grand Canyon Railway** provides a 65-mile, two-and-a-quarter-hour scenic journey from Williams, Arizona, to the South Rim of the Grand Canyon. This is a tourist train, not an Amtrak route. Musicians perform on the train, and the conductors tell stories. The train departs daily at 9:30 am with a return trip at 3:30 in the afternoon, with a layover of nearly four hours at the Grand Canyon. (Or stay at one of the hotels in Grand Canyon Village and return on a future day.)

Rates: Round-trip tickets start at $65 ($29 for children ages two to 15) up to $219 for Luxury Parlor Class, which includes a private bar and access to an open-air platform. TheTrain.com

●**The Durango & Silverton Railroad** uses old-fashioned steam engines to slowly traverse 45 miles of narrow-gauge rail line through the breathtaking mountains of southwestern Colorado's San Juan National Forest. The route travels along shelves blasted into mountainsides and across bridges over wild mountain streams—it is among the most scenic train trips in the country. The trip takes three-and-a-half hours each way and is offered from early May through late October (shorter trips are available in the off-season). There's a two-hour layover in Silverton, a tiny former silver-mining town.

Rates: Standard-class round-trip tickets cost $89 ($55 ages four to 11)...but prices climb as high as $199 for Presidential Class (ages 21 and up), which features large seats and access to an open-air viewing platform. DurangoSilvertonRailroad.com

AMTRAK SLEEPERS

Amtrak travelers on overnight routes can sleep in coach seats, just as travelers do on red-eye airline flights, but roomettes and bedrooms also are likely to be available at a higher price. Each person in a roomette or bedroom pays a basic rail fare (the cost of a coach seat), but there is only one supplementary charge for the room regardless of whether it is occupied by one or two people (or three or four people in the case of a family bedroom, which accommodates two adults and two children). The supplementary fare for the room covers dining car meals for all occupants.

A roomette is a compact private cabin for up to two travelers. Its seats convert into a bed, and a second berth folds down from above. Some travelers find the upper berths in roomettes claustrophobic, and both sleeping spaces are too small for most couples to comfortably share. Some roomettes have a private toilet and wash basin.

Many Amtrak overnight routes also offer bedrooms, which feature larger berths as well as private toilets and showers…and/or "family bedrooms," which include two adult-size berths plus two shorter berths for children but no private shower or toilet. Either of these bedroom options is likely to be at least twice as expensive as a roomette.

Go on Safari! See Wild Animals in the Wild

Susan Farewell, widely published travel journalist and founder of Farewell Travels LLC, a travel concierge that provides ideas, recommendations and referrals for worldwide travel. Based in Westport, Connecticut, she has traveled extensively throughout Africa and advises private clients about which safaris are best for them. FarewellTravels.com

---

Seeing a giraffe snacking on a sky-high treetop, a family of lion cubs cavorting around a log, a line of elephants making their solemn way across a river—nothing quite matches watching the great animals of Africa in the wild. And what a backdrop—landscapes that range from expansive plains to deep forests, from the mighty Zambezi River to the red desert sands of Namibia. A safari is an exciting trip at any age—ideal for families, couples or individual travelers. But how do you begin planning such a trip?

WHAT'S YOUR DREAM SAFARI?

Start by asking yourself the following questions…

What animals do you want to see? The wildlife you hope to spot while in Africa can determine which country or countries you visit and what time of year you go. For example, if you want to see the high-profile animals (the new name for what hunters refer to as the Big 5—lion, leopard, elephant, buffalo, rhinoceros), your best bet is to go to Botswana, Zimbabwe, Kenya, Tanzania or certain reserves in South Africa. If your lifelong dream has been to track gorillas, choose Rwanda or Uganda. If you're looking for big cats, travel to the Masai Mara in Kenya during the great wildebeest migration—for predators, it's the equivalent of a hot new restaurant opening. Almost everywhere in Africa, you will want to have binoculars handy for focusing in on birds, but if you are looking for the pink flamingos you've seen on TV, they're in Kenya.

How active do you want to be? Traditional safaris include at least two game drives a day, one as early as 5:00 am…the other in the late afternoon. This can mean lots of bumping along in 4-by-4s—not exactly getting lots of exercise. If you want to be more active, consider a safari that includes animal tracking on foot. There are certain parks and reserves within each country—and certain camps within those areas—that are better for walking than others. Most of them can be found in Zimbabwe, Zambia and select parts of South Africa, Botswana and Tanzania.

How much time do you have? It's a long trip to Africa. Example: A direct flight from New York City to Johannesburg is about 16 hours. To reach Nairobi, you may need to take a connecting flight, usually through London. Either way, you will have to allow for a few travel days on either end of the itinerary. Plan on spending at least 10 days from start to finish, or even better, two weeks.

What's your budget? The cost of a safari can vary dramatically depending on how long the trip is, how you travel between camps (flying safaris are quite common in some areas—you take Cessnas between camps) and the level of lodging you are seeking. Accommodations range from simple canvas tents to off-the-charts luxurious thatched tents with private soaking pools, expansive decks and open-air sleeping lofts. In general, prices range from $5,000 to $17,000 per person (including international airfare).

GREAT ADD-ONS

Safaris pair up nicely with other experiences in Africa, and since you're traveling the distance, it makes sense to add on. *Here are some to consider...*

● **See one of the Seven Natural Wonders of the World.** Victoria Falls, in both Zambia and Zimbabwe, is the largest waterfall on the planet (based on width and height). You can take a river cruise on the Zambezi in its mist...bungee jump into the gorge...soar above it in a microlight sightseeing flight...or simply don the provided raincoats and wander the sometimes very wet trails beside it.

● **Visit the Batwa Pygmies in Uganda.** In the Bwindi Impenetrable Forest, you can visit the last remaining community of Batwa Pygmies, an ancient tribe that has lived side by side with one-half of the world's population of mountain gorillas for generations.

● Tour the winelands of South Africa. The rugged hills and valley scenery are compelling on their own, but add tastings at the wine estates and restaurants throughout the winelands outside Cape Town, and it's all-out dreamy.

● **Visit the Cape of Good Hope.** It's not just a point on the map, but a dramatic meeting of cliffs and sea. An easy drive south of South Africa's Cape Town, it can include whale watching (between mid-July and December, southern right whales can be seen just offshore, where they mate and calve) and an up-close view of the small colony of African penguins that have made their home on the rocky coast and beach at Simon's Town.

● **Hit the beaches.** The Kenyan coast has white-sand beaches...Tanzania is home to the Spice Islands (Pemba and Zanzibar), which are excellent for snorkeling and diving...in South Africa, there's surfing at Long Beach...and there's Mozambique—with more than 1,500 miles of Indian Ocean coastline.

● **Climb Mount Kilimanjaro.** It's the ultimate adventure, but guess what? It doesn't require technical skill. Anyone who is reasonably active and in good health can climb Africa's highest mountain, which stands on its own in Tanzania (and is the highest freestanding mountain in the world).

PUTTING IT TOGETHER

Some of the big established travel companies have been arranging safaris for years.

Examples: Abercrombie & Kent (800-554-7016, AbercrombieKent.com) and Micato (800-642-2861, Micato.com). But increasingly, there also are smaller companies that specialize in customizing safaris.

Examples: Intrepid Expeditions (800-893-1157, IntrepidExpeditions.com) and Expert Africa (800-242-2434, ExpertAfrica.com).

Here is a sampling of what's available. Prices are for land only—air can be arranged through the safari companies.

"Tanzania Safari in Style" takes you to the Ngorongoro Crater, to a Maasai village and the plains of the Serengeti, 10 days. From $7,495 per person. Abercrombie & Kent.

A 12-day "Best of South Africa" trip includes Cape Town, Johannesburg and Sabi Sands Reserve. From $4,972 per person. Intrepid Expeditions.

Europe Too Expensive? Not with Pauline's Insider Secrets

Pauline Frommer, creator of the series of Pauline Frommer guidebooks, guides designed to help vacationers save money on trips in the US and to Europe and other destinations. Frommers.com/pauline. She is the daughter of the legendary travel expert Arthur Frommer.

Don't give up plans for a European vacation just because the dollar has gone down in value. Yes, in the past few years, the dollar has lost value compared with other currencies. *There are still great places you can visit without spending a fortune...*

KRAKOW, POLAND

Located on the beautiful Vistula River, Krakow is a city rich in history. The capital of Poland for more than 400 years (until 1596), Krakow is home to centuries-old churches and synagogues. Another gem is Wawel Royal Castle, a 16th-century structure that reflects architectural styles from many parts of Europe. Or if you want to shop for bargain jewelry, clothing or food, stroll through Rynek Główny, an 800-year-old market square.

A half hour from Krakow is Auschwitz. After seeing the former death camp, few people ever look at history in the same way.

Small hotels and bed-and-breakfasts in Krakow cost as little as $70 to $80 a night for two, and you can figure on $20 to $30 per person more for food and sightseeing costs. Also, the dollar is currently strong in Poland.

BOHEMIA, THE CZECH REPUBLIC

The capital of the Czech Republic, Prague has become as expensive as Rome, Madrid and other popular European cities, but the nearby countryside of Bohemia is a bargain. Top-rated hotels in many charming Bohemian villages charge less than $75 a night for a room for two, and meals and sightseeing typically run about $20 to $25 a day per person.

Bohemia is known for its nature trails, music festivals, historic castles and spas. Cesky Krumlov, for instance, is a UNESCO World Heritage site on the banks of the Vitava River. (The designation is given to only 851 sites that are judged to be among the most historically important in the world.)

Visitors can go boating, walk through castles and stop by the town's many cultural attractions, including the Egon Schiele Art Centrum, devoted to works of influential classical and contemporary art. Or tour the breweries in the town of Cesky Budějovice, whose name became Budweiser in the US.

In addition to the many travel booking websites, Czech Republic Bookings (BohemianHostels.com) lists bargain accommodations near Prague.

LISBON

The capital of Portugal, Lisbon is 20% to 25% less expensive than most other European capitals. The city is also one of the most beautiful, with great boulevards, magnificent parks and vestiges of its Roman and Moorish past. The Alfama neighborhood, for instance, dates from the Moorish occupation of the eighth century.

Or visit Saint George's Castle, located on a hill that overlooks the city. It was built in the sixth century and recaptured from the Moors 600 years later. If it's nightlife you're after, spend the evening in the Bairro Alto, home to dozens of friendly restaurants and clubs.

Spring is a great time to visit Lisbon. While it's still cool and damp in northern Europe, Lisbon—on the southwestern tip of the continent—usually sees lots of sunny days with temperatures in the 60s and 70s.

It's easy to save money in this city by renting an apartment for as short a time as a day or two. The agency Travelling to Lisbon (351-21-888-6072, TravelingToLisbon.com) links apartment owners with vacationers and often offers lodgings for as little as $75 a night per family. The dollar has also grown in value over the past year or two here.

LONDON

Though it's one of the most expensive cities in Europe, you can save substantially by going off season, booking a package deal and/or staying in one of a number of low-cost hotels or in a private house.

Airlines, hotels and even many restaurants lower their prices from October through April. Overall, a week in London is often 50% cheaper than it would be in July or August, the peak season.

Off season is high season for theater. You can see new shows long before they come to the US. So, bundle up and have a ball!

No matter when you go, to save on food, eat in pubs. They tend to be much less expensive than touristy restaurants.

To save on accommodations, consider EasyHotel (EasyHotel.com), a new chain of inexpensive hotels. I would especially recommend the one in Kensington, a quiet area of London that is a short subway ride from the theater district and many other attractions. Rates start at about $90 per night double occupancy.

Typical rates in a private house are about $150 per couple per night. Home owners who rent apartments and rooms to tourists can be located through AirBNB.com and At Home In London (AtHomeIn London.co.uk).

PARIS

While top hotels often charge more than $700 a night, Paris still has dozens of excellent hotels where two people can stay for less than $150 a night. The website Paris.org is useful in finding them.

You can often save even more by staying in an apartment instead of a hotel. The agency Parisian Home (ParisianHome.com) links up apartment owners with travelers. Some well-located studio apartments listed on the site recently rented for about $42 a night.

For the most authentic and affordable meals, ask a local for advice (and avoid restaurants that have English language menus posted outside). Examples: A helpful local might send you to Le Pré Verre (8 rue Thénard), where a high-quality three-course, prix-fixe meal would be about $53... or to Café Constant (139 rue St. Dominique), where you can feast for about $40.

Most museums in Paris offer free admission at least one day a month.

Example: The Musée du Louvre is free on the first Sunday of the month. Check the websites of other museums for their free days.

How to Get VIP Treatment Wherever You Go

How to Get Exactly What You Need from Your Doctor

Robert M. Arnold, MD, professor and director of palliative care services and the Leo H. Criep chair in patient care at the University of Pittsburgh School of Medicine. His research focuses on helping doctors communicate better with patients with life-threatening illnesses.

How many times have you left a doctor's appointment and realized that you forgot to ask an important question or didn't fully understand your physician's instructions?

It happens to everyone. Fortunately, there are simple steps you can take to avoid the common mistakes that keep you from getting exactly what you need at the doctor's office…

MISTAKE 1: **Making your list too long.** Most people know to write down their concerns and bring the list to their appointment. But many people make the mistake of trying to include every question they may have. The average doctor's appointment lasts only about 15 minutes, so you'll probably get to cover only a few issues in a single appointment.

What works best: Edit your list, and be sure that the problems that trouble you the most are the ones you bring up first. If you can't decide what's most important, hand your list to your doctor and say, "I'd like you to help me figure out which of these we should discuss today." If you believe all the issues are crucial, consider booking a double appointment, but be aware that insurance may not cover the extra cost.

MISTAKE 2: **Diagnosing, not describing.** If you tell your doctor that you have "neuropathic pain," he/she will have no idea whether you are knowledgeable enough to make that judgment. Instead, be descriptive. Say, "I have burning pain, numbness and tingling." What helps doctors make the best diagnosis is your data—unfiltered. Even if another doctor has given you a diagnosis, describe your problem to your current doctor in your own words.

What works best: Think like a reporter. Interview yourself before your appointment, and write down your answers. When did the problem start? How does it feel? Where does it hurt? What makes it better? What makes it worse?

MISTAKE 3: **Being on a different page from the person who accompanies you to your visit.** As we all know, bringing a friend or family member to your appointment can help you remember crucial information and remind you of details you wanted to share with your doctor. But if your companion's agenda is different from yours, it can interfere with your care.

What works best: Let your companion know ahead of time what your goals are for the visit and how he can help you reach them. Also ask about his concerns, and if he has questions for the doctor, tell that to the doctor at the beginning of the appointment.

MISTAKE 4: **Letting your doctor cut you off.** The widely publicized studies that showed doctors interrupt patients within 18 seconds are misleading. The researchers counted anything the doctor said—including "uh-huh" or "go on"—as interruptions. That said, doctors often don't let patients finish, mostly because they are thinking ahead to what the problem might be and they jump in with questions.

What works best: Say, "What I need to tell you will take only about another 30 seconds. May I finish telling you what's going on? Then I'll answer your questions." Similarly, some doctors appear distracted—for example, he may be talking to you and taking notes on the computer at the same time. Of course, you do want him to take good notes, but if you're truly bothered, you can move your chair or otherwise position yourself so the doctor can see you and the screen. Or simply say, "You know, doctor, having your full attention would really help me."

MISTAKE 5: **Thinking your doctor is "dismissing" you.** Sometimes your doctor won't agree with you. If you think that you have a certain condition but he doesn't agree, don't assume that he hasn't considered what you said. It probably just means that based on your symptoms and his experience, he disagrees.

What works best: Ask yourself if your theory about your ailment could be wrong and what harm there would be in trying your doctor's advice. If you don't want to take the chance or still believe the doctor was dismissive of your concern, get a second opinion.

MISTAKE 6: **Not being completely honest.** In an ideal world, patients would be comfortable telling their doctors anything, but in reality, some things are embarrassing. Doctors know this— that's why many will say things like, "How are you doing with your medicines? It must be hard to remember to take them all." This is their way of letting you know it's OK to be honest.

What works best: Be straight with your doctor about your habits—good and bad. If you say you're taking your blood pressure medicine and your blood pressure is still high, the doctor may increase the dose or add another drug. That's bad because it may expose you unnecessarily to side effects.

But if you are honest and tell your doctor that you haven't been taking the medication as directed, you can talk to him about the reason. Maybe you can't afford a certain drug or it's causing side effects. In many cases, there are alternatives that will work for you.

MISTAKE 7: **Forgetting the wrap-up.** At the end of every doctor's appointment, summarize the conversation and be sure that you understand what to expect and what your next steps are.

What works best: Write down what's new from your appointment. Are there new medicines? How will you know if they are working? Do you need tests? How do you schedule them? And always ask, "When do you want to see me again?"

MISTAKE 8: **Being afraid to "break up" with your doctor.** It's important to find a doctor who fits your personality. But in order to do that, you must know yourself and your needs. Do you want a doctor who's always on time and is all about the facts? Or is it more important that your doctor be soothing and responsive to your emotional needs? Should he be someone who worries about unusual things and will order tests that other doctors normally wouldn't?

What works best: Ask friends or family for recommendations, but realize that it often takes a visit or two to find out if you're in sync with a particular doctor. If not, don't be embarrassed to move on to someone else.

It's OK to say: "I like you, but I think I need a doctor who is more like X. Can you recommend someone?" Most doctors know their colleagues well enough to give you the right referral.

Get In to See Your Busy Doctor

Charles B. Inlander, a consumer advocate and health-care consultant based in Fogelsville, Pennsylvania. He was founding president of the nonprofit People's Medical Society, a consumer advocacy organization credited with key improvements in the quality of US health care, and is author or coauthor of more than 20 consumer-health books.

Not too long ago, I was concerned about what I thought was a suspicious lesion on my back, so I called my dermatologist's office for an appointment. The receptionist told me that the earliest available appointment was two months away. Before I hung up, though, I got scheduled for an appointment just two days away! Below, I'll tell you how I did it.

But first, let me explain what's happening all over the country. Over the past few years, more and more patients have been complaining about how long it takes to get appointments with their doctors—even doctors they have been seeing for years. While the problem tends to occur more often with specialists, who are harder to come by than primary care doctors in some locales, the declining number of primary care doctors is creating a backlog for some practices, too. But with the help of the following secrets, you'll greatly increase your chances of getting a medical appointment sooner. *What works best…*

•**Talk to the right person.** The receptionist answering the phone at a medical practice usually has little discretion over scheduling. She'll book you into an opening on the calendar, often weeks or months away. If you need a quicker appointment, ask to speak to the nurse who works with your doctor. That's what I did to get my appointment with the dermatologist so much quicker. Even if you have never been to the practice before, this usually works.

Insider secret: **Don't cry wolf.** When you talk to the nurse, give a legitimate medical reason (such as a recurrence of a previously treated condition) for the expedited appointment.

•**Do not ask about a "waiting list."** If you can't get through to the nurse, you'll probably assume that you should ask to be put on a waiting list (so you'll be called if there's a cancellation).

Insider secret: **Don't do that!** Instead of mentioning a waiting list, ask the receptionist if you can be put on the "quick call" list. This is the term that most medical practices use when referring to the list for people who get priority appointments when a cancellation or opening occurs. Asking for the quick call list tells the receptionist that you are something of an insider, which will help you get priority status.

•**Consider an urgent-care center.** If you are having a nonemergency problem (such as flulike symptoms or pain due to a minor injury) but cannot get a timely appointment with your primary care doctor or a specialist, head to your nearest hospital-affiliated or freestanding urgent-care center or even one at your local drugstore or supermarket. These walk-in practices can quickly determine if you need to see a specialist (or need hospital care)…and, if needed, usually can get you a quick appointment with an affiliated specialist (sometimes on the same day). If you're trying to see a specialist for an initial appointment, a call from your primary care doctor may help you get in sooner.

Important: For serious problems, such as chest pains, high fever, breathing difficulties or burns, go to an emergency room!

•**Get a new doctor.** If one of your current doctors regularly makes you wait several weeks or longer for an appointment, don't hesitate to find a new doctor. While he/she may be busy, your time is valuable too, and it's reasonable to expect to be seen within a month for a routine appointment or within a few days for a special need.

How to Charm Your Doctor

Charles B. Inlander is a consumer advocate and health-care consultant based in Fogelsville, Pennsylvania. He was the founding president of the nonprofit People's Medical Society, a consumer advocacy organization credited with key improvements in the quality of US health care, and is the author or coauthor of more than 20 consumer-health books.

My mother, who lived to age 91, always called her doctors by their first names. Even with a new doctor she would say,

"Just call me Betty. And I'll call you by your first name." Not one doctor ever balked!

Here was her thinking: Being on a first-name basis with her doctors automatically eased the communication barriers between them. Too often, patients are intimidated by doctors, making them afraid to ask questions. Now research is confirming that my mother was really on to something—the better your communication with a doctor, the better your medical outcomes tend to be. But even if it's not your style to address your doctor by his/her first name, there are other steps you can take to make the most of your communications. *My advice...*

●**Be "real."** We hear a lot about "partnering" with our doctors, but what does that really mean? Just as you would expect in any healthy relationship, you and your doctor need to be open and honest with each other.

What also helps: It's common to be somewhat nervous when you see a doctor. But instead of freezing up, be open and tell him a little about yourself and your family. Where have you lived or traveled? What is (or was) your occupation? The more nonmedical information your doctor knows about you, the more likely he will better understand you as a person.

●**Be direct.** As soon as possible, talk to your doctor about your expectations—as well as his. For example, five years ago, my wife was diagnosed with breast cancer. We told the surgeon and oncologist that we wanted to be sure that we could reach them personally with important questions throughout the lengthy course of treatment. Realizing that they were very busy, we assured them the direct contacts would be about only serious matters. Both gave us their personal cell-phone numbers, and one gave us his home number. We contacted them several times on those private lines, and they responded promptly and personally. If your doctor won't do this, ask how to reach an on-call physician 24/7.

●**Bring cookies.** Sure this sounds like a bribe or some type of subversive ploy, but bringing the doctor (and his staff) a small gift or offering helps to create friendships. A friend of mine who started bringing cookies to her doctor appointments says she now gets quicker appointments and faster responses, and the doctor spends more time with her.

Insider tip: "Gifts" can take many forms. I often bring my doctor articles I have seen online about bicycling (an activity I know he likes). A friend of mine brought his golf-loving doctor a box of fancy golf balls that he won at a raffle. Little things can make a big difference in opening the lines of communication.

●**Have a chat with the nurse.** If your doctor is not responding well to your concerns—or seems too detached—talk about it with his nurse. Knowing him well, she can communicate this to the doctor "professional-to-professional." And he will likely be much more responsive to you.

Be prepared: If the nurse says that's just the way he is, think seriously about switching doctors. The core of a good patient/doctor relationship is communication. Remember, it's your health that's at stake, and it's your doctor's job to take care of you.

How to Take Charge in the ER

Steven Z. Kussin, MD, a gastroenterologist and founder of The Shared Decision Center in Utica, New York. Dr. Kussin is the author of *Doctor, Your Patient Will See You Now: Gaining the Upper Hand in Your Medical Care.* MedicalAdvocate.com

Emergency rooms are crowded, chaotic and confusing places. Americans now make about 130 million ER visits each year. It's estimated that about half of all hospital admissions now come from ER referrals.

Problem: Patients who are seen in ERs (or "emergency departments") and/or admitted to the hospital may be subjected to disjointed care, medication errors, misdiagnoses and poor outcomes.

Solution: To protect yourself or a loved one, it's more important than ever to be both assertive and savvy about managing your own care in the ER and/or hospital.

IN THE ER

People have been known to die in ER waiting rooms. It's not uncommon to wait three hours or longer. But if you're really sick and getting sicker, you need to get attention now. *Here's how…*

•**Go to the head of the line.** ER nurses assess each new arrival (this is called triage), and the sickest or most badly hurt patients see doctors first. When you're asked why you're there, don't waffle or give a long-winded reason. Keep to the point. Say something like "chest pain" or "excruciating headache."

•**Stick to your worst symptoms.** Pain and other symptoms tend to cycle from bad to bearable. Don't downplay discomfort. If your pain was severe two hours earlier, focus on that. This is not the time to be stoic. Get their attention.

•**Go over their heads.** If you're not getting triaged or end up sitting for hours after you're put in an examining room, you (or a family member) should check in every 20 minutes or so with the triage nurse. If this doesn't help, ask to see a caseworker. They're responsible for coordinating medical care and making sure that patients get what they need—including a nurse's or doctor's attention.

Important: If your condition is worsening, notify the ER staff immediately.

•**Get your test results.** When you leave the ER, get copies of the results of any tests you received. It might take extra time, but it's worth the wait. Even though you'd assume that the ER would forward this to the proper hospital floor if you're admitted (and to your personal doctor), it's safer to have these test results with you. This ensures that hospital physicians have the information they need to treat you.

IN THE HOSPITAL

If you are admitted to a hospital for any reason, be sure to bring your relevant medical records and the prescription bottles for any medications you're taking. If you aren't able to do this, send a relative to your primary care physician's office to get copies of your records from at least the last year and to your home to get your pill bottles.

Poor communication causes about 40% of all medication errors—one-quarter of which occur when doctors don't get a complete medical history or fail to review your prior medical records. Fortunately, many hospitals now have electronic medical records, which allow doctors to easily access most records. *What to do…*

•**Get your doctor on board.** Most hospital care is now managed by hospitalists, doctors who are trained in acute and inpatient care. But a hospitalist will not know you.

Why it matters: Your regular doctor knows your health background, which can affect treatment. The hospitalist will not. If you are the patient, you are likely to be very sick and unable to communicate clearly on your own behalf. If this is the case, try to have a family member—one who isn't afraid to speak up—with you at all times.

Important: Find out which hospitalist is assigned to your case, and let your regular doctor know who it is. Ask your doctor if he/she will drop by every other day to check on things…talk to the hospitalist…and review your test results. Also let the hospitalist know the name of your primary care doctor in case he wants to make contact.

•**Wait for test results.** Hospitals discharge patients much more quickly than they used to—even when all of the tests haven't been completed. One study found that 40% of test results were still pending when patients left hospitals—and some of these tests could have affected treatment options or even the diagnosis.

My advice: When you check into a hospital, ask to meet with the hospitalist and the discharge planner. Tell them that you'd like to have your entire hospital record—including all test results—on the day you're discharged. If the hospital staff says that only a discharge summary can be made available, ask your primary care doctor to follow up within 48 hours for your full hospital record.

•**See your doctor soon after you leave the hospital.** Don't wait more than two weeks—sooner is better. Research has shown that patients who don't schedule follow-up visits with their doctors are up to 10 times more likely to be readmitted to the hospital within 30 days.

GO TO THE RIGHT ER FOR SEVERE INJURIES

Choosing the right ER before an emergency can greatly improve your quality of care…and could save your life. If you've suffered a severe injury (for example, in a serious car accident or a bad fall) and are able to express your preference regarding the hospital you go to, ask to be taken to a Level I trauma center, or if that's not possible, a Level II trauma center. Both types of ERs are always staffed with surgeons, anesthesiologists and other specialists. However, a Level II center, unlike a Level I center, may not have research/training programs. (Such programs may mean that more emergency medicine physicians are likely to be working in the ER.) To find a trauma center near you, go to FACS. org/trauma/verified.html.

Important: I don't recommend urgent-care centers or nonhospital-affiliated emergency facilities for serious emergencies. Use them only for problems that you already know aren't too serious—or when they're the only facilities that you can get to in a hurry.

Remember: You're the Customer

Charles B. Inlander, a consumer advocate and healthcare consultant based in Fogelsville, Pennsylvania. He was founding president of the nonprofit People's Medical Society, a consumer advocacy organization credited with key improvements in the quality of US health care, and is author or coauthor of more than 20 consumer-health books.

For most of us, a hospital stay feels like being in custody. We're awakened at all hours to have our temperature taken. We're carted off for a test and wait for more than an hour before it's given. Our doctor, who was supposed to be there at 9 am, doesn't show up until 3 pm. Being in the hospital can definitely make you feel like a second-class citizen. But it doesn't have to be that way. In fact, you can take charge of much of your hospital stay and command the respect you deserve by remembering that you're the customer and that hospital personnel (including doctors) are working for you. *What to do…*

●**Make signs.** Today's hospitals are bigger and busier than ever. This means that you may not see the same nurses, aides or even in-house doctors on each day of your stay. As a result, the staff barely gets to know you. And unless they scrupulously review your complete record (which rarely happens), they may not know that you have only one kidney, are allergic to certain medications or that you are hard of hearing. So before you go to the hospital, make bold-lettered signs that you or a family member can tape above your hospital bed saying, for example: "ALLERGIC TO PENICILLIN" or "Hard of hearing—SPEAK UP."

●**Use the phone.** When I was in the hospital some time ago, the nurses were not responding when I pushed the "call button." Finally, I picked up the bedside telephone, dialed the hospital operator and asked to be connected to my unit's nurse station. Someone picked up right away, and I told her that I needed help. From that point on, I had a quick response whenever I pushed the button.

Insider tip: Use the bedside phone to call for what you need. If you have an unanswered question about your care, call your personal doctor at his/her office. Or if you have a question about a medication that you are being given, call the hospital pharmacy. You'll usually get quick answers from a knowledgeable pharmacist.

●**Bring your own creature comforts.** Hospitals are notoriously noisy places. For most of us, it's hard to sleep with all the endless clatter and chatter. So bring your own earplugs, noise-reducing headphones or a portable DVD player and headset to help block out disturbing noises.

Another comfort: Bring a favorite pillow and/or cozy quilt.

Also: You can bring your own regularly used medications with you, including vitamins. This could save you a bundle if you have a high-deductible insurance policy, since the same hospital drugs are usually much more costly. For example, the hospital may charge $3 for an over-the-counter baby aspirin that you could buy retail for 3 cents! You may have to sign a waiver absolving the hospital of any liability, but if you can bring the pill yourself, do it.

Insider tip: If you bring your own medications or supplements, just be sure to check with your doctor to make sure that taking them while hospitalized is OK.

● **Don't be afraid to say "NO!"** If someone comes to give you a new drug or take you to a test that you weren't informed about, just say "NO." This puts you in the driver's seat, forcing the hospital to send a doctor or nurse to explain to you who ordered the drug or test and why. If you're satisfied, you can say "yes," but either way, you're in control!

Don't Forget Your Nurse

Rebecca Shannonhouse, editor, *Bottom Line/Health.*

Nurses are the health-care professionals most likely to help prevent the 44,000 to 98,000 deaths that occur in hospitals every year because of medical errors, according to the Institute of Medicine. If a doctor writes an incorrect drug dose or schedules you for the wrong test, nurses are in the best position to catch the mistake.

Unfortunately, heavy workloads and inadequate staffing make their jobs difficult. A survey of 2,203 nurses found that 92% say they're unable to spend enough time with patients to provide optimal care.

But patients can help nurses help them, I was told by Dorie Byers, RN, a clinical instructor at the Indiana University School of Nursing in Indianapolis. One important—but often overlooked—way to do this is to engage nurses. *Here's how…*

● **Get personal.** Nurses are trained to treat everyone the same, but you'll get more attentive care when you're not just another face. Introduce yourself to the nurses—and get to know them.

Also helpful: Introduce frequent visitors—your spouse, children, etc.—to the nurses. You'll get better care when everyone is working together.

● **Ask how you can help them.** Nurses love it when patients do things for themselves that their condition permits. An assertive, can-do attitude will earn respect from all the members of your health-care team.

● **Ask detailed questions about drug doses, tests, etc.** Nurses enjoy using their knowledge, particularly when it helps them catch errors that others might have missed.

Lesson: Don't be passive. Patients who take the initiative tend to have better health outcomes.

How to Get Faster Test Results

Charles B. Inlander is a consumer advocate and health-care consultant based in Fogelsville, Pennsylvania. He was the founding president of the nonprofit People's Medical Society, a consumer advocacy organization credited with key improvements in the quality of US health care, and is the author or coauthor of more than 20 consumer-health books.

Sometimes, waiting for your medical test results can cause more anxiety than the actual findings. That's particularly true if you or your doctor suspects that you might have a problem. The longer you have to wait, the more worried you become. But it doesn't have to be that way. *Here are smart steps you can take to get your test results as soon as possible…*

● **Get immediate results.** Immediate results may sound like a very high order, but they are possible. The key is to work closely with your doctor. It probably sounds obvious, but the first step is to let your doctor know that you want to get results as soon as possible—either good or bad news. This increases the chance that your doctor will pass results on quickly to you and that he/she will recommend a lab or center that is known for providing quick results.

Don't assume that you have to wait…and wait. For imaging tests, such as mammograms and other scans, many imaging centers will give you the radiologist-reviewed results on the spot. Ask your doctor to recommend such imaging centers in your area. Or call several centers near you and ask what their policies are on giving patients immediate results. Other centers will let you know if everything is OK but tell you to contact your doctor if there is a problem. In that case, you should immediately call your physician to discuss the results.

My story: When an MRI of my brain found I had a tumor a while back, the results were sent to my physician while I was at the imaging center, and we talked on the phone while I was still there about the next steps.

•**Find out when results will be available.** Of course, not all test results are immediately available. Blood work and other types of tests, such as tissue analysis of a biopsy, can often take several days or even weeks to be analyzed by a pathologist or other medical professional. And quite often your doctor will need to review the results and even discuss them with the pathologist and/or other physicians to make an accurate interpretation of the results. But you can still help move things along by calling your doctor's office as soon as you have completed the test. Let the office know what test you had…where it was done…when it was done…and the best way to reach you as soon as the doctor has the results. Again, let the doctor's office know that you want the results as soon as possible.

Note: If you have a condition, such as cancer, that may require frequent tests and/or biopsies that tend to take a long time for results, be sure to ask your doctor at your follow-up appointments if any future tests are likely or needed and if you should have them sooner rather than later.

•**Go online.** Most major hospitals and large medical practices, along with laboratories and imaging centers that are owned or affiliated with them, now make test results available to the patient online at the same time they become available to the doctor.

Important: The onus is on you to sign up or register for this service. Ask the doctors, hospitals, labs and imaging centers that you use if they offer such online services and how you can enroll.

Helpful: After you have a test but before you get the results, schedule an appointment with your doctor to go over the results.

Note: Some doctors prefer to do this over the phone, which is fine. But be sure to speak directly with the doctor, especially if the results are worrisome.

Get More from Your Insurance

Charles B. Inlander is a consumer advocate and health-care consultant based in Fogelsville, Pennsylvania. He was the founding president of the nonprofit People's Medical Society, a consumer advocacy organization credited with key improvements in the quality of US health care, and is the author or coauthor of more than 20 consumer-health books.

With the Affordable Care Act (ACA), also known as Obamacare, the traditional "open season" that gives us a chance to sign up or switch health insurance plans has a few more moving parts. Open season now includes three basic categories of health insurance—Medicare and employer health plans, as in the past, and ACA health policies for people who buy insurance on their own, who haven't been able to afford it or who have been denied coverage. Regardless of the type of insurance you have or need, making the right choices can be complicated. *Key points to consider…*

•**Cost.** No matter what type of health policy you might be shopping for, one of the biggest mistakes people make is paying more attention to a policy's premium cost than its actual coverage. In addition to the premium cost, consider the co-payments, deductibles and other out-of-pocket costs you'll owe if you use doctors, hospitals or medications not fully covered by the plan. These issues apply to Medicare, employer plans (if multiple plans are offered where you work) and to those plans that will be offered via the Obamacare Health Insurance Marketplaces, also known as Health Exchanges.

What helps: Make a list of the doctors, hospitals, medications and services you use, and see whether they are covered by any plan you are considering. Then compare the co-pays for those services or any limits on the number of treatments allowed (such as 20 physical therapy sessions per year) for each plan. Add those costs to the premiums before choosing a policy.

•**Does the plan fit your needs?** While cost is important, it's crucial that you opt for a plan that meets your family's health-care needs. For example, if your 55-year-old spouse has Parkinson's disease, you can anticipate needing more health services in the future than you did prior to that diagnosis.

What helps: Ask your doctor what health services you (and your family members) may need in the next year or two. Use that as a guide to find a plan that best matches your needs.

•**Don't miss the deadline!** Believe me, this is one deadline you don't want to miss. If you do, you'll keep your current plan (except in circumstances such as marriage or divorce).

Here are the specific dates you need to know: If you're on Medicare, open season begins October 15, and ends December 7. If you have an employer plan, open season usually occurs during November and December—check with your employer about it today. If you're buying an individual or family health policy from a private insurance company or are purchasing through an ACA-created Health Exchange, you need to sign up by December 31, for coverage to begin January 1.

Best places to get help: Medicare's website, Medicare.gov, compares various Medicare plans on a state-by-state basis. Or call 1-800-MEDICARE. If you're shopping for an individual or a family plan under the ACA Health Exchanges, Healthcare.gov is an excellent resource or call 1-800-318-2596. If you have an employer plan, check with the company's human resources office.

Travel Discounts for Seniors

Roundup of experts on travel and other discounts for seniors, reported at HuffingtonPost.com.

Amtrak gives 15% off the lowest available fare for most trains for travelers age 62 and older. Southwest Airlines provides fully refundable senior fares for fliers age 65 and older whose plans change—although these may not be the lowest fares offered. Verizon Wireless discounts cell-phone service for people 65 and older. Walgreens and RiteAid have monthly senior-discount days, when most non-prescription items are discounted by 20% to 25%.

5 Ways to Get Through Airport Security Faster

George Hobica, founder of AirfareWatchdog.com, which reports on airfare bargains. He previously was a travel writer for *Travel + Leisure*, *National Geographic Traveler* and other magazines.

The average wait time at Los Angeles International Airport security checkpoints is 40 minutes, according to the airport-delay monitoring app MiFlight. Waits longer than three hours have occurred at Chicago's O'Hare…Miami International Airport…and New York City's John F. Kennedy International Airport. It's not unheard of for travelers to spend more time getting though airport security at US airports than they do in the air. It even has become common to miss flights because of extensive security delays.

Enrolling in the "PreCheck" expedited security program administered by the Transportation Security Administration (TSA) was supposed to allow travelers to sidestep these delays—but the PreCheck program has had problems of its own.

Travelers who sign up for PreCheck and fly on participating airlines get to use special security lines where several time-consuming steps are not required—they do not have to remove their shoes and belts…or take their electronic devices out of their luggage, for example.

In theory, that should make PreCheck security lines a big time-saver. In practice, PreCheck has experienced a huge surge in popularity in the past year, and a growing glut of PreCheck travelers means that its lines sometimes take longer than standard airport-security lines.

What's more, these days it can take upward of one month just to get the in-person interview that is required by the PreCheck application process. Travelers must pay an $85 nonrefundable application fee and pass a security vetting process to participate in PreCheck. Certain high-end credit cards will cover this fee for you. Visit TSA.gov/precheck for a list of credit cards and application information.

Fortunately, PreCheck is not the only way to get though airport security faster. *Potentially better options include…*

•**Global Entry,** a government program that lets preapproved travelers speed through customs and immigration checkpoints in more than 50 US and international airports. And if you are a Global Entry member, you also qualify to use PreCheck security lines. To take advantage of PreCheck if you are a Global Entry member, enter your Global Entry membership number (which is in the upper-left corner on the back of your Global Entry "Trusted Traveler" card) into the "Known Traveler Number" field when you book flights on participating airlines—or enter it on your frequent-flier profile with the airline.

As noted above, those PreCheck lines are not always as quick as they should be, but Global Entry membership truly does reduce delays at customs and immigration. And it outdoes PreCheck in another way—the Global Entry interview-and-approval process often is weeks quicker than the PreCheck process, though this does vary by location. (Go to CBP.gov, then select "Global Entry" from the "Travel" menu.)

Cost: Global Entry has a $100 application fee. That's only $15 more than the application fee for PreCheck alone, so Global Entry is the better deal. After approval, renewal is not required for five years, so the annual cost is just $20.

You even can avoid this expense by charging Global Entry's application fee to a credit card that provides a statement credit to cover it. Predictably, these tend to be cards that have high annual fees, however, including The Platinum Card from American Express ($450 annual fee, American Express.com)…and Citi Prestige and Citi AAdvantage Executive World Elite MasterCard (both with a $450 annual fee, Citi.com).

•**Clear, a private security-screening alternative to the government-run PreCheck and Global Entry programs.** Clear features high-tech, automated biometric authentication—that is, fingerprint or retinal scanners—and usually is much faster than all other airport security options. Often there is virtually no Clear line at all…except when those high-tech biometric scanners go down, which does happen on occasion (ClearMe.com).

Clear currently is available in 16 airports—Austin…Baltimore…Dallas/Ft. Worth…Denver…Houston's George Bush and William Hobby airports…Las Vegas…Miami…Orlando…San Antonio…San Francisco…San Jose…Seattle…Washington's Dulles and Ronald Reagan National airports…and Westchester County, New York, in the New York City area. The company that runs Clear expects to offer the service in the Detroit airport soon, and Clear is available in a number of major league sports stadiums, where it enables you to avoid the sometimes lengthy security checkpoint lines.

Because of the cost, most people will find that it's worth enrolling in Clear only if they frequently use at least one of the currently served airports or, perhaps, if they have season tickets with a team that plays in a stadium that offers Clear.

Cost: $179 per year, or $79 to $99 per year for Delta SkyMiles members. Family members 18 and over can be added for $50 each. Family members under 18 can use Clear for free when traveling with a Clear member.

Other possible ways to avoid long security lines…

•**Paying airlines for expedited security occasionally is possible.** JetBlue and United offer passengers the option of paying a modest fee for onetime access to a special security line in some airports. (Travelers who have elite status in an airline's frequent-flier program and/or who are flying business or first class often qualify for access to a special security line without paying an added fee.)

This option typically is offered at the airport check-in kiosk or desk when available.

Strategy: Check the length of security lines before checking in to a JetBlue or United flight.

Pay the extra fee if the lines look longer than is acceptable to you.

Cost: JetBlue's Even More Speed starts at $10... United's Premier Access starts at $15. (Some other airlines offer VIP airport services that include significantly expedited security, such as the American Airlines Five Star Service program. But these programs tend to cost hundreds of dollars per flight and often are available to only first-class passengers.)

•**Investigate alternative security checkpoints.** Many large airports have multiple security checkpoints—and one might have significantly shorter lines than another.

Ask an airport or Transportation Security Administration employee whether there is another security checkpoint where the lines tend to be shorter. It might be a long walk to get to the other checkpoint, but even so, this can be a time-saver.

Helpful: Apps including GateGuru (free, iOS, Android and Windows. GateGuru.com) and MiFlight (free, iOS, GoMiFlight.com) can help you locate alternate security checkpoints and sometimes provide user-generated wait-time estimates.

How to Get the Best Airline Seats

Roundup of experts on airline seating, reported at Money TalksNews.com; *Travel + Leisure* magazine.

To get the best airline seats without paying heavily for an upgrade...

•**Compare planes and seats online** at websites such as SeatGuru.com, SeatExpert.com and SeatPlans.com.

•**Join an airline's frequent-flier program.**

•**Book early** to have the widest selection of seats.

•**Use a travel agent**—he/she sometimes has access to better seats and may charge only $20 to $30 for simple bookings.

•**If you must book a middle seat,** sign up with a notification site such as ExpertFlyer.com to be notified immediately if a better seat opens up—you may be able to change seats without cost.

For a better chance of having an empty seat next to you when flying, choose an aisle seat near the back of the plane—and ask if the middle seat is free when making your reservation or check online.

Helpful: Most airlines release premium seats that they hold for frequent fliers exactly 24 hours before flight time.

To get the best possible seat in coach: Fly at off-peak times, when the chance is higher that you can get a good seat or change seats after everyone is aboard. If you have elite status in a frequent-flier plan, you may be able to get a better seat at no extra cost.

Research Senior Discounts

Kiplinger.com

Discounts available to people of all ages or at specific websites can sometimes be better than senior discounts. *For instance...*

•**AARP members get 5%-to-20% discounts at certain hotel chains.**

Examples: A recent AARP discount at Holiday Inn Chicago-O'Hare Airport brought the one-night rate to $114.95. But a seven-day, advance-purchase rate for any traveler was $106.95—total savings of $8.

•**A booking through the Last Minute Travel app** was $101—a $14 savings over the AARP rate.

•**For car rentals,** deals through Hotwire.com may be 50% lower than Avis and Budget rates with AARP discounts.

•**Lower-than-senior-discount rates** also are available at daily-deal websites such as Groupon and LivingSocial.

Best Concert Tickets at the Best Prices

SmartMoney.com.

Fan club websites often offer members early access to tickets, which makes it easier to get the cheapest seats. (Membership typically is free.) American Express, Chase and Citibank may offer credit card holders early access and/or preferred seating. Citibank announced that customers can use their ThankYou rewards points to pay for tickets at Live Nation.com, a concert search engine. Search engines such as FanSnap.com and SeatGeek.com allow you to compare prices for tickets being resold at sites such as StubHub.com and RazorGator.com. Prices of these secondary market tickets tend to fall in the last 48 to 72 hours before a show.

Your Quick & Easy Retirement Planner

The key questions you need to ask to live the life you want, with fewer worries and more fun!

Use a separate pad or open a document on your computer to record your answers to these questions. Include the date and update this document as time goes on.

1. What do you want to do?

We start with this seemingly mundane question because, unless you're working part-time, you're going to have a LOT of extra time on your hands in retirement. You never know what it feels like until you're in the thick of it. This free time can be both a blessing and source of frustration and conflict. It all depends on how you plan for it. Some key questions to ask yourself and your partner include (so you're both on the "same page" moving forward)...

At what age do you want to retire? What about your spouse or partner?

Where do you want to live?

How and where do you plan to live at each stage of the rest of your life? In the same place, and the same city as you are now? Do you want to split your time between different locations?

What hobbies, passions, and activities do you want to pursue?

What new things do you want to learn?

If one of you is still working full-time, what will the other person do during that time?

If you want to travel, where do you want to go? What special trips do you dream about? (List)

What are your priorities for the next 30 years of your life?

How do you envision a typical day?

What sort of activities do you like or want to do alone?

What sort of activities do you want to do together?

Are you and your life partner "on the same page"? If not, how can you resolve your differences?

2. Do you have enough money to live the life you want?

Do you keep track of your expenses?

215

Do you have a monthly budget now? In other words, do you know how much you spend each month, so you can plan to withdraw that amount from your savings?

How much money will you need in retirement to maintain your current lifestyle?

A healthy man or woman retiring today at 65 can be expected to live until age 85. And that's the average, so you could easily live longer than that. Have you saved enough to generate the income you need to support your lifestyle for the next 20 years?

Some experts say you should have enough money saved to generate 70% of your pre-retirement income.[1] Other experts say you should calculate how much money you *spend* each year. Then multiply that number by twenty. (*Example*: If you spend $80,000 a year after taxes, your target savings would be $1.6 million.)[2] Twenty times what you need for income will enable you to take out 5% a year and hit that $80k target.

However, there's an old rule of thumb that says you should aim to withdraw only 4% a year. In 1994, financial expert William Bengen studied historical stock market returns from the 1930s to the 1970s. He determined that even in volatile markets, you could withdraw 4% annually without exhausting your retirement portfolio in less than 33 years.[3]

You could also try one of the many online retirement calculators that will give you an estimate of your "magic number" to save for retirement.

Our recommendation: Set a cautious target of 20 times annual spending and aim to take out only 4% a year. See page 469 of *Say No to Nursing Homes* for a novel way of "crash-proofing" your retirement portfolio.

Can you afford to delay taking Social Security or converting your IRA, so they continue to grow tax-free?

How much money do you have now? Is it well organized and well-managed?

It's okay for one person in the household to take the lead in managing the finances. But both of you should be aware of how much money there is, where it's located, where all the paperwork is, and be familiar with your financial advisor, if you have one.

You both should be comfortable with the way your money is being managed, too. Is the level of investment risk appropriate for your age and comfort level? Are you in the right investments?

Will you outlive your money?

There are strategies that practically guarantee you'll never outlive your money. These include "reverse allocation" for your investment portfolio and a new type of annuity for later in life. See page 469[4] of *Say No to Nursing Homes* and your FREE Report, *Retirement Riches*,[5] for all the details.

What can you do if you haven't saved enough money at this point in your life?

Could you work a few more years than you originally planned? That could add more years for saving and delay the date when you start drawing from Social Security and your savings. Both of these steps can help make up for lost time and ensure that you have more money later in life.

Do you have the insurance coverage you need?

Should you scale back your life insurance at some point? Is long-term health insurance right for you? See page 507 of *Say No to Nursing Homes* for when it makes sense to get long-term care insurance, and when it doesn't.

What would happen to your finances if one of you were to die?

Have you completed a Will and set up Powers of Attorney for managing your finances and healthcare?

Does your spouse or partner know where all the records for pensions, insurance policies, Social Security, and other sources of income are located?

Is there a trusted advisor the surviving spouse can turn to?

Will you have enough money for healthcare for you and your partner?

3. Are you protecting your health and wellness?

Do you have the "four pillars of a healthy life" covered?

1. Diet: Are you preparing healthier meals, with more plant-based foods, fewer carbohydrates, more protein, vegetables and fruits?

2. Exercise: Do you get at least (minimum) 30 minutes of moderate exercise (such as walking) at least three times a week? Do you get more than that? Are you expanding your exercise habits to include new things such as yoga, Tai Chi, weight-training and more?

3. Sleep: Have you developed good sleep habits? Do you try to go to sleep at the same time every day? Do you avoid "screens" (TV, computers, cell phones, tablets) for at least an hour before going to sleep?

4. Stress: Have you learned how to reduce your stress levels? Such as deep-breathing techniques, meditation, moderate exercise or chanting?

Are there any chronic health problems that you're dealing with now? Have you researched and found the best options for overcoming them?

What diseases run in your family? What can you do to reduce your risk of suffering from them?

What are you doing for your spiritual or emotional health?

What changes to your diet, exercise, sleep patterns or stress levels do you want to make? Do you have a written list or plan for making those changes?

If you were to develop difficulties with the Activities of Daily Living (ADLs), would you want to stay in your home with in-home caregivers? Or move to an assisted-living facility?

Have you explored ways to become more resilient? To bounce back faster from life's inevitable setbacks?

4. What's on your "bucket list"?

What amazing places would you like to visit?

Do you want to spend more time with children or grandchildren? How are you going to do that?

Is there a course or skill you'd like to learn or master?

If money were no object, what amazing thing would you want to do?

5. What sort of legacy do you want to leave behind?

Do you plan to leave money to your children? If so, how much, and how?

Have you spoken with an accountant or estate attorney about the best way to leave this money to your children, and to minimize taxes?

Have you made your estate and gift wishes known to your children, to avoid any conflicts in the future?

Are there any charities you want to support… now or with a legacy gift?

What is the best way for you to leave a financial legacy? An outright gift? A planned giving vehicle? A family foundation? If you've identified a particular cause or charity, they often have professionals who can help you plan and structure your charitable gift in the most efficient way.

Do you want to volunteer with any organizations?

To whom would you like to give your most cherished possessions?

Have you made your wishes for end-of-life care known to your children?

Have you made your wishes for your funeral and burial arrangements known to your children or relatives, and put them in writing?

Have you pre-planned and pre-paid your funeral, to relieve your loved ones of that burden?

How would you like to be remembered?

Does this affect your plans for the next few years?

---

[1] http://www.kiplinger.com/article/retirement/T047-C000-S002-how-much-you-need-to-retire.html

[2] https://www.tonyrobbins.com/wealth-lifestyle/much-need-retire/

[3] http://www.investopedia.com/terms/f/four-percent-rule.asp

[4] Common wisdom says that to protect your retirement assets you should slowly scale back your exposure to stocks throughout your retirement years. But the truth is, it may be safer and smarter to slash your stock holdings as you near retirement or in early retirement, then slowly increase the allocation to stocks over time during retirement.

[5] For many people, a QLAC is the best way to guarantee that they won't run out of money if they live past age 85. And it has big tax advantages (see below). http://bottomlineinc.com/retirement-income-life/